DENOTATIONAL SEMANTICS:

THE SCOTT-STRACHEY APPROACH

TO PROGRAMMING LANGUAGE THEORY

The MIT Press Series in Computer Science

1. Denotational Semantics: The Scott-Strachey Approach to Programming Language Theory, Joseph E. Stoy, 1977

DENOTATIONAL SEMANTICS:

THE SCOTT-STRACHEY APPROACH

TO PROGRAMMING LANGUAGE THEORY

Joseph E. Stoy

The MIT Press

Cambridge, Massachusetts, and London, England

Publisher's Note

This format is intended to reduce the cost of publishing certain works in book form and to shorten the gap between editorial preparation and final publication. Detailed editing and composition have been avoided by photographing the text of this book directly from the author's typescript.

Printed and bound in the United States of America.

Library of Congress Cataloging in Publication Data

Stoy, Joseph.
  Denotational semantics.

  Bibliography: p.
  Includes index.
  1. Programming languages (Electronic computers)--Semantics. I. Title.
QA76.7.S74 001.6'424 77-11962
ISBN 0-262-19147-4

To Gabrielle

PREFACE

This book is an account of the theory and techniques of denotational semantics. It is intended for graduate students, for specialist undergraduate courses, and for any who desire an introduction to this approach to the definition and analysis of programming languages, which owes its origin to the pioneering work of Dana Scott and Christopher Strachey. Although some of this material has been described before, in the papers of Scott and Strachey themselves, for example (see references [48] to [59] in the Bibliography), or in the expository paper by Bob Tennent [61], this is as far as I know the first introductory text book to include not only an account of Scott's theory of computation, but also a detailed treatment of the use of denotational semantics as a tool for programming language definition.

The book falls into several parts. The first two chapters are introductory, and the third provides a simple example of denotational semantics as a definition technique. Chapter 4 is in some sense a digression, intended for students unfamiliar with the idea of regarding functions as data objects in their own right: those who take this notion for granted may prefer to omit this chapter, except perhaps for the final section on functions, algorithms and approximations. Chapter 5 concerns the λ-calculus: it introduces a notation which is used extensively throughout the book, and leads to a discussion of various theoretical difficulties, which it is the purpose of the following two chapters to resolve. Chapters 6 and 7 comprise an account of Scott's approach to the theory of computation, involving continuous functions on continuous lattices, and his model for the value spaces needed in programming language semantics. Those who are concerned with denotational semantics simply as a definition tool, and are not too interested in the underlying theory, might legitimately scan these two chapters fairly lightly, or perhaps even defer them altogether. Chapter 8 and the following chapters treat the formal semantic definitions of various kinds of language: first the λ-calculus itself; then a simple language embodying the concept of state and commands acting on the state; then several extensions of this language. Chapter 11 carries this part still further, with a treatment of jumps; and Chapter 12 covers the assignment command. The remaining two chapters deal mainly with applications: Chapter 13 discusses matters concerned with the correctness of language implementations; and Chapter 14 treats the connection with proofs of the correctness of programs, as well as various other miscellaneous topics.

The book is partly based on the graduate course (Formal Semantics of Programming Languages) which I gave in the Fall Term of 1973, while I was a visitor at MIT. In outline this course followed similar courses previously given by Strachey in Oxford. The part dealing with the λ-calculus, lattices and reflexive domains used the lecture notes by John Sanderson [46], though part of this material has been superseded in the present book by the treatment of Pω and LAMBDA, based on more recent work by Scott (described by him in [53]). My debt to these people is very great; but of course any errors or opacities which remain in this book are my sole responsibility.

I also wish to thank Mrs. Barbara Halpern for providing the line drawing of her brother Christopher (at page xiv), and to Dana Scott for his Foreword, which is an account of Strachey's rôle in the development of denotational semantics (and complements Scott's account of his own work, in his Turing lecture, to be published in the Communications of the ACM). I am grateful to the Massachusetts Institute of Technology for offering me a visiting appointment for the year 1973-74 (partly supported by a grant from the National Science Foundation), and the University of Oxford for granting me leave of absence; to my many friends and colleagues at Project MAC (now the Laboratory for Computer Science) for providing such a stimulating and enjoyable environment; and to my friends, colleagues and students at the Programming Research Group here in Oxford (particularly those who have taught or been taught from earlier drafts of this text), for the thoughtful criticism which has been an invaluable aid to the book's final production.

Balliol College, Oxford.
June, 1977.

CONTENTS

CHRISTOPHER STRACHEY 1916–1975

FOREWORD

by Dana S. Scott

An Appreciation of Christopher Strachey and his Work

We all wish that Christopher were writing these introductory words for this book. His untimely death at the age of 58 in May, 1975, left a permanent void in the lives of his relatives, colleagues, students and many friends, academic and non-academic. In the ten years he worked in Oxford, where he had held a personal chair since 1971, his field grew and changed remarkably, in no little measure owing to his own many original ideas and his influence on the work of others. This was generously acknowledged when the British Computer Society made him one of its first Distinguished Fellows in 1972.

Strachey's own publications were few, however, though that was not always his fault. In the last year before his brief, final illness Strachey laboured on the Milne-Strachey book, since he saw the need for a comprehensive account of the approach to programming language semantics he advocated. A preliminary manuscript was completed in late 1974, but he was unable to start on the necessary revisions for publication. The book published in 1976 by Robert Milne under their earlier title *A Theory of Programming Language Semantics* (see reference [34] in the Bibliography) was completely rewritten by Milne and contains in a very substantial portion his own important and original contributions, which developed as an outgrowth of his earlier Cambridge Ph.D. work done (at Oxford) under Strachey's direction. It is not being unfair to Milne to say that the published book is not what Strachey would have written: their styles of exposition were just very, very different, and Milne had hardly any other option than to start over in order to produce a consistent and complete text. It could not really serve as a starting place for the ordinary student requiring an introduction, but it will prove a most valuable reference work for any number of topics, and Joe Stoy often cites it in the present text.

To me, in any case, it is also doubtful whether Strachey could have written a satisfactory beginning text himself. His lecturing style was by turns crisp, muddled, cryptic, delightful, maddening, sarcastic, always highly spontaneous, but - to those that had ears - unfailingly stimulating. What he could have done, and did do on several occasions, was to produce shorter pieces which would, with great clarity, put forward what were the basic ideas and important problems, since his unique experience gave him special insight. True, he had his prejudices and hobby-horses, but we could, and did, forgive him everything for the sake of his excellent ideas. This is not meant to imply that he was incapable of sustained work, since that is far from the truth, but academic writing was a considerable chore for him and in a certain sense was a waste of his time. Of course, no one had any idea just how limited his time was; so we can be doubly grateful that Stoy has taken the responsibility as a long-time assistant and co-worker with Strachey to set down not only what he learnt from him, and others, but what he developed himself for exposition over a considerable period of lecturing at Oxford and during a sabbatical year at MIT. Again this may not be exactly the book Strachey would have wanted, but it will complement the Milne work very well indeed and will introduce the approach to a wide audience. It will be clear in many places what good use Stoy has made of his teaching experience and what effort he has put into trying to make the material understandable.

It should also not be thought that Milne and Stoy are the only workers in this direction of language definition. References to many other names can be found in the bibliographies of these two books, and in the papers to which they in turn refer. Furthermore, the other well-known approaches, in particular the Vienna Definition method, the Algol 68 method and the axiomatic method, all had influence on Strachey's ideas. Sometimes he disagreed strongly with certain features of the other approaches, but he took full account of what they were doing - though his approach was quite different. It should also not be thought that Strachey was not concerned with the details of the semantics, even though he did not write so much himself. In the first place during many protracted periods we would all talk things over with him almost daily. In the second place, he lectured every year at Oxford, and many of the formulations and examples are his, though it might be difficult to trace back to the exact origin of every point. Finally, he could be very critical and emphatic about exactness and clarity, so that sometimes proposals went through many versions. It is difficult, therefore, to give precise credit to him, but we are all glad to say how great a debt we feel.

The remarks just made will, I hope, be seconded by his doctoral students. It will be noted from the list* below that language definition was not by any means the only interest of Strachey and his group. His field was *computing* in a dynamic sense: how to get the machine to do what *you* want. Thus, a programming language is obviously a necessary tool. Strachey felt that people had made as bad design mistakes on the language level as they had on the machine or operating system level, and he was concerned with rationality on all levels. Personally I

---

* Doctor's Theses written under Strachey in Oxford:

C.P. Wadsworth (D.Phil. 1971): *The Semantics and Pragmatics of the λ-calculus*.
P.H.F. McGregor (D.Phil. 1973): *Design of Computer Instruction Sets*.
N.P. Derrett (D.Phil. 1975): *Design of Computing Mechanisms*.
R.E. Milne (Ph.D. Cambridge 1975): *The Formal Semantics of Computer Languages and their Implementation*.
P.D. Mosses (D.Phil. 1975): *Mathematical Semantics and Compiler Generation*.
G.T. Ligler (D.Phil. 1975): *Proof Rules, Mathematical Semantics and Programming Language Design*.
A.C. Bamford (D.Phil. 1976): *Procedure-calling Mechanisms*.
P.J.L.Wallis (D.Phil. 1977, begun under Strachey): *Language Design for Structured Programming*.
(Three or four other graduate students who started their work under Strachey are still working on their theses.)

think one of our greatest losses in his death is that his design philosophy was not yet more widely known. Philosophy in design of machines (or algorithms or languages) is something that has to be learned by doing it. Strachey should have been allowed much greater scope to develop and pass on his ideas; but we can be thankful that in his last decade he was given a group at all, first by the Science Research Council and later (though at a reduced level) as taken over by Oxford University. His ideas and philosophy will certainly live on, however, in the work of his students and associates.

To understand the context of this work, and the aim of this book by Stoy in particular, we should review Strachey's somewhat unorthodox early career. (Much of the information that follows is taken either from the *Times* obituary of 23 May 1975, from a personal reminiscence by Professor David Barron published in the *Computer Bulletin* for September 1975, from the King's College Cambridge obituary, or from the historical preface written for the Milne-Strachey manuscript, but not employed by Milne in [34].)

On 16 November 1916 Christopher Strachey was born into the middle of the Bloomsbury set, with complicated connections on both sides of his remarkable family. His father was Oliver Strachey, an older brother of Lytton Strachey, whose career was not in literature but in cryptography. From his father Christopher perhaps took his lifelong interest in recreational puzzles. His mother was Ray Costelloe, a strong woman from a line of strong women, and perhaps from her he inherited his own special independence of mind. From Gresham's School he went up to King's as a Mathematical Scholar in 1935. His undergraduate career was academically undistinguished, and Strachey never took an advanced degree. Graduating just before the war, he worked throughout it as a physicist in the Valve Research Laboratories of Standard Telephone and Cables Ltd., where experience with a differential analyser awakened his interest in mathematical machines.

Surprisingly, he became a schoolmaster after the war, first at St. Edmund's Canterbury (1945-1949) and then at Harrow (1949-1951). It was a very important experience in his development, however, since it affected his whole approach to teaching and making people understand things. Once in a great while I found him being rather too much the schoolmaster, but I was always most envious of the magician's way he had of capturing a person's attention and interest. At Oxford, for example, he had particular success with vacation courses in computing for undergraduates, and he was also excellent with pupils from schools. In an oblique way one might say computing can be like playing a musical instrument, and talent shows itself early. (Strachey himself was also a keen amateur musician.) But often the standard school curriculum provides little opportunity for music and even less for computing. Certainly the "New Maths" seems to have been rather a failure in this direction, probably by being too abstract.

Here, in computing for schools, is another line where Strachey's special qualifications remained to too great an extent unfulfilled. On the other hand he was quite opposed to "Computing Science" as an undergraduate course *in itself* (that is, according to the British pattern, where a student would study nothing else). At that age students should learn serious things that they will need later, rather than the latest "state-of-the-art" mish-mash which will be out of date before they graduate. At least that was his opinion, and perhaps he was right, but surely *some* education is needed. A mix of required subjects and computing options is perhaps the answer - both in a mathematics curriculum and in engineering. (Alas, at Oxford we do not even have the resources to do that: I know from his remarks to me that the extremely slow development of his subject at Oxford was profoundly discouraging to Strachey in his last few years.)

Suddenly in 1950, while still a schoolmaster and an unknown amateur, Strachey appeared at the National Physical Laboratory with a draught-playing program for their Pilot ACE. His next big achievement, a simulator for the Manchester Mark I, was far larger than any previous program for that machine, and this achievement firmly established his position in the computing field in Britain.

In 1951 he joined the National Research and Development Corporation, where he was responsible for the overall design for the Ferranti Pegasus computer, which successfully embodied his belief that ease of programming should guide the design of machines.

Seconded to Toronto, he programmed most of a backwater simulation for the St. Lawrence Seaway. This was another *tour de force*, and advanced the opening of the Great Lakes to shipping by many years. Later, along with one or two others, he became interested in the use of a computer for several *concurrent* tasks; indeed, it was he who published the earliest paper on this, though he attached little significance to the fact.

From 1959 Strachey was a freelance consultant (somewhat unusual in those days), and his business even prospered sufficiently to employ an assistant (Peter Landin). He was living in London then, and he formed a select discussion group for people interested in the then new field of "automatic programming", which met monthly at his home. In 1962 he gave up his private consulting and went to work at the Mathematical Laboratory in Cambridge, where he was also a Senior Research Fellow of Churchill College.

About Cambridge, David Barron writes: "At the time we were designing the hardware and software of the Titan computer (later known as Atlas 2), and I was in charge of the University software team. One day I was summoned to [Professor M.V.] Wilkes's office and told that Strachey was going to join my team. I was staggered by the idea that Christopher should be working for me, and indeed I might as well have tried to hold a (friendly) tiger by the tail. In fact that is a fairly apt simile. We were supossed to be designing a language and writing a compiler. Christopher set off, and the rest of us were pulled somewhat breathlessly behind. We never did get a compiler, but at the end of it he had formulated some of the fundamental ideas of modern programming languages, had sown the seed for the work on formal semantics that he and Peter Landin were later to pursue, and I had gained an understanding of programming languages the depth of which I have only recently come to appreciate."

Concerning some of those fundamental ideas, Strachey wrote: "Algol 60, surely one of the most successful pieces of original work by a committee, had already introduced some important ideas, including the concept of scope. Without experience it is not possible to be certain, but it is generally felt that John McCarthy played a large part in this. At the time, McCarthy was working on Lisp which is closely based on Church's λ-calculus. The λ-calculus has been widely used as an aid in examining the semantics of programming languages precisely because it brings out very clearly the connection between a name and the entity it denotes, even in cases where the same name is used for more than one purpose. The earliest suggestion that λ-calculus might be useful in this way that has come to our notice was in a verbal communication from Roger Penrose to [me] in about 1958. At the time this suggestion fell on stony ground and had virtually no influence."

David Barron continues: "We devoted a lot of time in the early days [at Cambridge] to syntactic matters, particularly to the problem of defining operator precedence so that the 'obvious' mathematical meaning of an expression is retained. However, this preoccupation with syntax was short lived, being terminated by the enunciation of Strachey's first law of programming: *Decide what you want to say before you worry about how you are going to say it.*"

On the rôle of syntax, Strachey himself said: "The syntactic problem was the first to be recognised and, with the introduction and general acceptance of BNF, the first to receive a satisfactory solution. The problems of syntax are much easier than those of semantics. This had the natural but unfortunate consequence that great attention was given to syntactic questions - so much so, indeed, as to give rise to the idea that syntax and grammar were the whole of a programming language. Nothing could be further from the truth as the widespread and continuing misunderstandings about even the most basic concepts, such as names and values, illustrate vividly."

On his work at Cambridge, Strachey also commented: "From about 1962 until 1966 [I] was engaged with several collaborators at Cambridge and London on the design of a general purpose programming language which came to be known as CPL (an acronym which stood for so many different titles in the course of its existence that it finally acquired a life of its own). During the course of this design work a rather large number of concepts became clear, including many of those concerned with the store such as the distinctions between L- and R- modes of evaluation and between scope and extent. Though both these distinctions were originally due to myself they were refined in further discussions. CPL was never satisfactorily implemented and only inadequately publicized; the most complete document concerning it was only circulated privately (although quite widely)."

The influence of CPL was remarkable, however, and an implementation of a variant of CPL, devised by Strachey's student Martin Richards and called BCPL, has established itself as an important implementation language in its own right (see ref. [44]). BCPL was used to very good advantage by Strachey later at Oxford when he developed the operating system for his Modular One machine at his Programming Research Group.

After leaving Cambridge and before coming to Oxford in 1965 to set up his group, Strachey spent an influential year at MIT. 1964 saw the advent of two crucial papers: Landin's paper on the mechanical evaluation of expressions [25], and Strachey's *Towards a Formal Semantics* [56] (published in 1966 but delivered at a working conference in 1964). Strachey comments: "Although Landin's influence on the development of our semantic method has been considerable, it has been largely indirect. We prefer in the first instance to use a more abstract approach and the standard semantics differs from the work of Landin in that it does not depend in any way on a machine involving anonymous quantities and linkage information not explicitly available to the programmer." And further: "[Paper [56]] introduced the general method of giving mathematical semantics as a set of recursively defined functions from syntactic domains to semantic domains which included high-order functions. The approach was deliberately informal, and, as subsequent events proved, gravely lacking in rigour - but, in spite of these defects, it certainly laid down the outline of our subsequent work."

The kind of work Landin did (and others, as in the Vienna method [27],) comes to the fore again in describing precisely how to *implement* a language. This is discussed in Chapter 13 of the present work, and in great detail in [34]. The distinction drawn between language *definition* and language *implementation* is a vital point in understanding Strachey's approach, and the theme is touched on again and again by Stoy in this book.

The fullest discussion of the first phase of Strachey's work on the conceptual basis of programming languages was contained in a series of lectures given by him at the International Summer School in Computer Programming at Copenhagen in August 1967. The paper Strachey wrote [57] was privately circulated, but unfortunately the editor did not publish the proceedings of the meeting. The essential content was incorporated into the first draft of [34], but at the present no example of Strachey's writing on this important theme is in print.

Concerning the basic ideas of these papers, Milne

and Strachey remarked in the introduction to the draft of [34] that there were four features of mathematical semantics as it now stands which were not in the 1964 paper and which they did not consider their own work. "The first is that the store, σ, is a function from locations to their contents, following a suggestion made by Rod Burstall to [Strachey] in 1964. Before then we had made no detailed model of the store and had merely assumed the existence of certain basic functions operating on it. The construction of a proper model helped to bring out the fact that storing commands (or procedures) led to severe mathematical problems." With all the proper background and a discussion of the foundations, this topic is presented here in Chapter 12.

The second divergence they mention is the separation of the *store* from the *environment*. This was a suggestion of mine made in the fall of 1969 when our joint work was just starting. The idea is common from logic and the semantics of the "static" languages employed in the theory of models as understood by logicians. In the present book it figures first in Chapter 8 and then throughout the following examples.

The third contribution in their list was my own construction of λ-calculus models and more complicated reflexive domains in November of 1969. I have written about this discovery, and Strachey's influence, in my Turing lecture, which will be published in the Communications of the ACM later this year. The essential idea is the content of Chapters 6 and 7 of this book. The main point is to have an *extensional* theory of functions, related directly to computability, where functions (rather than syntactic representations or programs for the functions) can be treated as objects in themselves. More background on the idea can be found in the papers of mine (and in the joint paper with Strachey [54]) cited in the Bibliography. Many people have taken up this idea for a variety of purposes, and it is becoming a flexible tool for a theory of computability on abstract domains with some real applications.

The final piece of the puzzle mentioned by Milne and Strachey is the introduction of *continuations* to deal with the complicated problems of jumps and error exits from procedures. This was due to Christopher Wadsworth, and independently Lockwood Morris, and is an application of an idea of A. Mazurkiewicz in a paper of 1970. This is the subject of Chapter 11.

They continue: "There is another facet to the development of mathematical rigour in the discussion of programming languages which is perhaps more technically mathematical than most of those so far discussed. This is the development of *induction rules* and the closely related *fixed-point operators*. The relevant theorems about fixed points, due to Knaster and Tarski, had little impact on computing [as distinct from recursive function theory] until the work of David Park and Scott. Landin in his 1964 paper made use of the 'paradoxical combinator', Y, discussed by Curry and Feys. In λ-calculus Y has the formal properties of a fixed-point operator, the definition of which requires the application of a function to itself. After Scott had completed his theory of reflexive domains, Park showed that this operator could be identified with the [minimal fixed-point function; c.f. Theorem 7.19 of this book]. The paradoxical combinator was extensively used in the early stages of mathematical semantics as a minimal fixpoint operator without any satisfactory mathematical justification; fortunately, subsequent events showed that these uses were in fact substantially correct. The development of induction rules for mathematical semantics was started by McCarthy, who introduced 'recursion induction'. This rule turned out to be inadequate; more satisfactory rules were discussed by de Bakker and Scott." The point here is that McCarthy's domains of computation were too limited, and the rôle of continuity of functions and inclusivity of predicates was not apparent. When the better domains were introduced, better induction rules were required (see the discussion in Chapter 9). Much more has to be done in developing practical proof techniques, and many people are working on this problem at the present time.

In effect Strachey lived to see the completion of the second main phase of the work on mathematical semantics, and this book of Stoy's is going to be a most helpful summary. For the future the problems of an adequate proof theory and of explaining non-determinism loom very large. In evaluating Strachey's own contribution we can at a very minimum say that he *founded* a subject, and with his inspiration in mind we can now set about making it useful.

Merton College, Oxford.
June, 1977.

DENOTATIONAL SEMANTICS:

THE SCOTT-STRACHEY APPROACH

TO PROGRAMMING LANGUAGE THEORY

Chapter 1

INTRODUCTION

This book is an introduction to the method developed by Dana Scott and Christopher Strachey for describing the formal semantics of programming languages. This method is known as "denotational" semantics, or sometimes "mathematical" or "functional" semantics. In the first two chapters we shall attempt to describe the special flavour of this kind of semantics, and also to answer some more fundamental questions, such as why we need a formal semantics at all.

Programming languages are certainly not the first formal notation for specifying operations of a fairly specialized nature. Others, for example, are the notations of matrix algebra or the calculus. Yet usually there is no attempt to give a formal semantics of these other notations. What is so special about programming languages?

Part of the answer is the sheer *amount* of new notation involved in programming languages. This has evolved so quickly over the last quarter century that it has not had time to be assimilated naturally by workers in the field. Notation for the calculus, for example, developed at a far more relaxed rate (mainly, of course, because of the absence of commercial pressures); people proposed variants from time to time, until nowadays the few which proved to be most useful are generally accepted and universally taught.

In programming languages, on the other hand, one notation may even be used in different languages to mean different things. Consider, for example, how the meaning of an expression like $f(x)$ depends on the different rules about parameter passing in different languages. Moreover, the rate of growth of these languages has meant that the development of the notation has outstripped the development of our conceptual understanding of computing, so that the notation does not always mirror faithfully the structure of the underlying mathematics. For both these reasons, formal and rigorous definitions of our notation are essential to avoid misconception and error.

In particular, programming languages contain some features (especially the "imperative" features) which go against our experience of ordinary mathematics. For example, we would normally expect the assertion

$$x = x$$

to be obviously and always true. But this is just not so for programming languages: consider the Algol 60 expression

$$Random = Random.$$

Mathematics has very many generally accepted conventions about matters like these, and many of them are adopted by various programming languages. It is when we adopt different conventions that the need for formality arises again, for unless we take great care in these situations we shall find ourselves accidentally slipping back into the old ways.

Mathematicians normally deal with their notations (the details of the syntax and so on) very informally and, quite reasonably, expect the educated reader to make allowances for minor inconsistencies. Computers, on the other hand, require that programs presented to them follow a precise set of rules (and will continue to do so at least until Artificial Intelligence finally triumphs and we can begin to have informal conversations with our machines about our requirements). The rules are often difficult to describe precisely, and this is another reason for requiring great care and formality. As an example of these difficulties, we mention the rules about substitution. In particular, every one knows that the name of a variable of integration may be changed to another without affecting the value of the integral. Thus

$$\int_a^b \ldots x \ldots \mathrm{d}x = \int_a^b \ldots y \ldots \mathrm{d}y$$

where $\ldots x \ldots$ is some expression involving x, and $\ldots y \ldots$ is the same expression using y instead. But if

$$\int_a^b \ldots x \ldots \mathrm{d}x \quad \text{is} \quad \int_a^b (x^2 + \int_c^d x\ y\ \mathrm{d}y)\ \mathrm{d}x$$

then we could not simply change all the x's to y's: the process of substitution would have to involve changing the name of the dummy variable of the inner integration in order to avoid a clash of names. There have been many incorrect attempts to give the rules of substitution formally in various contexts (e.g. by Hilbert and Ackermann, Hilbert and Bernays, Gödel, Quine — all of them famous mathematicians). Later on we shall meet one version of the correct rules.

Referential Transparency

One particularly important convention in mathematics, which we have in fact already mentioned above, may be summed up in the phrase "referential transparency". This is a phrase which has been used by various authors with slightly different meanings. It was first used by Whitehead and Russell [69] to compare the logic of the following two syllogisms.

All men are mortal;
Socrates is a man;
Therefore Socrates is mortal. (i)

Everything Xenophon said about Socrates is true;
Xenophon said: "Socrates is mortal";
So Socrates is mortal. (ii)

A statement, they said, is not referentially transparent if questions arise not merely about its content but also about the circumstances of its assertion (for example, was it Xenophon who said it?). In (i) all the statements are transparent: all that matters is what they assert. But the statement "Socrates is mortal" is used non-transparently in (ii): the fact that Xenophon said it is crucial to the argument.

Quine [40] uses the phrase slightly differently to refer to the substitutivity of identities: that is, the interchangeability of two expressions denoting the same thing. For example, in the sentence

"Tully was a Roman"

the word "Tully" may be replaced by "Cicero", which was another name of the same man. But the phrase

"William Rufus was so-called because of the colour of his hair"

becomes untrue if we replace "William Rufus" by the alternative description of the same man, "King William II". "Tully" is being used transparently in the first sentence, but "Rufus" is used opaquely in the second.

Our use of the phrase "referential transparency" draws something from each of these two meanings. We use it to refer to the fact of mathematics which says:

The only thing that matters about an expression is its value, and any subexpression can be replaced by any other equal in value. Moreover, the value of an expression is, within certain limits, the same whenever it occurs.

The word "subexpression" is important, as we are not allowed to replace arbitrary chunks of an expression: for example, we can say $sin(1+5) = sin(6)$, but not $21+57 = 267$. The qualification "within certain limits" is necessary because of the way we use variable names. For example, if $x = 6$ then the expressions *sin*(1+5), *sin*(6), *sin*(x) are all interchangeable and their value is independent of position *provided* that *sin*(x) is not placed in some other context where x has been defined to refer to some value other than 6. When a name is introduced in normal mathematics it is usually obvious how much of the surrounding text is affected by the definition: this area is called the *scope* of the definition. The value of an expression is independent of its position only provided we remain within the scopes of the definitions which apply to the names occurring in the expression. This restriction is not irksome, as these scopes are specific areas of text which are easily ascertainable by fairly superficial examination.

In most programming languages referential transparency appears to be destroyed. For example, the fact that we have deduced $x=6$ would not imply that we could replace x by 6 everywhere within the scope of the declaration of x; if the program contains a statement like

if $x > y$ **then** $x := x-1$

then the value of x is not independent of position — afterwards it even depends on the value of y.

This is fairly catastrophic: it is one of the main reasons why some mathematicians tend to be put off computers by their first acquaintance with programming languages. The principle thus violated does, after all, form one of the cornerstones of mathematical argument. We shall see what we can salvage from the situation later on. We bring up the concept at this early stage partly as an example of the kind of rule which is often taken for granted, which implies the need for great care in situations where it does not apply, and partly because we shall be concerned to emphasise that this principle *does* apply throughout the formalism we shall use in describing semantics.

Purpose of a Formal Semantics

It may still reasonably be asked why we bother with giving a formal description at all. In fact the uses to which such descriptions are put have changed over the years. Initially, the objective was to give a sufficiently precise description for *implementers* of the language to construct a correct compiler. Nowadays, the emphasis is more on a description sufficiently precise for *programmers* to make rigorous statements about the behaviour of the programs they write. In the future, the most important benefit will probably be to *language designers*, who will be guided towards the design of better (cleaner) programming languages, with simpler formal descriptions. And the advantage of that will be that the programs which we concoct by the usual informal methods will be more probably correct, because we will less likely have forgotten about the crucial little exception to some general rule that applies in our particular case.

We shall see that the different methods of formal semantics appear to be inspired by, and to concentrate on, different objectives in the list we have given.

Syntax and Semantics

We may think of programming languages (and, indeed, mathematical models generally) in either of two ways. We may regard them as *free* objects — as objects of study in their own right without any implied meaning — or we may think of them together with an *interpretation* of their meaning.

Syntax deals with the free properties of a language. The sorts of question that arise here are: Is X a grammatically correct program? What are the proper subexpressions of the expression E?

The *semantics* of a language attempts to give the language an interpretation, and to supply a meaning, or value, to the expressions, programs etc. in the language.

The boundary between syntax and semantics is a bit fuzzy in places. For example, is the question whether the occurrence of a name is within the scope of some definition of that name a matter of syntax or semantics? We could regard it as a (context-sensitive) syntactic question, or we could do as most compilers do, and make it part of the semantics. We should not be worried by the fuzziness, however: the distinction remains obvious, important and useful for the majority of cases.

Incidentally, the fuzziness of the boundary is much worse when dealing with natural languages. There are many situations (for example, "Time flies like an arrow", compared with "Fruit flies like a banana") where semantic questions (the existence or otherwise of fruit flies and time flies) affect the parse. In other examples (e.g. "Our mothers bore us") the probable characteristics of the objects described affect the syntax. The situation is much easier with artificial languages — we design them ourselves, so we can take care to avoid such horrors. This may indicate that "language" is the wrong word to use for the objects of our study, and that perhaps the word "notation" would give a more accurate impression of what we are about: we do not normally talk about "the language of tensors", or "Leibnitz's language for the integral calculus". But we are bedevilled by over-inflated jargon in computing (usually implying unwarranted anthropomorphisation), and we must learn to live with it.

We can apparently get quite a long way expounding the properties of a language with purely syntactic rules and transformations, particularly for languages without commands (with no jumps or assignments, for example). One such language is the λ-calculus and, as we shall see, it can be presented solely as a formal system with syntactic conversion rules. Backus [1], for example, believes in defining languages this way. But we must remember that when working like this all we are doing is manipulating symbols — we have *no idea* at all of what we are talking about. To solve any real problem, we must give some semantic interpretation. We must say, for example, "these symbols represent the integers" — and then we are faced with the problem of proving that they do so consistently.

The need for a semantic interpretation is even more apparent when we are dealing with the imperative features of languages. In the assignment command, for example, we are specifying a change that is to happen somewhere else, in the computer store (we prefer the less anthropomorphic English term "store" rather than the American "memory"). We cannot satisfactorily explain this merely in terms of syntactic transformation to the program itself: the *meaning* of the command is the change to the store, and that is its *semantics*.

There is a temptation to become preoccupied with questions in the theory of syntax, partly because there is some well-developed mathematics there to build on (Chomsky grammars, for example). People who succumb can frequently be recognised by their excessive preoccupation with the actual symbols as written. At the extreme, they do not allow one to speak of a program's being "wrong": either it is syntactically incorrect, in which case it is not a program at all; or it is a perfectly good program, though perhaps not the one the programmer expected to write. Our point of view is rather that a program is intended to model the behaviour of something, be it the prime numbers, the flow of viscous fluids, the structure of knowledge, or an infinite universe of cellular automata. Whether the program is "right" or "wrong" depends on whether it faithfully models the behaviour of these other things.

In these notes we shall take syntactic matters very much for granted, and shall not be exploring the properties of various kinds of grammar. We shall assume that there exist methods of parsing our programs: that is, for going from the string of symbols on paper or cards etc. — a *concrete representation* of the program — to a parse tree, indicating the structure of expressions and subexpressions in the program — an *abstract representation*. Most of the time we shall start from such a parse tree.

It is time now to bring this introductory and somewhat discursive chapter to a close: we go on to introduce the method called "denotational semantics", and to discuss how it compares with the other approaches.

Chapter 2

DENOTATIONAL SEMANTICS

Methods of Formal Semantics

Three main methods have developed for giving semantic descriptions of programming languages.

The Operational Approach. We define an "abstract machine", which has a state, possibly with several components, and some set of primitive instructions. We define the machine by specifying how the components of the state are changed by each of the instructions. Then we define the semantics of our particular programming language in terms of that. The idea is that although the abstract machine is probably completely unrealistic from a practical point of view, it is so simple that no misunderstanding can possibly arise with respect to its order code. The semantic description of the programming language specifies a translation into this code. Once this code is understood, one merely has to trace through the translated program step by step to determine its precise effect. Languages defined in this way include PL/I (by the Vienna Definition Method [27]) and, underneath its inimitable description method, Algol 68 [62].

The Denotational Approach. We give "semantic valuation functions", which map syntactic constructs in the program to the abstract values (numbers, truth values, functions etc.) which they denote. These valuation functions are usually recursively defined:

the value denoted by a construct is specified in terms of the values denoted by its syntactic subcomponents, and it is this emphasis on the values *denoted* by all these constructs that gives the approach its name. There may or may not be an obvious way of working out the results of these functions in any particular case: that is, the defining equations may or may not suggest a way of implementing the language.

The Axiomatic Approach. We associate an "axiom" with each kind of statement in the programming language, which states what we may assert after execution of that statement in terms of what was true beforehand.

We shall defer any further consideration of the axiomatic approach for the present, and relate the other two approaches with the help of a diagram (Fig.2.1).

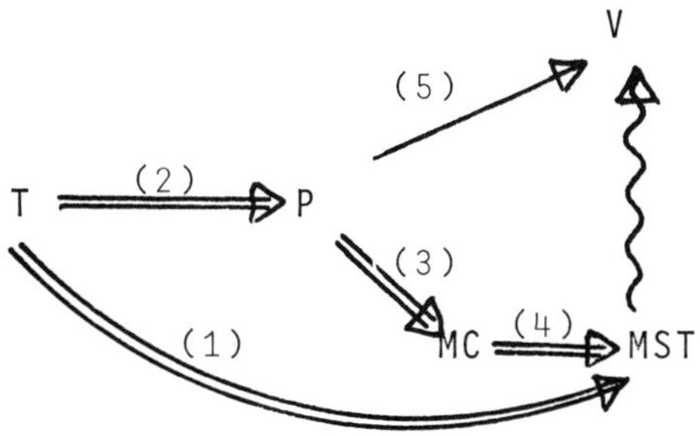

Fig. 2.1. Semantic approaches compared.

In Fig.2.1, T stands for the text of some program in our programming language, and we are considering how to describe the semantics of all such programs. One way (1) is to specify in detail a complete implementation. This used to be quite common: languages would be "as defined by" some particular compiler. To get the semantics of a particular program T it is necessary to determine its behaviour under the standard implementation, in terms of the machine state transformation MST which it produces in the computer. This method involves us in all the details of an actual compiler. Moreover, the job of proving the correctness of any other implementation, constructed along different lines, is horrendous.

Paths (2), (3) and (4) may be introduced to simplify matters. In the first place, (2) represents the translation of the program text T into a parse tree P, which indicates the syntactic structure of the program The definition of this transformation (the specification of the grammar of the language) and its implementation (the lexical analysis and parsing algorithms) are matters which, as we have intimated earlier, will not concern us greatly in this book.

(3) represents a translation of the parse tree into a program MC in the machine code of some standard machine, and (4) represents the execution of the machine code program to produce the machine state transformation MST. (3) is defined by giving the translation rules for generating code from the tree, and (4) by specifying the operations of the machine. Other languages can also be described by giving their

translation into the same machine code. So the combination of (2), (3) and (4) gives a standard implementation of the programming language. Of course, other, more efficient, direct implementations can be constructed, but they must all be equivalent to the standard one.

Notice that so far everything is purely formal symbol manipulation — either translation or implementation, which is the manipulation of representations by a machine. We have not yet given any abstract "meaning" to constructs in the language. (This applies to the routes marked with double lines ⇒.)

(5) specifies for each construct in **P** its mathematical value in some suitable abstract value space **V**. This is what gives a "meaning" to the construct, and it allows us to talk about *equality* in **P**: two expressions are equal if they both denote the same value in **V**.

The implementation parts (⇒) and the denotational parts (→) of the diagram are not, however, unrelated. Now that the denotational definition gives us some criteria, we have an opportunity to prove of some implementation: (*a*) that it is correct (in the sense that equal expressions remain equal under the machinations of the implementation); (*b*) how effective it is (one possible standard is that if some expression has a discrete value — e.g. an integer, rather than an infinitary value like a real number or a function — then the implementation will find it exactly).

Our approach, of course, will be along the single-line route. We shall obviously require a language in which to describe the association (5) between programming language elements and abstract values, and we shall mainly use the informal methods and notations of ordinary mathematics. As we have already hinted, such informality is perfectly satisfactory only in a situation where there is an opportunity for dialogue, so that points of ambiguity can be clarified; this process continues until a bell rings in the mind of the listener, and finally he understands (the process does not necessarily terminate). Mathematics is no different in this from any other kind of communication with language — scientific, poetic, theological and so on. Since we do not have the opportunity for dialogue here, we use the traditional forms of mathematics in the hope that the conversations necessary to arrive at a consensus of understanding will already have taken place, in various classrooms and elsewhere, before the reader comes to this book.

Example of the Two Approaches

As a simple example for comparison of the two approaches, we briefly consider the λ-calculus. (We shall be studying this in very much more detail later, and the reader is urged to be patient if any undefined terms are encountered.)

Various rules exist (the conversion rules of the λ-calculus) for syntactic transformations on λ-expressions. For example, we may say

$(\lambda x.3 \times x)4 \quad \text{cnv}_{\beta} \quad 3 \times 4$.

If we also define a particular order in which to apply these rules whenever there is any choice, they can form the principle of operation for an evaluation machine. So, in particular,

1. One particular order of evaluation is called *normal order*; we can define a machine based on this which reduces any λ-expression to its so-called "normal form" if it has one, and then stops; if the expression does not have a normal form the machine continues indefinitely (normal form and normal order will be defined later).

2. Peter Landin's SECD machine [25] is another machine for evaluating λ-expressions. It is not as powerful as the previous one, in the sense that there are some expressions for which this one will continue forever but the other would find a normal form; but when this one does find the answer it is often faster.

3. Various other machines have been proposed [64] which combine some of the advantages of the previous two.

So there may be several machines which each purport to evaluate, and even to define, the same language. Some may not even be correct. Proving that two of them are equivalent is not a trivial task (in the λ-calculus it involves the Church-Rosser theorem). Moreover, except for history, there seems to be no very convincing argument for taking any particular one of them as canonical.

The semantic equations, however, do define a canonical function. There may, of course, be more than one formulation of the denotational semantics, but they all define the same function. (The task of proving two formulations equivalent is now a matter of showing the identity of two functions, conceptually much more straightforward than the equivalence of two different implementations.)

In the case of the λ-calculus, we say that we are attempting to model the concepts of function and functional application and abstraction. As we shall see, we have to be rather careful about exactly what class of functions is represented by λ-expressions; but once that is established we can define a semantic function associating each λ-expression with a member of that class. Then we can (and shall) prove that the conversion rules mentioned above are correct; that is to say, that they preserve identity in the class of functions.

Many people, however, are unwilling to treat functions as abstract objects, and so there is a strong temptation to stick to the syntactic rules. Such an attitude does no positive harm — the denotational definition of the semantics causes not one jot or tittle to pass from the rules, since they remain provably correct — though it may be sometimes inadequate. On the other hand, many expositions of λ-calculus treat normal order evaluation as the *touchstone* of correctness; then, however, the fact that the system can be thought of as modelling functions is merely a matter of good fortune. We start with the functions, and then we find rules whose correctness we can prove.

Comments on the Operational Approach

In this approach we usually translate our programs into the machine code of some abstract machine. This is a natural development of the original view of high-level languages, which was as a kind of shorthand for writing machine code: it was at the machine code level that the real computing was analysed. (Nowadays we tend to think of high-level languages more in their own terms and at their own level, but the name FORTRAN survives as a reminder of the older view.) The first observation that we may make about the operational method is that we still have the problem of rigorously defining the abstract machine; that is, of giving a formal semantics for the machine code. In a sense we have merely pushed the problem of semantics one level back.

More serious, however, as Dijkstra has remarked [9], is that the method tends to be regarded as one which gives the result only of specific computations. Starting with some particular program, and some particular input data one may "crank the handle" of the defined abstract machine and obtain the particular final result. This job is, however, precisely what the computer is for. It is much more useful for us to be able to consider the class of all the computations that can possibly be evoked by the program, or even by a class of programs. When we do this, we are in effect considering the function that the program and its implementation together define. We are, in fact, moving towards a functional approach.

That suggests that this difference between the two

approaches is basically one of attitude. Although this is partly true, it is not entirely so. The crux of the distinction is that by considering the function associated with a program by an operational definition of semantics, we may be begging the question of whether such a function exists and is well-defined. Again, for some particular programs it may be obvious; but when giving the semantics of a language we must consider all programs that could possibly be written in the language. To verify that such a well-defined function exists for *any* program in the language is a fundamental task of any mathematical theory of semantics.

An operational definition can, of course, be made mathematically rigorous. Indeed, in our Chapter 13 on non-standard semantics we shall be giving some very simple examples of such definitions. But even then there is a further difference between an operational definition and a denotational one. The former defines the value of a program in terms of what an abstract machine does with the complete program. Its structure, therefore, need not correlate with the way the programmer thinks about his program, when he selects particular syntactic components and combines them together in particular ways. In the denotational definition, on the other hand, the value of a program is defined in terms of the values of its subcomponents; it is more easily possible for us to confine our treatment to any particular part of the program we wish to examine. This may make it a more satisfactory tool for the language designer and also for those concerned with validating various techniques for proving the correctness of particular programs.

Operational definitions of semantics tend to suggest techniques for implementing the language to the compiler writers — this, indeed, may be one of their main benefits. But we have already mentioned the enormous difficulty in showing the equivalence of two implementations, constructed along different lines. A standard denotational definition does not contain details of a particular implementation; so although it is a complicated job to show that an implementation is faithful to the denotational semantics, the problem is not compounded by the need to reconcile opposing implementation techniques. (This point will be illustrated by simple examples in Chapter 13).

Comments on the Axiomatic Approach

In this method a rule is associated with each statement of the language. These rules allow us to say what will be true after the statement has been executed and to relate it to what was true beforehand. For example, given the statement

while E **do** Γ

where E is an expression and Γ is a command, we know that after the statement terminates (if it terminates) the value of the expression E will be *false*. (Other assertions can also be made, depending on the initial conditions and on the properties of Γ.)

This approach grew out of Floyd's work [13] on attaching assertions to the links of flowcharts. Its application to high level languages, mainly the work of Hoare [19], has made an important contribution to the art of proving the correctness of programs. Its main advantage is that the assertions it involves are expressed in the programming language itself (sometimes with a modicum of extra apparatus, such as quantifiers), and there is a minimum of new notation. This is significant, as it is to be hoped that the proof of a program's correctness will become the responsibility of the programmers, and it is unreasonable to expect them to do the programming and the proving in two different languages.

At present, however, the axioms are hedged about with restrictions, and apply only in simplish situations. For example, even the simple result cited above might not apply if E had a side effect. With a given language it is often not clear in what situations the various axioms are applicable. On the other hand, the very paucity of extra apparatus makes it difficult, when designing a language, to discuss how to arrange that the necessary conditions hold.

In our approach we shall be able to prove these "axioms" as theorems deriving from our denotational semantics: then, of course, the conditions of applicability will be clearly apparent. Indeed, the derivation of these theorems is a most important part of the application of our method: we shall discuss one particular example in Chapter 14.

It might perhaps be thought that it is pure wishful thinking to hope that programmers would become expected to prove the correctness of their programs. But it is difficult to speculate with any confidence on the future of a profession as young as computing, or even about how many of its practitioners will still be programmers in our sense of the word. Yet in any case we are not suggesting that each program be accompanied by a formal proof. Dijkstra has remarked that a formal proof of a program is in the same relation to the programmer's informal sense of its correctness as the text of an Act of Parliament is to one's sense of justice. In both cases there arise difficult situations where the rules are not clear; to resolve them recourse must be had to the formal text, and this is usually a job for professionals. But if these situations arise too frequently then something is wrong, either with the rules or with the upbringing or training of the people concerned. Our job as designers is to frame the rules so that they are sufficiently simple and universally applicable that they may be faithfully followed even in informal argument.

Comments on Our Approach

We are now reaching the end of our comparison of the various methods of formal semantics, and our discussion of the relationship between the denotational approach and the others. We have, of course, been making a case for the denotational point of view, which is the principal subject of this book. Apologia for the other methods may be found elsewhere.

It may appear that the operational method is likely to be of most value to the implementer, the axiomatic to the programmer, and the denotational to the language designer. This impression is not so far from the truth, but it is something of an oversimplification. Neither the three methods nor the three sorts of activity are as disjoint as the division suggests, and there are techniques for moving from one formulation to another in studying a language. Our proof of one of the "axioms" in Chapter 14 is one example of this, and so is our discussion of non-standard semantics in Chapter 13. We claim, too, that the denotational semantics provides a *normative* definition of a language: it is the most convenient standard for settling questions about the correctness both of implementations and of programs written in the language. Operational definitions, on the one hand, contain extra implementation details which, unless they are explicitly relevant to a particular problem, serve merely to complicate further an area which is already complex. On the other hand, the axiomatic semantics gives less than a complete definition of a language. This, of course, is by design, as it lets the programmer concentrate on the properties which concern him; it means, however, that a set of axioms is unsatisfactory as a *definition* of a language, as it is not obvious that a language exists for which the axioms are satisfied. Demonstrating the existence of such a language is most easily done by giving its denotational semantics.

The special contributions of the denotational approach to the study of computing are two. Firstly, there is the investigation of the mathematical foundations of computing. This concerns the nature of the abstract space V in Fig. 2.1.; this part is mainly the work of Dana Scott. Secondly, there are the techniques for defining actual languages ((5) in Fig.2.1); this part is mainly the work of Christopher Strachey. The second part obviously relies on the first for logical justification; but the relationship is rather like that between real arithmetic and the theory of Dedekind cuts. Thus the definition techniques rarely use the basic theory explicitly, and take it for granted most of the time — indeed, they even predated it by several years. We shall follow the logical order, however, and study the fundamental theory before we come to any techniques that rely on it. But first we introduce the definition method by means of a simple example in which no theoretical difficulties arise.

Chapter 3

BINARY NUMERALS

For a simple example of the method of language definition we consider the binary numerals which, as every schoolboy knows, are a possible representation for the non-negative integers. In fact they form a simple "language" for these numbers, and we can give the syntax and semantics of this language as follows.

Syntax

N ::= 0|1|N0|N1

The syntax is presented in a variant of Backus-Naur form ([38]), with which we assume the reader is familiar. The difference is that we use Greek capital letters for the metalinguistic variables, instead of names in angle brackets. In this case N is an element of the set of numerals, which we call Nml. So

N ∈ Nml.

The syntactic definition says that Nml consists of arbitrary finite strings of 0s and 1s. But so far we have no idea about what any of them might mean.

Semantics

The non-negative integers are abstract mathematical objects which are defined quite independently of the numerals, by Peano's axioms. For the present we call the set of non-negative integers N, and refer to them simply as "numbers".

We still do not know how the numerals are related to the numbers. We do not know anything about which end the most significant digit is — or even what it signifies.*

We want each numeral to represent a unique number, so we must define a semantic function

$\mathcal{N}$: Nml → N.

If we like, we may say that $\mathcal{N}$ "evaluates" a numeral and gives the corresponding number.

The syntactic definition of Nml was a recursive definition with four alternative clauses. We can therefore expect a similar structure for the definition of $\mathcal{N}$. The definition is as follows:

$$\mathcal{N}(\underline{0}) = 0$$
$$\mathcal{N}(\underline{1}) = 1$$
$$\mathcal{N}(\underline{N0}) = 2 \times \mathcal{N}(\underline{N})$$
$$\mathcal{N}(\underline{N1}) = 2 \times \mathcal{N}(\underline{N}) + 1.$$

Here there is an important difference between those symbols that are underlined and those that are not.

---

*The decision which way round the digits run is, of course, mathematically trivial. Indeed, one early British computer had numbers running from right to left (because the spot on an oscilloscope tube runs from left to right, but in serial logic the least significant digits are dealt with first). Turing used to mystify audiences at public lectures when, quite by accident, he would slip into this mode even for decimal arithmetic, and write things like 73+42=16. The next version of the machine was made more conventional simply by crossing the *x*-deflection wires: this, however, worried the engineers, whose waveforms were all backwards. That problem was in turn solved by providing a little window so that the engineers (who tended to be behind the computer anyway) could view the oscilloscope screen from the back. [C. Strachey — private communication.]

The underlined symbols are parts of *numerals*: either they are symbols in the *object language* (the language we are defining), or they are variables ranging over elements of Nml. All the other symbols are in the metalanguage and represent mathematical objects which, except for the function $\mathcal{N}$ being defined, are all known about already: they include zero, unity, the successor of unity, and the primitive recursive functions of addition and multiplication. To each member of Nml precisely one of the four equations is applicable, depending on which of the four productions in the syntax corresponds to it. In the third and fourth equations $\mathcal{N}$ is applied recursively to a subcomponent of the numeral in an obvious way.

Let us be just a little more pedantic. Strictly speaking, perhaps, the symbols N should not have been underlined. N is really a variable in the metalanguage, whose *values* are objects in the object language. The underlined 0 and 1, on the other hand, are not variables, and simply stand for themselves: they are effectively quoted. (We ignore philosophical quibbles about whether they are really standing for themselves or are merely instantiations of some abstract paradigm; moreover, we shall assume that we know what we mean by saying that two characters are "the same".) So by N0 we mean

$$N \smile \ulcorner 0 \urcorner$$

where the quoted 0 is a direct component of the value and the unquoted N is a variable; the variable is replaced by its value and the two strings concatenated. We can (and sometimes shall) write instead

$\ulcorner$NO$\urcorner$

as an alternative notation, suggested by Quine [40], for the same operation. Since these square quotes do not indicate true and complete quotation, they are called Quine's quasi-quotes.

More frequently, however, instead of writing

$\mathcal{N}\ulcorner$NO$\urcorner$

we shall write

$\mathcal{N}[\![$NO$]\!]$

The brackets $[\![\ ]\!]$, used round an argument of a semantic function, always enclose expressions in the object language, possibly including metalanguage variables.

In this discussion so far we have been thinking in terms of the concrete syntax. An alternative treatment (which we shall discuss further in Chapter 8 below) is to think of the syntactic definition of Nml as specifying the structure of valid parse trees. Thus the four alternative clauses specify four alternative kinds of node in a tree, and we can regard the 0s and 1s in the productions merely as indicating which particular kind is currently being considered. We think of Nml as the set of valid parse trees; expressions in the metalanguage denoting elements of such syntactic value spaces are, by convention, enclosed in $[\![\ ]\!]$ brackets.

So strings like 011010 are particular elements of the object language Nml; the same strings surrounded by quasi-quotes or $[\![\ ]\!]$ brackets, together with all other symbols in the equations, are elements of our metalanguage which we are using to discuss the relationship between elements of Nml and elements of the abstract value space N.

We have now given the semantics of the binary numerals, and we should prove that our definition is reasonable.

Exercises.

1. Show that every numeral represents a single number. (Use induction on the length of N).

2. Show that every number is represented by at least one numeral. (Use simple number theory about division by 2.)

Numerals *vs*. Numbers

Confusion easily arises about the relationship between numerals and numbers. Sometimes it is said that the numerals are the *names* of the numbers. But we prefer to think of names as atomic objects, whose internal structure is irrelevant except insofar as it enables us to say whether two names are the same. (Names can, of course, be given to several different kinds of object, and it is sometimes convenient to use some characteristic of the name as a mnemonic to remind ourselves what kind of object it is denoting. The initial letter rule of Fortran, and our own naming conventions — N_0, N_1 for numerals, E_0, E_1 for expressions, bold type for domains, etc. — are examples of this. But this is merely for convenience, and adds very little to our conceptual understanding.)

In this sense 0 and 1 are names; the other numerals, however, are *expressions*, with a syntax and semantics as defined above. Because the special syntactic rules for numerals are applied on the small scale, inside other expression constructions in a programming language, they are sometimes called *microsyntax*.

The confusion between numerals and numbers is made more common because for N there exists a *complete canonical* representation in the form of reduced numerals (numerals without leading zeros). The syntax for these is

N′::= 0|1|1N

where N′ ∈ Nml′, the set of reduced numerals, and N ∈ Nml as defined before. Notice that it is not quite as easy to give a semantic function $\mathcal{N}'$: Nml′→N for the reduced numerals: the most convenient way is by means of an auxiliary function $\mathcal{L}$: Nml→**N**, which gives the "length" of a numeral (see also Knuth [23]). Reduced numerals are in 1-1 correspondence with numbers.

Exercise.

3. Define $\mathcal{N}'$, and prove that reduced numerals are in 1-1 correspondence with numbers.

We are therefore tempted to work with reduced numerals and to confuse them with numbers (though we are more likely to do so in decimal). Since numerals are merely a *notation* for numbers this is muddled thinking; but as the representation is complete and canonical it does not tend to give wrong answers. The situation is quite different in cases where no complete canonical representation exists, such as the real numbers or functions: confusion can then indeed lead to error.

The Value of a Good Notation

From our use of '0' and '1' on both sides of our semantic equations it might appear that our definitions are somewhat circular. We have tried to indicate that this is not the case. What we have been doing with the semantic equations is explaining (or defining) the *positional notation* for numerals. This is not an obvious notation: in fact it is one of the great inventions of mathematics. It is by no means a necessary part of arithmetic: the concepts of zero, unity, addition, multiplication, prime numbers, etc. are quite independent of the decimal or binary notations. In principle we could do the whole of number theory without these notations, perhaps using Roman numerals to represent particular numbers. But it cannot be denied that the positional notation is an enormous convenience, as anyone who has tried to divide CCXLVII by XIII will realise.

One of the effects of the introduction of the positional notation was to popularise mathematics: to take what was previously the concern only of specialists and make it available to the general public. Fortran began a similar process for computing, but there is still a long way to go. Another effect was that operations like addition and division became almost completely mechanical, thus allowing mathematical minds to start thinking about something else instead. It is by no longer having to think about things that civilisation progresses. (For a more extended discussion of this, see Whitehead [68], particularly Chapter V on *The Symbolism of Mathematics*.)

In fact a good notation is more than mere "convenience", for it also allows us to structure our *ideas* hierarchically: we can focus our attention at the appropriate level. For example, when we actually need to consider the structure of a numeral (to find out what number it represents), the details of the positional notation are important. At higher levels of abstraction, however, the notation is so concise and compact that it is easy to regard the numeral as a single object (a molecule, perhaps). A good notation thus conceals much of the inner workings behind suitable abbreviations, while allowing us to consider it in more detail if we require: matrix and tensor notations provide further good examples of this. It may be summed up in the saying: "A notation is important for what it leaves out."

The moral of this digression is twofold: firstly, it justifies the use of programming languages at all. Our semantic metalanguage is too complicated for use in general programming (as is also machine code): high level languages are provided instead, in accordance with the principle already mentioned of avoiding the need to think about inessentials. Secondly, it points to the need for care in formulating the notation of our semantic metalanguage. One example of a decision about metanotation has already arisen: our use of single Greek letters in place of longer names (N for <*numeral*>). This stems from the belief that our mental pattern-recognisers find a concise statement more intelligible than a longer version with the same structure. (This is not an argument for one-line programs, where a longer

version may very well have a cleaner structure.)
But it should be noted that notational decisions are liable to be altered in the light of experience; so the particular notation used in these notes should not be regarded as permanently fixed.

Questions of Implementation: Addition

This example has so far concentrated on the relationship between a language and the abstract space of values: the upper half of Fig.2.1 (page 13). Now, still using the numerals, we give an example of the sort of thing we can say about matters of implementation.

As we have said, the standard arithmetic functions are purely abstract functions on numbers (quite independent of the numerals), with standard primitive recursive definitions. Addition, for example, is defined as follows:

$$a+b = \begin{cases} a & \text{if } b=0 \\ Suc(a)+c & \text{if } b=Suc(c) \end{cases}$$

where $Suc(x)$ means the successor of x. But we have also said that the positional notation allows these functions to be treated as mechanical operations. So, for example, addition may be *implemented* by means of the usual digitwise addition rule, which "adds" two numerals to give another numeral. Let us denote this operation by $\oplus$; so

$\oplus : (\mathrm{Nml} \times \mathrm{Nml}) \rightarrow \mathrm{Nml}.$

Now that we have given the semantics for the positional notation we can try to prove that this implementation works correctly; that is to say, for all N_1 and

N_2,

$$\mathcal{N}[\![N_1 \oplus N_2]\!] = \mathcal{N}[\![N_1]\!] + \mathcal{N}[\![N_2]\!]$$

where the + denotes mathematical addition of two numbers.

We must first define ⊕. Like N, it is defined recursively by cases, as shown in Table 3.1.

N_2 \ N_1	0	1	$N_1'0$	$N_1'1$
0	0	1	$N_1'0$	$N_1'1$
1	1	10	$N_1'1$	$(N_1' \oplus 1)0$
$N_2'0$	$N_2'0$	$N_2'1$	$(N_1' \oplus N_2')0$	$(N_1' \oplus N_2')1$
$N_2'1$	$N_2'1$	$(N_2' \oplus 1)0$	$(N_1' \oplus N_2')1$	$((N_1' \oplus N_2') \oplus 1)0$

Table 3.1. Definition of ⊕.

Here, in a somewhat informal notation, $(N_1' \oplus 1)0$ indicates that 0 is to be concatenated to the numeral which results from $N_1' \oplus 1$, and so on.

The proof is now by induction on this table. A crucial first step is to show that

$$\mathcal{N}[\![N \oplus 1]\!] = \mathcal{N}[\![N]\!] + 1$$

This also requires an induction on the clauses for N , but most of the cases are directly in the table.
One of the basis steps is to show

$$\mathcal{N}[\![1 \oplus 1]\!] = \mathcal{N}[\![1]\!] + 1$$

LHS $= \mathcal{N}[\![1 \oplus 1]\!] = \mathcal{N}[\![10]\!] = 2 \times \mathcal{N}[\![1]\!] = 2 \times 1 = 2.$

RHS $= \mathcal{N}[\![1]\!] + 1 = 1 + 1 = 2.$

We leave the task of filling in the remainder of the proof as an exercise. As a further exercise, just in case any further convincing is required that giving semantics to numerals is non-nugatory, we invite the reader to look at another language, with syntax identical to that of the numerals, but with a different semantics.

Exercises

4. Complete the proof that
$$\mathcal{N}[\![N_1 \oplus N_2]\!] = \mathcal{N}[\![N_1]\!] + \mathcal{N}[\![N_2]\!]$$

5. Consider the language defined as follows.

Syntax (same as for Nml)

$\Sigma ::= 0 \mid 1 \mid \Sigma 0 \mid \Sigma 1$

Semantics

$\mathcal{S}[\![0]\!] = 0$

$\mathcal{S}[\![1]\!] = 1$

$\mathcal{S}[\![\Sigma 0]\!] = -2 \times \mathcal{S}[\![\Sigma]\!]$

$\mathcal{S}[\![\Sigma 1]\!] = -2 \times \mathcal{S}[\![\Sigma]\!] + 1$

a) Prove that each integer (positive or negative) has a corresponding numeral.

b) Devise a digitwise addition rule $\oplus$ for this language, and prove that it is correct.

We now have completed our introduction to the techniques of semantic description using the numerals as examples. We now proceed to something with a little more meat.

Chapter 4

FIRST-CLASS FUNCTIONS

Many treatments split programming languages up into two parts: a descriptive part (sometimes called the applicative part) and an imperative part; these are also sometimes known as the expression part and the command part. One possible plan is to study the descriptive part of a language first, so that the ideas there may be thoroughly understood before the extra complications of commands are introduced. That is the plan we shall adopt, and for the descriptive part we shall use the λ-calculus as our particular object of study.

The λ-calculus has a free-wheeling approach to functions which is unfamiliar to the average programmer. So in this chapter, somewhat by way of digression, it may be appropriate and beneficial to introduce this less inhibited approach to functions by example using a more or less conventional programming language. In doing this, of course, we must anticipate many features of these languages which will not be formally introduced until much later, and we ask the reader's forbearance.

First and Second Class Objects

Even mathematicians are accustomed to treating functions as underprivileged objects. This attitude starts young. In an expression like

$$(x + y) \times (x - y)$$

the "x" and "y" are regarded as variables, but not "+", "-", or "×". Similarly, in the expression

$f(x)$

f is usually thought of as a constant. A similar restriction usually applies in programming languages: for example, one is not allowed to write

(**if** $x > 0$ **then** *sin* **else** *cos*)(y)

in Algol 60.

In the context of programming languages, what are the rights and privileges of first-class citizens? We list some of them:

1. they may be assigned to variables;
2. they may be passed as parameters to subroutines;
3. they may be returned as the results of function calls;
4. they may be selected by means of conditional expressions,
5. entered in arrays,

and so on.

In Algol 60, the only types which have all these properties are **real**, **integer**, and **boolean**. All types have property 2 but **procedures**, for example, have in addition to 2 only the ability to be obeyed.

We wish to gain some familiarity with functions treated as first-class objects; so we shall examine an example to see what happens when we allow variable functions, function-producing functions and so on. Further examples and some exercises may be found in an Appendix. For these examples we do not employ any existing programming language (though our notation is like that of Algol 60): we hope that the notation will cause no difficulty.

Example: Curried Functions

By a device introduced by Schönfinkel [47] and extensively used by Curry [7], to any function of two (or more) arguments there corresponds an equivalent one which takes one argument at a time. So to $f(x,y)$ there corresponds $f'(x)(y)$. f' is called the *curried* version of f. It is a function of one argument, x; the result, $f'(x)$, is also a function of one argument, y: the result of this, $f'(x)(y)$, is equal to the original $f(x,y)$. For example, we may define the function *Add* to add a pair of integers; so

$$Add(3,4) = 7$$

and

$$Add\colon (N \times N) \to N$$

(using N now for the set of all integers). If *Add'* is the curried version of *Add*, we have

$$Add'\colon N \to (N \to N)$$

and

$$Add'(3)(4) = 7.$$

Note that we are assuming, and shall throughout these notes, that functional application associates to the left, so that $Add'(3)(4)$ means $(Add'(3))(4)$, not $Add'(3(4))$.

We now wish to define the function *Curry*, which is to convert a function of two arguments to its curried equivalent. So

Curry(*Add*) = *Add'*

and so on. The functionality of *Curry* is therefore as follows:

Curry: ((N×N)→N) → (N→(N→N)).

A possible solution is the following:

```
let Curry(f) = g
    where g(x) = h
          where h(y) = f(x,y)
```

An alternative formulation in a more Algol-like syntax, avoiding the where-clause, is:

```
function Curry(f);
begin function g(x);
      begin function h(y);
            resultis f(x,y);
      resultis h                    || result of g(x)
      end;
resultis g                          || result of Curry(f)
end
```

If we knew λ-notation, we could say simply

$$Curry(f) = \lambda x.\ \lambda y.\ f(x,y)$$

The reader is urged to check through these definitions and to make sure he thoroughly understands what they are saying.

Implementation

Let us consider what difficulties may be involved in implementing languages like these. The principal difficulty concerns the *extent* (or lifetime) of variables.

It is important to distinguish clearly between the two concepts *scope* and *extent*. As we noted in Chapter 1, the scope of a variable definition is the area of program text within which an occurrence of the name refers to that definition; the extent, on the other hand, is the length of time during which the variable exists. So scope is a spatial concept and extent is a temporal one. In the following Algol 60 program, for example, the inner definition of *x* causes what we call a *hole in the scope* of the outer definition (whose scope is as indicated by the arrows); the extent, however, continues throughout, until control finally leaves the block. So of course, "4" will be printed.

```
begin real x;
      x := 4;
      begin real x;
            x := 3
      end;
      print(x)
end
```

It may be worth cautioning the reader at this point against the jargon of Algol 68. This uses many of the same words as everyone else, but often they have different meanings. For example, "name" is used to mean address. And, in particular, "scope" means something much more like extent.

In Algol 60 the extent of a variable ends when control finally leaves the block in which it was declared (i.e. it survives through any temporary excursions such as procedure calls). The extent of a procedure parameter is for the duration of the corresponding activation of that procedure. This is not good enough for *Curry* where, for example, the parameter f is required to persist *after* the activation of the procedure *Curry*. We therefore require a language in which extents are semi-infinite (in implementation terms this entails a garbage collection facility, so that storage can in fact be reused when the implementation can determine that the original use is no longer relevant). Algol 68 has some storage where extents are semi-infinite, called the heap; *Curry* still cannot be written in Algol 68, however, as part of the mechanism for referring to variables on the heap is itself still of limited extent.

Let us consider in a little more detail what happens when Curry is defined and used. A function definition does not define a function unless we also know the values of the variables it mentions without definition (the non-local variables). For example, the definition

let $h(y) \;=\; f(x,y)$

does not define a function (of y) unless we know what f and x are. So in the machine representation of a fully-fledged function there are two components:

1. the code of the algorithm;
2. a list (the *free variable list*), giving the values denoted by the non-local variables.

(Some people prefer to think of item 2 as the entire

environment; that is, a list of the values of all the variables the algorithm could possibly use. This does no harm, but all that is required are the values of the variables it actually does mention: this can allow economies in an implementation.) The structure consisting of these two components together is called a *closure*, and we draw it like this:

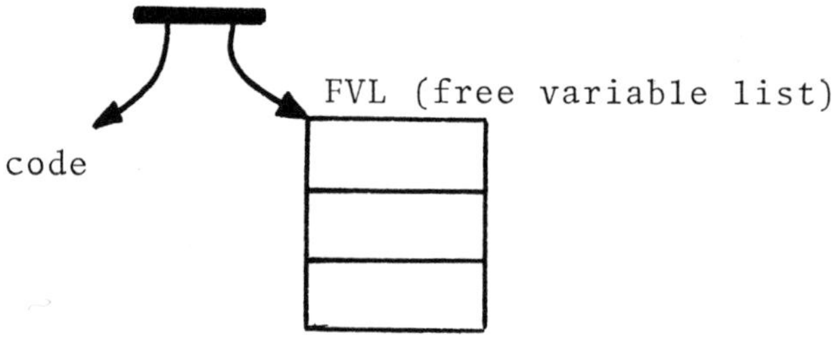

Curry itself has no free variables, so its closure is

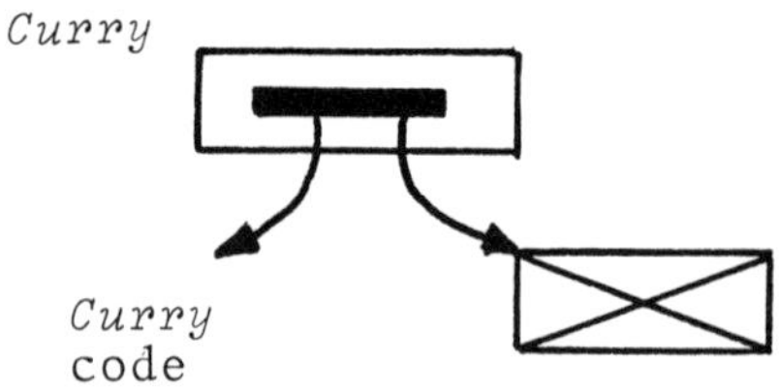

(Here *Curry* is the name of a location or cell ("pigeon-hole") containing the closure representing the function.)

Suppose we say

*Add*1 := *Curry*(*Add*).

Curry is invoked, and a closure for *g* is created. *g* has one free variable, *f*, the parameter of *Curry*, and its value is *Add*. Now the values in a free variable list might be the cells denoted by the non-local variables (represented by pointers to them), or instead they might be the contents of these cells at the time the function definition is executed.

In most languages with functions the semantics corresponds to the first choice, so we adopt that here. Finally, since *g* is the result of *Curry*, the value contained in the cell *g* gets placed in *Add*1. The final situation looks like this (we shall draw parameter cells on the right of our pictures):

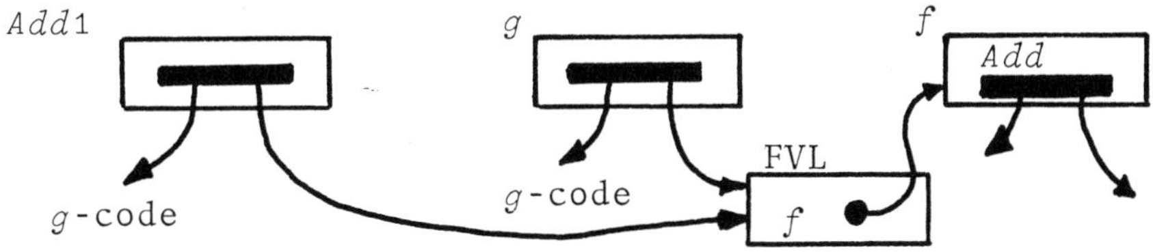

Notice that after this the cell *g* is no longer required, as nothing refers to it; however, the FVL of *g* and the cell for the parameter *f* must both remain.

Now suppose the following is obeyed:

*Add*3 := *Add*1(3).

*Add*1 is invoked, which causes the execution of the code of *g*. *h* is defined, so its closure is constructed. This has two free variables: *x*, the parameter of *Add*1, which is 3, and *f*, which is found in *Add*1's FVL. *h* is the result of *g* (or *Add*1), so its value is assigned to *Add*3, and the complete final situation is as follows:

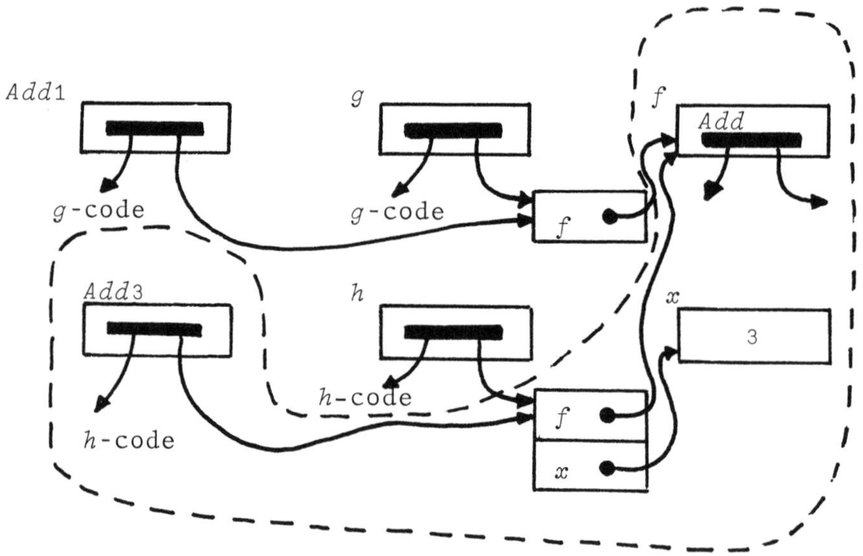

The dotted line surrounds the full representation of *Add*3, with all the ramifications. *Add*3 cannot be used if any of this ceases to exist. Unless such a catastrophe occurs, however, we could say

n := *Add*3(4) .

This would cause an invocation of *Add*3, so the code of *h* would be executed with the appropriate free variables *f* and *x* (*Add* and 3) and parameter *y* (4).

All the necessary information is available.

The problem caused here by inadequate extents is very closely related to the so-called *funarg* problem of LISP, particularly the upward funarg problem. In LISP, however, the problem is compounded with other effects which arise because the representation of a LAMBDA expression (the normal functionlike object) does not contain the values of the non-local variables at all. This "binding" is done only when the function is executed, and sometimes the wrong variable is found instead. So this feature of LISP does not deal with the definition of *functions*, which is why we did not choose LISP as the vehicle for our present discussion. In fact the extent problem is not confined to functions; it arises whenever objects which can be assigned or can be returned as the result of a function call (that is to say, objects which can be carried "outside the scope" of their original definitions) might be represented by structures containing pointers to other entities. This applies not only to the closures of functions but also, for example, to arrays and other forms of data structure.

Notice in passing that this approach involves our considering what happens at the definition time of a function (which is when the closure is created) as well as activation time (which is when the closure is applied).

Functions, Algorithms and Approximations

We make one final comment on this example before moving on. Mathematically, a function is regarded as a mapping, from arguments to results. Most are infinite mappings: that is, they are defined on an infinite domain. Being infinite, these objects cannot be represented inside a finite computer as an explicit table of arguments and results. Some functions are indeed represented by explicit (and finite) mappings: one example is the computer store, which is a mapping from addresses to contents maintained explicitly in the core. Usually, however, a function is represented by means of an algorithm, which is itself represented inside the machine by a closure.

An algorithm does not explicitly give us any of the function mapping. However, it does allow us to generate whatever (finite) portion of it we require, by applying the algorithm to appropriate arguments; at any stage in the execution, the behaviour of the program will be influenced only by that finite portion of the mapping corresponding to the arguments already supplied to the algorithm. In effect, what we are doing as execution proceeds and we go on applying a function to more and more arguments is gradually building up an *approximation* of the actual mapping which is good enough for the purposes of the particular program and data.

It is easy to confuse functions with the algorithms representing them, just as it was easy to confuse numbers and numerals. A careful distinction is, however, even more vital in the case of functions: on the one hand, a single function may have several algorithms (the reader probably knows more than one algorithm for the factorial function); on the other hand, the number of functions (uncountable) is greater than the number of algorithms (countable, at any rate if we regard an algorithm as specified by a finite string of letters drawn from a finite — or even countably infinite — alphabet), and so there are many functions which have no algorithm at all.

We have to represent functions by algorithms (or possibly by finite approximations to the explicit mapping) because of the infinitary nature of the function itself. The situation is similar to that of the real numbers, most of which cannot be written as finite decimal numerals. In such cases, too, we must either be content with a finite approximation (such as 3.14159 for π) or, if possible, give a rule (such as $0.\dot{1}4285\dot{7}$) which will enable the number to be computed to whatever (finite) degree of accuracy is required. Here, though, our greater familiarity with the number system helps us from confusing the numbers with the recurrence rule: we are even happy to say that $0.24\dot{9} = 0.25$.

In our example we have various functions whose value depends on that of other functions. *Add*1 and *Add*3, for example, both depend on *Add*. In *Add*3 we actually get round to applying *Add* to some arguments. That is to say, we are building up our required approximation to *Add*3 by building up an approximation to *Add*, on which it depends. Moreover, it must be possible to reach an approximation to *Add*3 sufficiently good for the purpose of any particular program by using a sufficiently good, but still finite, approximation to *Add*.

Other cases are like *Add*1: here we do not evaluate f in any way, but merely pass it on. But in the end, all we can do to find out anything about f is apply it to a finite number of arguments*. So we build up our approximation to *Add*1 by supplying it with a finite set of arguments, for each of these it gives back something like *Add*3. And the only way we can find out about this approximation is by applying these things like *Add*3 to arguments and so building up approximations to them: this in turn can only be done by building up approximations to the functions like *Add* on which they depend. So the whole thing relies on being successfully able to refine approximations by refining other approximations — for that is in general the only way in which we can compute with infinitary objects inside a finite machine (or, indeed, in a finite universe).

All this is by way of an initial flirtation with an idea (the notion of *continuity*) which will be of crucial importance later.

---

* We are ignoring things like the facilities in LISP which allow us to dissect the actual text of the algorithm in a very non-referentially-transparent manner (cf. the example about William Rufus in Chapter 1). These, however, would not invalidate the argument; for we would say that functions and the quoted texts of algorithms are different kinds of data objects, one of which can be applied to arguments, and the other dissected. Then our analysis of these extra complications of LISP would focus on the process of switching from one to the other (a kind of Gödelisation). Another way of looking at it is that for us to be able to regard some program as depending on a value which is a *function*, it must give the same result for *any* closure representing that same mapping; but this can never be true of anything that works by analysing the algorithm.

Further examples of the use of functions as first-class objects, together with some exercises, may be found in the Appendix.

Chapter 5

THE λ-CALCULUS

Now that we have acquired some familiarity with the treatment of functions as objects of computation, we return to the study of a language, the λ-calculus, which achieves all its power from the behaviour of functions. This study will lead us into difficulties, and to solve these we shall have to undertake a closer investigation of the properties of the abstract value space which is the universe of discourse of the λ-calculus. This will be contained in chapters 6 and 7, and it introduces us to the lattice-theory approach to the theory of computation. Then, in Chapter 8, having sorted out these difficulties, we shall return to the formal semantics of the λ-calculus language itself.

Our first task is to introduce some more suitable notation for treating functions as "first-class" objects. Because we are now regarding functions and their arguments as of equal status, we use a more symmetric notation for the operation of applying one to the other: instead of $f(x)$ we write

fx.

Here f is a variable taking values drawn from some set of functions, and x takes values drawn from some set of suitable operands. Actually, later on we shall be trying to arrange that f and x take values drawn from the *same* set; then there will be no restrictions about using functions as arguments of functions.

So now, instead of having many primitive operations

(such as ×, -, + etc.) we have just one: application, denoted by juxtaposition. Thus, for example, if a denotes the addition function, s subtraction and m multiplication, then $m(axy)(sxy)$ and $\times(+xy)(-xy)$ both now denote what we used to write as $(x+y)\times(x-y)$. However, if we vary the values denoted by m, a and s (or, indeed, ×, + and -) these expressions may denote many other quite different values. (Note that since functions can at present have only one argument all our functions are *curried*: this notational device was explained in the previous chapter.)

Of course, we shall relax a little from this purist behaviour, and feel free to use the more conventional infixed notation ($a+b$ etc.) when it leads to no ambiguity. Similarly, we shall if we wish surround either argument of an application with brackets; but in order to avoid too many of these we shall adopt the convention that application associates to the left. So abc denotes $(ab)c$ rather than $a(bc)$.

Using the application operator we can now write many expressions involving variables ranging over suitable sets of functions and other values. As yet, however, we have no notation for defining new functions. For example, the expression $+ \ x \ 1$ denotes let us say, integer values — though of course we will not know what value $+ \ x \ 1$ denotes until we know the value of x. Moreover, the value of $+ \ x \ 1$ varies as we vary x. But if we try to say without more ado that therefore $+ \ x \ 1$ denotes a *function* of x we soon land in confusion. Consider, for example, the expression *abc*. Is this a function of one variable or two or three, and in which order are they applied?

We could resolve these ambiguities by writing, for example,

f where $fa = abc$

or

g where $gx = + \; x \; 1$.

(Note that we still do not know what function f denotes until we know the values of b and c.) This technique works, but it has the disadvantage that we cannot define a function without giving it a name. In fact we shall often want to use functions as subexpressions of larger expressions, and to be forced to name them would lead to undue complication. After all, if we had to give names to *all* subexpressions, our original example

$(x+y)\times(x-y)$

would become

e where $e = c\times d$ where $c = x+y$ and $d = x-y$

and we would lose much of the power of the more concise notation: it would be rather like programming in assembly language.

To avoid this difficulty Church [6] introduced an operation called *abstraction*, represented by λ-notation.

5.1 *Definition.* If M is an expression taking values in some domain D, then

$\lambda x\!:\!D'.M$

denotes the function f:D′→D such that $f(x)$ for any $x \in$ D′ may be obtained by evaluating M using that value for x. We write simply λx.M if D′ can be inferred from the context. This linguistic operation of forming a function definition from an expression is called *abstraction*.

So our previous examples become

$\lambda a.abc$

and

$\lambda x.+ \ x \ 1.$

If the first of these functions is applied to some value y (assuming that y is suitable) the result will by Definition 5.1 be given by

$ybc.$

Similarly, the second example is the successor function, and $(\lambda x.+ \ x \ 1)z = + \ z \ 1$; hence $(\lambda x.+ \ x \ 1)3 = 4$ and so on.

More generally, suppose N is some expression taking values in D′. Then (λx:D′.M)N is by Definition 5.1 equivalent to f(N), where f denotes the function whose result for any $x \in$ D′ may be found by evaluating M using that value for x. Since any expression may be replaced by any other with the same value, we see that (λx:D′.M)N may thus be evaluated by substituting the expression N for every occurrence of x in M. (We may have to use some parentheses to control the grouping, and we shall have to get rather more precise about what we mean by "substitution" and "occurrence" to avoid difficulties with name clashes.) Later, when we set up this notation as a formal calculus, this observation will become one of the formal rules (the rule of β-conversion). At present, however, our concern is to investigate a convenient notation for functions, and so we regard this observation merely as a consequence of our definition of the notion of abstraction.

Two important axioms describe properties of abstraction and application.

5.2 *Axiom of Comprehension.* If M is a valid expression (whether or not it contains occurrences of x) which takes values in D, then there exists a function $f{:}D'\to D$ such that $fx = M$ for all $x \in D'$.

5.3 *Axiom of Extensionality.* If two functions f and g are defined on the same domain and give equal values for all arguments, they are equal; that is

for $f,g : D'\to D$, if $fx = gx$ for all $x \in D'$, then $f = g$.

The axiom of comprehension guarantees that the abstraction operation can always be done; the axiom of extensionality (which can be regarded as the definition of equality of functions) ensures that a unique function results.

This, then is the λ-notation. It is a very convenient notation for writing down functions when we have independent knowledge of their existence: the good behaviour of this process is guaranteed by the two axioms we have just introduced. There are no logical difficulties involved in this activity, and we shall do it freely. Note that we are using λ-expressions as a notation for *functions* (mappings from arguments to results), not as a notation for algorithms (mechanical rules for calculating a result from a particular argument value). A function is represented by a λ-expression, and that expression will certainly suggest one possible algorithm; but our axiom of extensionality says that any other λ-expression specifying the same mapping would be an alternative representation for the same function: the two λ-expressions would be equal, even if the algorithms they embodied were completely different. As a simple example, note that

$$\lambda x.(x+3)\times(x-3) \quad = \quad \lambda x.x^2-9.$$

As usual, we are being careful to distinguish the abstract objects (functions) from their representations (λ-expressions).

The λ-Calculus

We now turn the λ-notation into a calculus, by giving a formal syntax and syntactic transformation (conversion) rules. The only justification now required for writing a particular λ-expression is no longer that it defines a known function, but merely that it conforms to the grammatical rules. So we shall have to investigate whether there exists any suitable set of values which expressions in our calculus could be denoting — as we shall see, this is not straightforward.

5.4 *Definition.* The *expressions* (also sometimes known as *well-formed formulae*, *wffs*, or *obs*) in the λ-calculus are made up according to the following syntax :

<expression> ::= *<variable>*
| *<expression><expression>*
| λ*<variable>*.*<expression>*
| (*<expression>*)

We assume that there is an infinite sequence of variables, or names. The expressions corresponding to the second line of the syntax above are known as *applications*, and the expressions corresponding to the third line are *abstractions*.

In parsing composite expressions we recall that application associates to the left, and we assume that when an abstraction such as $\lambda x.\mathrm{M}$ occurs in a larger expression, M is taken as extending as far as possible — that is, to the first unmatched closing bracket or the end of the expression, whichever is first. So, using parentheses to indicate grouping (as permitted in the final production of the syntax), an expression such as

$(\lambda x.\lambda y.\mathrm{N})ab$

becomes

$(\lambda x.(\lambda y.\mathrm{N}))ab$

and then

$((\lambda x.(\lambda y.\mathrm{N}))a)b.$

In our examples we shall use lower case italic letters for variables, and upper case letters to stand for arbitrary expressions. We sometimes adopt the convention of omitting a dot immediately before a λ; thus $\lambda x.\lambda y.\mathrm{N}$ above could have appeared as $\lambda x\lambda y.\mathrm{N}$, which we assume to be a variant of the same expression. (Some authors abbreviate still further and would write this last example as $\lambda xy.N$.)

Before we can define precisely what we mean by "substitution" as required for the conversion rules, we must tighten up our ideas about the occurrence of a variable in an expression. In particular, a variable can occur in an expression in two ways: *bound* or *free*. The basic idea is that a bound variable is one involved in an abstraction; when the abstraction is applied to some argument, it is the bound variables that get replaced by substitution. More formally, we define the new concepts as follows.

5.5 *Definition*.

1. x occurs free in x (but not in any other variable;
2. x occurs free in XY if it occurs free in X or Y (or both);
3. x occurs free in $\lambda y.X$ if x and y are different variables and x occurs free in X;
4. x occurs free in (X) if it occurs free in X.

5.6 *Definition*.

1. No variable occurs bound in an expression consisting just of a single variable;
2. x occurs bound in XY if it occurs bound in X or Y (or both);
3. x occurs bound in $\lambda y.X$ if x and y are the same variable or if x occurs bound in X;
4. x occurs bound in (X) if it occurs bound in X.

The clauses in these definitions thus cover separately each of the possible forms of expression. Notice that a particular variable can occur bound at one place in an expression and free at another place. Moreover, a particular occurrence of a variable can be free in some subexpression, but bound in the overall expression. For example, consider

$(\lambda x.ax)x$.

a and x both occur free in ax. In $\lambda x.ax$ a is still free, but x is bound. In the complete expression x occurs both bound (at its first two occurrences) and free (at the third occurrence).

For an abstraction $\lambda x.M$ it is convenient to call x the bound variable of the abstraction; the expression M is known as the *body* of the abstraction. As we have noted, the occurrences of the bound variable in the body may be regarded as markers indicating where the argument expression should be inserted when evaluating an application of the abstraction: the use of names rather than, say, a special symbol is necessary to avoid confusion when several abstractions occur in the same expression. Another more pictorial way of avoiding this confusion would be to draw lines between each marker in the body and the head of the particular abstraction in which it was bound. So, for example, the expression shown in Fig. 5.1 is one way of indicating the binding structure pictorially represented in Fig. 5.2. Notice that p is used in Fig. 5.1 to indicate two different bindings. By virtue of the definition above, the occurrences of p in $p(p\ q)$ are bound in $(\lambda p.p(p\ q))$; outside this subexpression the same name is available to indicate other bindings.

5.1. (λ*p*.(λ*q*.(λ*p*.*p*(*p* *q*))(λ*r*.+ *p* *r*))(+ *p* 4))2

5.2.

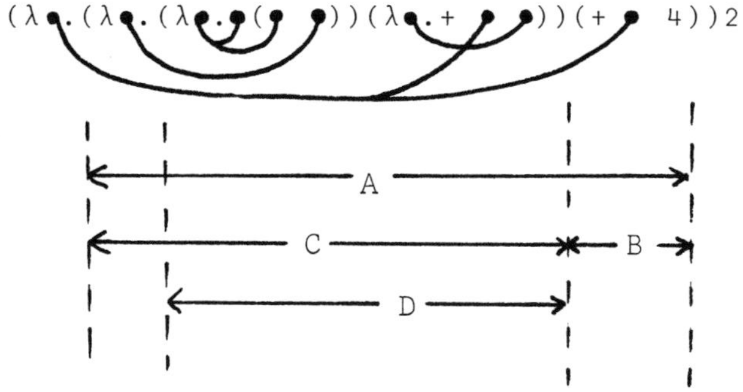

5.3.

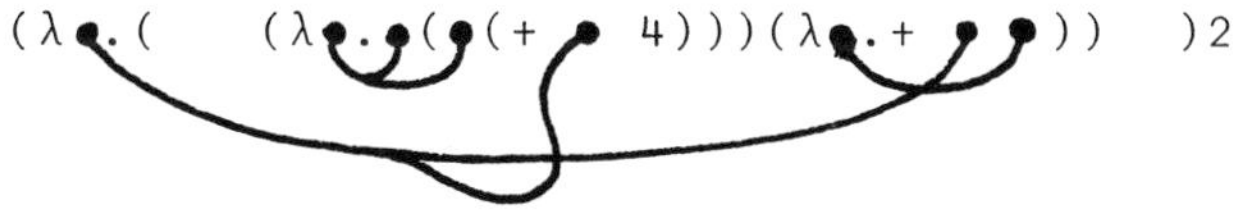

5.4.

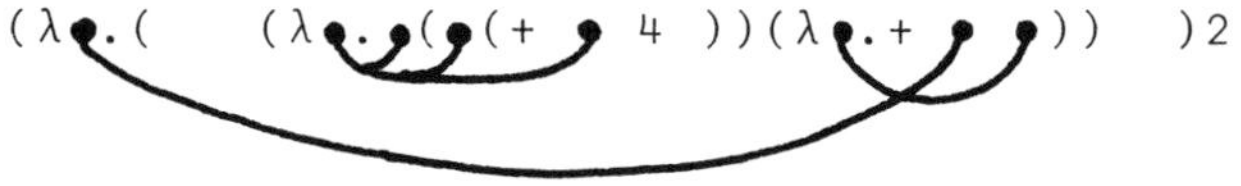

Figs. 5.1 - 5.4. Variable Binding (see pp. 60,62).

This picture may help us to see what is happening in the rather complicated definition of substitution which follows. Suppose we wish to evaluate the application marked A in Fig.5.2. According to the ideas developed earlier, what we must do is replace A by the expression obtained by substituting the argument (B) at the appropriate place or places within the body (D) of the abstraction (C). All the other bindings remain as they were, so the process changes Fig.5.2 into the expression shown in Fig.5.3. Again, of course, we could use names to indicate the bindings in this expression; but notice that we can no longer use p to indicate both bindings for which it was previously used. If we tried to do so we should find that all occurrences of p in

$(\lambda p.p(p(+\ p\ 4)))$

would be bound in that abstraction, so that instead of Fig.5.3 we would get Fig.5.4. We are therefore compelled to change the name we use for one of the bindings.

The following substitution rule spells out in formal syntactic detail exactly how to substitute M for x in X, with any necessary name changes.

5.7 *Definition*. Let x be a variable and M and X expressions. Then $[M/x]X$ is the expression X′ defined as follows:

1. X is a variable:
   1.1. If $X \equiv x$ then $X' \equiv M$.
   1.2. If $X \not\equiv x$ then $X' \equiv X$.

2. X is an application YZ:
   $X' \equiv ([M/x]Y)([M/x]Z)$.

3. X is an abstraction $\lambda y.Y$:
   3.1. If $y \equiv x$ then $X' \equiv X$.
   3.2. If $y \not\equiv x$ then
      3.2.1. if x does not occur free in Y or if y does not occur free in M then
      $X' \equiv \lambda y.[M/x]Y$;

      3.2.2. if x does occur free in Y and y does occur free in M then
      $X' \equiv \lambda z.[M/x]([z/y]Y)$
      where z is the first variable in the sequence of variables such that z does not occur free in M or Y.

The first two sections of this definition are straightforward. Case 3.1 applies on encountering an abstraction whose bound variable is the same as that being replaced; the new binding takes precedence and totally shields the body from the effects of the substitution. For the remaining abstractions, 3.2.1 copes with those cases where there is no possibility of a name clash, either because the body contains no free occurrence of the variable being replaced (so that no substitution will in fact be performed) or because the expression to be inserted contains no free occurrences (of y) which would be caught by the bound variable of the abstraction. If these conditions are not satisfied it is necessary to change the bound variable of the abstraction to some other name which does not clash, and 3.2.2 deals with this case. Thus, for the transformation illustrated in Figs. 5.1 to 5.3. we have

$[(+\ p\ 4)/q]((\lambda p.p(p\ q))(\lambda r.+\ p\ r))$

$\equiv\ ([(+\ p\ 4)/q](\lambda p.p(p\ q)))([(+\ p\ 4)/q](\lambda r.+\ p\ r)$

(by case 2)

$\equiv\ ([(+\ p\ 4)/q](\lambda p.p(p\ q)))(\lambda r.+\ p\ r)$

(by case 3.2.1, etc., since q does not occur free in $+\ p\ r$)

$\equiv\ (\lambda a.[(+\ p\ 4)/q]([a/p](p(p\ q))))(\lambda r.+\ p\ r)$

(by case 3.2.2)

$\equiv\ (\lambda a.a(a(+\ p\ 4)))(\lambda r.+\ p\ r).$

Now, having formally defined substitution, we can state the conversion rules for performing transformations on λ-expressions. We write

X **cnv** Y

to indicate that either side may be replaced by the other whenever one of them occurs as an expression or as a subexpression of a larger expression. We have met the first two rules informally already, for we have felt free to rename bound variables provided that we introduce no clashes, and we have encountered the substitution method for evaluating applications. The third rule which we shall consider, η-conversion, is related to the axiom of extensionality, since both $\lambda x.(\mathrm{M}x)$ and M give $\mathrm{M}y$ when applied to any y (unless x also occurs free in M). Remember that here, as usual, we are assuming that M is a proper sub-expression of $\mathrm{M}x$.

5.8. *Conversion Rules.*

α. If y is not free in X, then $\lambda x.X$ $\mathbf{cnv}_\alpha$ $\lambda y.[y/x]X$.

β. $(\lambda x.M)N$ $\mathbf{cnv}_\beta$ $[N/x]M$

η. If x is not free in M, then $\lambda x.Mx$ $\mathbf{cnv}_\eta$ M.

Notice that there is no need for any qualification in the β-conversion rule, as the details of the substitution rule, 5.7, take care of the potentially pathological cases.

In practice we use these rules to evaluate λ-expressions, which means that we try to eliminate as many abstractions as possible. α-conversion does not help in this, but the other two rules, when used in the left-to-right direction, both replace an expression containing an abstraction with some other expression which may well be simpler. For this reason this sort of conversion is called a *reduction* and the particular expression which is replaced is called a *redex*. So an expression of the form $(\lambda x.M)N$ is a β-redex, and $\lambda x.(Mx)$ is an η-redex (if x is not free in M). When indicating a reduction we often use the symbol **red** instead of **cnv**; A **red** B asserts that A may be transformed to B by one or more reduction steps, and perhaps some α-conversions. So, for example, we might have:

$$\begin{aligned}(\lambda x.\lambda y.y)ab\ &\mathbf{red}_\beta\ (\lambda y.y)b \\ &\mathbf{red}_\beta\ b\ .\end{aligned} \tag{5.9}$$

$$\begin{aligned}\lambda x.\lambda y.axy\ &\mathbf{red}_\eta\ \lambda x.ax \\ &\mathbf{red}_\eta\ a\ .\end{aligned} \tag{5.10}$$

As it happens the final result of these evaluations contains no redexes. Such an expression is said to be in *normal form*. It is not always possible to reduce an expression to normal form, as is shown by the following example

$$(\lambda x.xx)(\lambda x.xx) \tag{5.11}$$

Note that $(\lambda x.xx)$ has the form $(\lambda x.Mx)$, but it is not an η-redex because x occurs free in M. β-reduction gives

$$(\lambda x.xx)(\lambda x.xx) \ \mathrm{red}_\beta \ (\lambda x.xx)(\lambda x.xx)$$

So no progress can be made. This example also shows that reduction does not necessarily succeed in reducing the number of abstractions in an expression — indeed, it may even increase it, as in the following example.

$$(\lambda x.xxx)(\lambda x.xxx) \tag{5.12}$$
$$\mathrm{red}_\beta \ (\lambda x.xxx)(\lambda x.xxx)(\lambda x.xxx)$$
etc.

In all the examples so far there has only ever been one redex at a time. Let us consider what happens if there is a choice.

$$(\lambda x.\lambda y.y)((\lambda x.xx)(\lambda x.xx))b \tag{5.13}$$

By attacking the leftmost β-redex, we can reduce this to $(\lambda y.y)b$ and hence to b. On the other hand if we attack the other β-redex (the one we examined in Example 5.11) our attempts at evaluation may never terminate.

This difference in behaviour prompts another question: is it possible for two different reduction sequences to terminate with different results? This would seriously undermine our confidence in the system, but fortunately the answer is "no". This result follows from the following theorem.

5.14. *Church-Rosser Theorem I*. If X cnv Y then there exists an expression Z such that X red Z and Y red Z.

The classic proof of this theorem (and its companion theorem, 5.16 below) may be found in Curry and Feys [7] Chapter 4; a simpler proof appears in [18].

5.15. *Corollary*. No expression can be converted to two distinct normal forms (i.e. normal forms which are not α-convertible).

To show this, note that the two normal forms, if they did exist, would be convertible, by going from the first back to the original expression and thence to the second. Hence, by the theorem, there would exist a further expression to which both were reducible. But this could not be so, as normal forms have no redexes and cannot therefore be reduced at all.

Thus no two orders of evaluation can give different normal forms, though some may possibly fail to terminate at all. The further question therefore arises: is there an order of evaluation which is guaranteed to terminate whenever a particular expression is reducible to normal form? In Example 5.13 we achieved success by eliminating the offending subexpression $(\lambda x.xx)(\lambda x.xx)$ before we tried to evaluate it. The order of evaluation which does this whenever possible, called *normal order*, is that which at each stage reduces the leftmost redex in the expression. In normal order no expression in the argument position of a β-redex is evaluated until the redex has itself been reduced, which might eliminate the argument from the expression altogether. This helps us to see the truth of the following theorem.

5.16. *Church-Rosser Theorem II*. If A **red** B, and B is in normal form, then there exists a normal order reduction from A to B.

So normal order reduction is guaranteed to terminate with a normal form if any order of evaluation does. Another order, which more closely resembles the behaviour of many languages, is *applicative order*. Here, the operator and operand (function and argument) of an application (β-redex) are separately evaluated to normal form before the β-reduction is performed. Although, by the first Church-Rosser Theorem, we know that whenever it terminates this order will give the same result as normal order, it is less powerful than normal order: as we have seen, for example, it would fail to terminate on Example 5.13. However, when it does terminate it is often faster than normal order. This is because applicative order evaluates operands only once, before they are substituted into the body of the operator, whereas normal order evaluates them as many times as necessary, after the substitution. But this is also the secret of normal order's extra power: for "as many times as necessary" sometimes means "never".

The rules of normal and applicative order reduction (which partly resemble the "call by name" and "call by value" rules of Algol 60) can form the basis of mechanistic definitions of the semantics of the λ-calculus; the two versions will define slightly different languages, reflecting the different power of the two abstract machines. We shall see later whether we may specify which version we prefer by the mathematical semantics.

Exercises.

1. Reduce to normal form:

$(\lambda x.x)(yz)$,

$(\lambda x.xy)(\lambda z.z)$,

$\lambda x\lambda y.xy$,

$\lambda x\lambda y.yx$.

2. Let

S = $\lambda x\lambda y\lambda z.xz(yz)$,

K = $\lambda x\lambda y.x$,

B = $\lambda x\lambda y\lambda z.x(yz)$,

I = $\lambda x.x$.

(a) Reduce S(KI) and BI to normal form, and hence prove them both convertible to I.

(b) Show that

S(KS)K cnv B,

SKK cnv I.

The expressions defined here are examples of *combinators*, which are λ-expressions with no free variables; Curry experimented with these in an attempt to do without variables altogether. (b) is an illustration of how this may be achieved: in fact any λ-expression without free variables may be expressed instead as some combination of the two combinators S and K.

3. Let *Tw* be the abstraction that applies its first argument *twice* to its second, and *Th* the abstraction that does so thrice; so

$Tw = \lambda f \lambda x.f(fx)$,
$Th = \lambda f \lambda x.f(f(fx))$.

Assume that we have extra rules in our calculus for performing arithmetic evaluations involving integers, and let Sq be the *squaring* function; so $Sq = \lambda x.x \times x$ and Sq 4 cnv 16 etc. Show that $(Tw\ Sq)3$ cnv 81.

Evaluate:

$Th\ Tw\ Sq\ 3$,
$Tw\ Th\ Sq\ 3$,
$Th\ (Tw\ Sq)\ 3$.

4. Actually we have no need to add extra rules to deal with the integers, as we can *represent* the integers directly in the λ-calculus. In fact, Tw may be used to represent 2, and Th to represent 3. The general scheme is defined as follows.

Let 0 be represented by $\overline{0} = \lambda x \lambda y.y$,
1 by $\overline{1} = \lambda x \lambda y.xy$,
2 by $\overline{2} = \lambda x \lambda y.x(xy)$,
3 by $\overline{3} = \lambda x \lambda y.x(x(xy))$,

and, in general,

n by $\overline{n} = \lambda x \lambda y.\overbrace{x(x...(xy)...)}^{n \text{ times}}$.

Show that the λ-expression

$Suc \equiv \lambda x \lambda y \lambda z.y(xyz)$

applied to the representation of any integer is convertible to the representation of its successor.

5. If integers are represented as in the previous exercise find λ-expressions for $Plus$, $Times$ and Exp, such that

$Plus\ \overline{m}\ \overline{n}$ cnv $\overline{m+n}$,

$Times\ \overline{m}\ \overline{n}$ cnv $\overline{m\times n}$,

$Exp\ \overline{m}\ \overline{n}$ cnv $\overline{m^n}$.

Hint: note that the representation of n applies its first argument n times to its second argument.

6. It is also desirable to have representations of the truth values. These are often used to select one of two expressions, so it would be convenient if

$True\ x\ y$ cnv x,

$False\ x\ y$ cnv y.

The following definitions accomplish this.

Let $True \equiv \lambda x \lambda y . x$,

$False \equiv \lambda x \lambda y . y$,

and let

$IsZero = \lambda k . k(True(False))(True)$.

Show that

$IsZero\ \overline{n}$ cnv $True$ if $\overline{n} = \overline{0}$

cnv $False$ if $\overline{n}$ represents some other integer.

Recursive Definitions.

Consider the definition

$Fact = \lambda n.$ if $n=0$ then 1 else $n\times Fact(n-1)$,

which we could write in the notation introduced in the exercises as

$Fact = \lambda n. IsZero\ n\ \overline{1}\ (Times\ n\ (Fact(Pred\ n)))$,

where $Pred$ maps integer representations to their predecessors.

(One possible expression for *Pred* is

$\lambda k.(k(\lambda p\lambda u.u(Suc(p\ True))(p\ True))(\lambda u.u\ \bar{0}\ \bar{0}))False.$)

This is an equation which we have to try to solve for *Fact*, just as $x = 5/x$ is an equation to be solved for x. The existence of an equation, however, does not by itself guarantee the existence of a solution; $x = x+3$, for example, has no solution in the real numbers. Let us see if this particular equation has a solution.

Suppose we put

$H = \lambda f.\lambda n.$if $n=0$ then 1 else $n\times f(n-1)$.

Then we are seeking an expression for *Fact* that satisfies

Fact cnv *H Fact*

So *Fact* is to be a *fixed point* of *H*.

Now in general a fixed point of a function is a value in the function's domain which is mapped to itself by that function. Considering functions from integers to integers we have, for example, that the fixed point of $\lambda x.27$ is 27, and the fixed point of $\lambda x.6-x$ is 3. Not all such functions have exactly one fixed point: for example, $\lambda x.x+1$ has none, while $\lambda x.x$ has infinitely many.

Let us see whether for any *H* we can find an expression *E* convertible to *H E*. Casting around for possible approaches we remember that if *D* is $\lambda x.xx$, then

D D cnv *D D*

Can we adapt *D* so that *D D* cnv *H*(*D D*)? If so, *D D* will be a fixed point of *H*, as required. Fairly obviously, we should try defining D to be $\lambda x.H(xx)$, and then we find our requirements are satisfied: $(\lambda x.H(xx))(\lambda x.H(xx))$ is a fixed point of H. Moreover, by abstraction on H we can produce an expression Y, where

$$Y \equiv \lambda h.(\lambda x.h(xx))(\lambda x.h(xx)), \tag{5.17}$$

which, applied to any expression, renders a fixed point of that expression. In particular we can put

$$Fact \equiv Y\ H$$

to obtain our required solution of the equation for the factorial function.

Exercise

7. Evaluate $(Y\ H)3$. (Note that this application terminates in normal order but not in applicative order. Notice how the mechanics of the formula ensure that a fresh copy of $(Y\ H)$ becomes available for each recursive call.)

The argument we have just given may seem too slick to be satisfactory. It certainly leaves some unanswered questions, which must be settled before we can be happy with the above definition of $Fact$. If B has more than one fixed point, which one does YB produce? What happens when Y is applied to expressions such as $\lambda x.x+1$ which, as we have said, has no fixed points? It is questions like this last one that have earned Y the title of "paradoxical combinator".

An even more fundamental difficulty, however, is highlighted by the fact that our definition of Y involves the application of x to itself. The possibility of self-application can lead to paradoxes. For example, suppose we define

$u \equiv \lambda y.\ \text{if } y(y) = a \text{ then } b \text{ else } a.$

Then an attempt to evaluate $u(u)$ gives

$$u(u) = \text{if } u(u) = a \text{ then } b \text{ else } a \qquad (5.18)$$

which is a contradiction. But self-application is certainly allowed by the way we defined our calculus, when we allowed an application to be comprised of any two expressions juxtaposed.

Moreover, we remember that application was invented as a notation for describing the operation of mapping an argument to a result by means of a function. So saying that any expression may be applied to any other is tantamount to claiming that every expression denotes a function; indeed, this is implied by the η-conversion rule, which says that any expression is convertible to an abstraction. That is to say, it requires that our space of values be identified with the space of functions on those values. (In fact isomorphism is good enough – to each value there corresponds a unique function and vice versa — for then when we require to treat an object as a function we can simply take its image in the function space.) However, if *any* mapping between values is allowed in our function space then we cannot possibly achieve this isomorphism, for there are always more functions than values (except, indeed, for the trivial case where there exists only one value, and therefore only one function — this solution is hardly rich enough for a theory of computation).

Of course, we could avoid this difficulty simply by banning self-application. Using functions as arguments of other functions would not be prohibited altogether, but the spaces from which the functions and their arguments came would be quite separate, and no attempt would be made to set up an isomorphism. This approach can take us quite a long way towards a theory. However, not only is it of no help with the λ-calculus, but (more importantly, perhaps) it is also inadequate for more conventional programming languages, some of which (Algol 60, for example) allow self-application explicitly. Moreover, as we shall see, a state of the computer store defines a function from locations to their contents, and commands may be regarded as store transformation functions, mapping the original state of the store to a new one: so languages which allow commands themselves to be stored in locations also give rise to similar problems. And we must still give satisfactory answers to the questions raised earlier about fixed points, which affect any language in which one can write a loop. We cannot therefore abandon our search for a theory to solve these problems.

It is instructive at this stage to consider the position we have reached with regard to the λ-calculus itself. We have a formal syntactic system. This system indeed has been proved self-consistent, so we know that we shall never derive a contradiction from it*. We would very much like to be able to think of it as describing the behaviour of functions: this was why we set it up in the first place. We are as yet unable to do so, however, for we have not found a class of functions which it describes. So far we cannot regard it as describing anything: it is a system without semantics. We can, of course, give it trivial semantics by saying that it is talking about itself, describing the behaviour of merely syntactic objects (λ-expressions) under syntactic transformations (the conversion rules); but this is not helpful. The lack of any other semantic model is the reason why the λ-calculus had fallen into disrepute among some logicians, although computer people have always recognised its relevance to the study of programming languages. Fortunately, however, it has been rehabilitated by the theory we are about to study.

Notice that we shall not require that the semantic model we are seeking be in 1-1 correspondence with the set of finite λ-expressions, any more than the real numbers are in 1-1 correspondence with the finite decimal numerals. We shall require, however, to know that each λ-expression can be associated with some particular element in the model, even though there will be (uncountably many) elements in the model not associated with any λ-expression.

---

*In the pure λ-calculus, evaluation of the apparent contradiction 5.18 would not terminate; so within the calculus we would never arrive at a stage where we could recognise it as contradictory.

Exercises

8. Let $f \circ g = \lambda x.f(gx)$ for all f, g (this is simply functional composition). Let $\Delta = \lambda x.xx$. Show that $\Delta(f \circ \Delta)$ cnv $f(\Delta(f \circ \Delta))$, and hence that it is irreducible.

9. Let

$$\begin{aligned} Y_1 &\equiv \lambda f.\Delta(f \circ \Delta) \\ G &\equiv \lambda y \lambda f.f(yf) \\ Y_{n+1} &\equiv Y_n G. \end{aligned} \qquad (n = 1, 2, \ldots)$$

Prove

i. For all x, $Y_1 x$ cnv $x(Y_1 x)$;
ii. GY_1 cnv Y_1.

Hence prove by induction that, for all $n \geq 1$,

iii. For all x, $Y_n x$ cnv $x(Y_n x)$;
iv. GY_n cnv Y_n.

That is to say, (iii) all the Y_n are fixed point operators, and (iv) all the Y_n are fixed points of G.

10. Prove that Y_1 is *not* convertible to Y_2 (Böhm [5]). [This is quite tricky. Hint: count λ's.]

Chapter 6

LATTICES AND DOMAINS

The discussion at the end of the previous chapter has indicated that if our search for a semantic theory of the λ-calculus is to be successful we must find a way to restrict the class of functions we are allowed to consider. Otherwise there will be simply too many of them for us to find any non-trivial space with an isomorphic function space.

The logicians' usual solution is not to work with functions at all. Instead, they work with representations of functions. In short, they take Gödel numbers. They are usually dealing with functions over the integers, in which case the operation of Gödel-numbering maps into integers the functions expressible by algorithms of finite length (which form a countable set). When they wish to consider a function A which takes another function B as an argument, they can then formally supply A with the Gödel number of B.

This approach is satisfactory for use in arguments concerning decidability. The form these arguments usually take is: "Suppose you claim to have a function X which decides the halting problem; then I will be able to find another function W for which X fails to work". Of course, such workers do not expect to use the behaviour of these functions to model situations arising in other parts of mathematics, which is the computer programmer's job; indeed, the particular counter-examples used in these computability arguments tend to be fairly outlandish. But our interest is in semantics, and we are vitally concerned with the behaviour of individual functions. In particular, we have the axiom of extensionality (5.3 above, page 56), which states that if two functions behave the same then they *are* the same: that is, if f and g are such that $f(x) = g(x)$ for all x, then $f = g$. No mapping based on symbolic expressions of algorithms can preserve this equality, for two completely different algorithms may yet define the same mapping.

The Approximation Ordering.

Instead of using Gödel-numberings of algorithms, then, we shall adopt another approach which concentrates more on the functions, or mappings, themselves. Let us attempt to gain a little more insight by looking at another facet of our problems, the question of multiple fixed points. Consider the recursive definition:

$f = \lambda x.$ if $x = 0$ then 1
else if $x = 1$ then $f(3)$
else $f(x-2)$.

We see that we are looking for a fixed point of

$\lambda f.\lambda x.$ if $x = 0$ then 1
else if $x = 1$ then $f(3)$
else $f(x-2)$.

Our practical experience of computing with recursive functions may lead us to the solution

$$f'(x) = \begin{cases} 1 \quad (x \text{ even}) \\ \text{undefined} \ (x \text{ odd}). \end{cases}$$

But another solution is

$$f_1(x) = 1 \ (\text{all } x)$$

and so is

$$f_a(x) = \begin{cases} 1 & (x \text{ even}) \\ a & (x \text{ odd}) \end{cases}$$

where a is an arbitrary constant. Why should f' be the function that a computer implementation would provide in practice?

The answer is that the other solutions all contain arbitrary information (the value of a) which we should not expect the implementation to decide. f', on the other hand, contains only the information actually implied by the recursive definition. It is the minimal solution we require: the one containing the minimum amount of information. Let us now formalise this notion of an ordering of values based on their information contents: this will also allow us to incorporate the ideas about approximation we discussed earlier, at the end of Chapter 4.

To see how this ordering works, let us first look at a set of values which are simpler than functions. Consider one possible way of dealing with approximations to real numbers: the set of closed intervals, written $[\underline{x},\overline{x}]$ where $\underline{x}$ and $\overline{x}$ are real, and $\underline{x} \leqslant \overline{x}$. The idea is that the perfectly accurate value is somewhere between these two values.

Let $x = [\underline{x},\overline{x}]$ and $y = [\underline{y},\overline{y}]$. If $\underline{y} \leqslant \underline{x}$ and $\overline{x} \leqslant \overline{y}$ then x is consistent with y but more accurate. We may write $y \sqsubseteq x$, which we use to mean that y *approximates* x, that x is more accurate than y, (or at least no less accurate), that x contains more (or equal) information than y, but that no information in x contradicts any of the information we have about y. So in Fig.6.1, for example, $x \sqsubseteq z$ and $y \sqsubseteq z$, but neither $x \sqsubseteq y$ nor

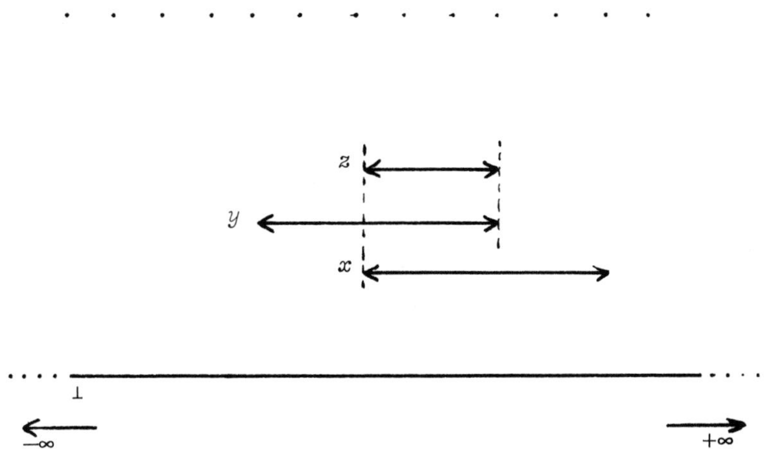

Fig. 6.1. Closed intervals.

$y \sqsubseteq x$ is true, as x and y each contain some values excluded by the other. In fact z in the figure contains all the information to be gleaned from x and y together: we may call z the "least upper bound" of x and y, and write $z = x \sqcup y$.

There are some special cases. One is the interval $[-\infty,\infty]$, the whole real line. This gives no information at all, and is therefore weaker than every other interval in our ordering. We call this element $\bot$ (pronounced "bottom"). Other special cases are the intervals $[x,x]$, which correspond to perfectly specified numbers. There are also values which contain inconsistent information, such as $[0,1] \sqcup [2,3]$: we may identify all such values and call them $\top$ ("top"). So $\bot$ denotes the absence of information, and $\top$ denotes too much information, to the extent of contradiction.

Other sets of values may be ordered according to their information content even more simply. The two truth values, for example, are incomparable; so if we add $\bot$ and $\top$ to denote the undefined and the overdefined truth values, we obtain the set shown in Fig.6.2. Similarly the integers are all incomparable, so the set appropriate to them is shown in Fig.6.3. These two sets, in which all the elements apart from $\bot$ and $\top$ are incomparable with each other, are examples of so-called *flat lattices*.

The relation $\sqsubseteq$ illustrated by these examples is a *partial ordering*. Some of the general properties of partially ordered sets are summarized in the next section. The proofs of the theorems are omitted; some of them may be found in Sanderson [46], Chapter 2, from which this summary is condensed.

Partially Ordered Sets.

6.1. Definition. A set P is *partially ordered* (p.o.) by $\sqsubseteq$ (pronounced "weaker than") if, for every $x,y,z \in$ P the following properties hold:

1. (Reflexivity) $x \sqsubseteq x$.
2. (Anti-symmetry) $x \sqsubseteq y$ and $y \sqsubseteq x$ implies $x \equiv y$.
3. (Transitivity) $x \sqsubseteq y$ and $y \sqsubseteq z$ implies $x \sqsubseteq z$.

Fig. 6.4. shows some examples of partially ordered sets. Notice that there is no requirement that *every* pair of elements in a set be related by $\sqsubseteq$: if $x \not\sqsubseteq y$ and $y \not\sqsubseteq x$ then x and y are said to be *incomparable*.

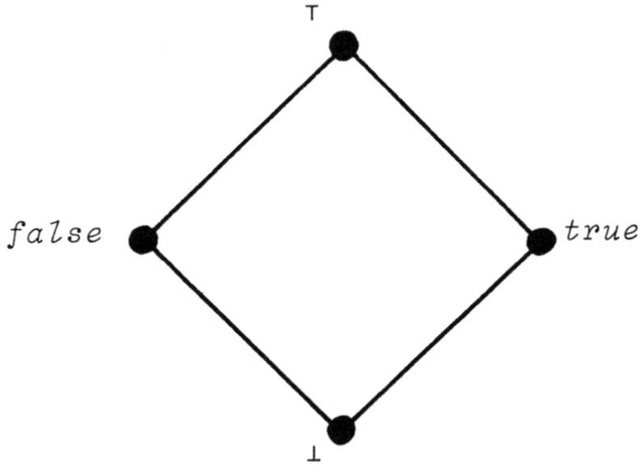

Fig. 6.2. The truth-value lattice.

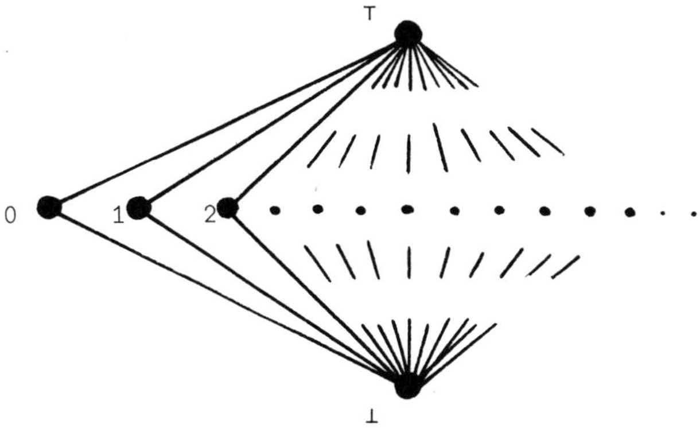

Fig. 6.3. The lattice of integers.

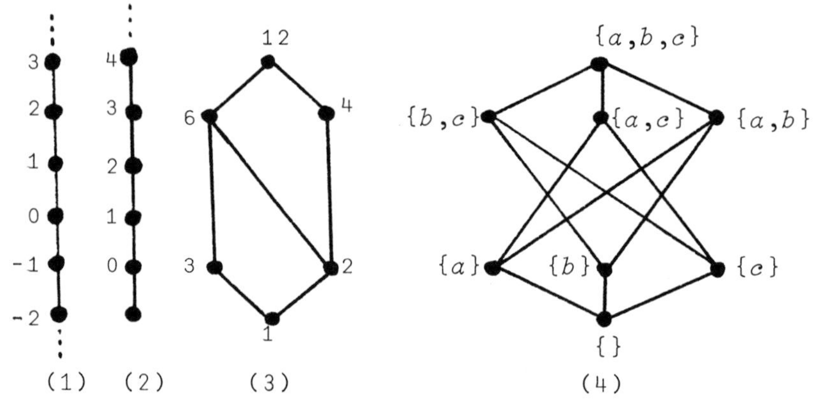

Fig. 6.4. Partially ordered sets.

(1) The integers ordered by $\leqslant$.
(2) The non-negative integers ordered by $\leqslant$.
(3) The factors of 12 ordered by divisibility.
(4) The subsets of a set of three elements, ordered by $\subseteq$.

6.2. Definition. A p.o. set P is a *chain* (alternatively called a *totally* or *linearly ordered* set) if for all $x,y \in$ P, $x \sqsubseteq y$ or $y \sqsubseteq x$.

In Fig.6.4 only (1) and (2) are chains; the p.o. sets (3) and (4) both contain incomparable elements. However, they all contain subsets which are chains: for example, {1,2,6,12} in (3).

6.3. Corollary. Every subset of a chain is a chain.

6.4. Theorem. Every finite non-empty chain P may be written with the elements numbered in the form

$\{p_1,p_2,\ldots,p_n\}$

where $p_i \sqsubseteq p_j$ whenever $i \leqslant j$.

6.5. Notation. Unless otherwise stated, P denotes a p.o. set. Small letters are used to denote elements and capital letters subsets of P.

$a \sqsubseteq X$ means $a \sqsubseteq x$ for all $x \in X$.

$X \sqsubseteq a$ means $x \sqsubseteq a$ for all $x \in X$.

$x \sqsupseteq y$ means $y \sqsubseteq x$. Similarly we may write $a \sqsupseteq X$ etc.

6.6. Theorem. For any $X \subseteq P$ there is at most one $a \in P$ such that for all $p \in P$, $a \sqsubseteq p$ if and only if $X \sqsubseteq p$. When a exists it is called the *least upper bound* (l.u.b.) of X.

Notice that not all $X \subseteq P$ need have least upper bounds. Sometimes a set has no upper bounds, while others have several (or even infinitely many) but none is weaker than all the others. Fig. 6.5 illustrates both these situations.

6.7. Notation. For any $X \subseteq P$ the least upper bound of X, when it exists, is denoted by $\bigsqcup X$. Thus by 6.6, for all $p \in P$, $\bigsqcup X \sqsubseteq p$ if and only if $X \sqsubseteq p$. By re-

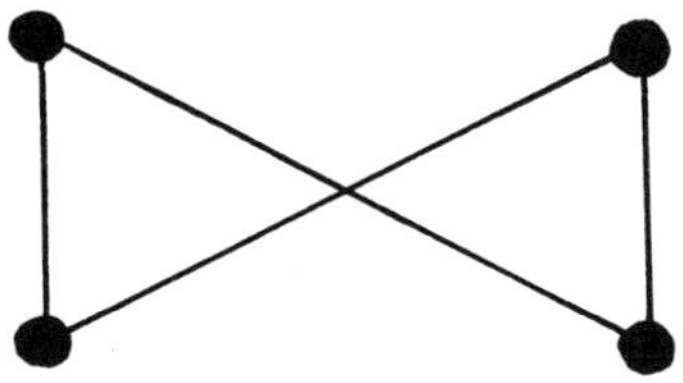

Fig. 6.5. A partially ordered set.

placing $\sqsubseteq$ by $\sqsupseteq$ throughout, we may similarly define $\bigsqcap X$, the *greatest lower bound* (g.l.b.) of X.

The form of these definitions allows us freely to interchange $\bigsqcup X \sqsubseteq p$ with $X \sqsubseteq p$ or $\bigsqcap X \sqsupseteq p$ with $X \sqsupseteq p$.

6.8. Theorem. If $X \sqsubseteq a$ and $a \in X$ then $a \equiv \bigsqcup X$.

6.9. Theorem. If X and Y are subsets of P, $X \subseteq Y$, and $\bigsqcup X$ and $\bigsqcup Y$ exist, then $\bigsqcup X \sqsubseteq \bigsqcup Y$.

6.10. Notation. Write $\top$ ('top') for P and $\bot$ ('bottom') for P.

Top and bottom (named from their position in the p.o. set diagram) need not exist any more than any other l.u.b. or g.l.b. In Fig. 6.4, (2) has 0 as bottom and no top, while (1) has neither.

6.11. Corollary. If a non-empty finite chain P is written with the elements numbered in the form $\{p_1, p_2, \ldots, p_n\}$, where $p_i \sqsubseteq p_j$ whenever $i \leqslant j$, then $\bigsqcap P = p_1$ and $\bigsqcup P = p_n$.

6.12. Theorem. For all $a \in P$, $\bigsqcup\{a\} = a$.

6.13. Notation. If x and y are any elements of P we write $x \sqcup y$ for $\bigsqcup\{x\ y\}$, and $x \sqcap y$ for $\bigsqcap\{x\ y\}$.

These dyadic operators are called *join* and *meet* respectively.

6.14. Corollary. Whenever $x \sqcup y$ exists, $x \sqsubseteq x \sqcup y$ and $y \sqsubseteq x \sqcup y$.

6.15. Theorem. Whenever $x \sqcup y$ exists, $x \sqcup y \equiv y$ if and only if $x \sqsubseteq y$.

6.16. Theorem. For all $x, y, z \in P$ for which $x \sqcup z$ and $y \sqcup z$ exist, if $x \sqsubseteq y$ then $x \sqcup z \sqsubseteq y \sqcup z$.

6.17. Theorem. Let R be a set of subsets of P. Then, provided all the necessary l.u.b's exist, $\bigsqcup(\bigcup_{X \in R} X) = \bigsqcup\{\bigsqcup X \mid X \in R\}$.

In particular $\bigsqcup(X \cup Y) = (\bigsqcup X) \sqcup (\bigsqcup Y)$.

6.18. Theorem. If $x,y,z \in P$ and the necessary joins and meets exist,

1. (Commutative Law) $x \sqcup y = y \sqcup x$.
2. (Associative Law) $x \sqcup (y \sqcup z) = (x \sqcup y) \sqcup z$.
3. (Idempotence Property) $x \sqcup x = x$.
4. (Absorption Law) $x \sqcup (x \sqcap y) = x$.

6.19. Definition. A continued join operator may be defined in terms of the dyadic operator by putting

$$\bigsqcup_{i=1}^{n} x_i = (\ldots((x_1 \sqcup x_2) \sqcup x_3) \sqcup \ldots\ldots) \sqcup x_n.$$

6.20. Theorem. If all the required joins of pairs of elements exist that are needed to form $a = \bigsqcup_{i=1}^{n} x_i$, then $\bigsqcup\{x_1, x_2, \ldots x_n\}$ exists and is equal to a. (The proof is by induction on n.)

On the basis of this theorem we may reasonably extend the definition of the continued join and meet operators to infinite sets, as follows.

6.21. Definition. If $X = \{x_1, x_2, \ldots\}$ is a countably infinite set we define $\bigsqcup_{i=1}^{\infty} x_i = \bigsqcup X$ and $\bigsqcap_{i=1}^{\infty} x_i = \bigsqcap X$.

Our discussion of $\bigsqcup X$ and $\bigsqcap X$ has so far covered the cases where X = P (the entire p.o. set), where X contains one or two elements, and where it is infinite;

there remains the case where X is empty. Now if we bear in mind that $(X \sqsubseteq p) = \bigwedge\{x \sqsubseteq p \mid x \in X\}$, we see that $\emptyset \sqsubseteq p$ reduces to $\bigwedge\emptyset$, which by convention is trivially true. Thus for $X = \emptyset$, 6.7 yields $\bigsqcup\emptyset \sqsubseteq p$ for all p; but $\perp \sqsubseteq p$ for all p, so $\bigsqcup\emptyset = \perp$ by an immediate consequence of Definition 6.1 (provided $\perp$ exists).

6.22. Convention. $\bigsqcup\emptyset = \perp$, provided $\perp$ exists in P.

Complete Lattices.

The reader will have noticed the continually reiterated restriction in the previous section: "provided the relevant l.u.b's exist". We could take this for granted if we assumed that all our values were elements of *complete lattices* under the information-content partial ordering, for these are simply p.o. sets in which all l.u.b's and g.l.b's exist. We do not lose generality by this assumption, since every p.o. set can be embedded in a complete lattice (see Theorem 6.29 below).

It should be noted, however, that some workers prefer not to work with complete lattices, as these are liable to contain extra elements in which they could not conceivably be interested. In particular, some people prefer to work without $\top$, so as not to have to take into account the possibility of self-contradictory values. Instead of complete lattices they use p.o. sets in which l.u.b's exist for all countable directed subsets (the concept of directed set will be explained below). For purposes of the semantics of programming languages, the choice is largely a matter of taste (though the situation might be different in the analysis of languages allowing parallel processing We prefer to use complete lattices, as they are more closely related to the model we shall study later, which seems to give us greater insight than the other approaches into such aspects as determining which values are actually computable. In any case, once the theory has been set up using complete lattices, there are techniques for filtering out some of the unwanted elements; we shall not, however, discuss these in any detail here (see Scott [53], Chapter 6).

6.23. Definition. A p.o. set S is a *lattice* if $\bigsqcup X$ and $\bigsqcap X$ exist for every non-empty, finite subset $X \subseteq S$.

Notice that this is not yet a complete lattice, since not all subsets of S need have bounds.

6.24. Theorem. S is a lattice if and only if $x \sqcup y$ and $x \sqcap y$ exist for all $x,y \in S$.

6.25. Corollary.. Every non-empty chain is a lattice.

6.26. Definition. The lattice D is *complete* if $\bigsqcup X$ and $\bigsqcap X$ exist for *every* subset $X \subseteq D$.

D will always denote a complete lattice from now on, unless otherwise stated.

6.27. Corollary. Every finite lattice is complete.

6.28. Corollary. Every complete lattice has a bottom and a top. Notice that the converse of 6.28 is not true. The p.o. set shown in Fig.6.6, for

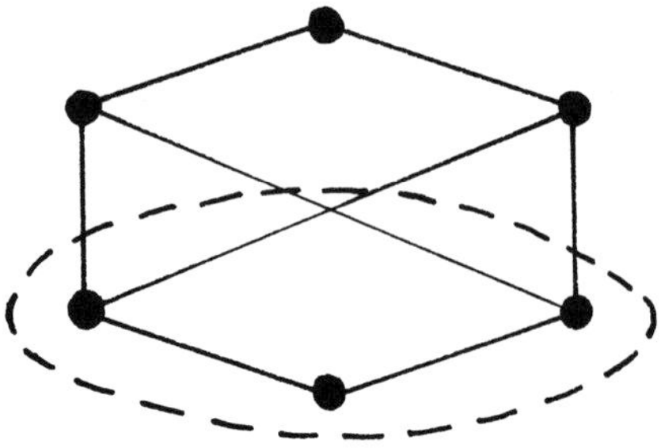

Fig. 6.6. A p.o. set which is not a lattice.

example, has a bottom and a top but is not even a lattice, as the subset X has no l.u.b.

In our earlier examples, the integers in Fig. 6.4 (1) form a lattice. If the elements $+\infty$ and $-\infty$ are adjoined at the top and bottom it becomes a complete lattice. Figs. 6.4(3) and (4) are complete lattices already; so are all the sets we introduced at the beginning of this chapter, of values ordered by their information content.

The rational numbers ordered by $\leqslant$ are an example of a lattice which cannot be completed merely by adding bottom and top ($-\infty$ and $+\infty$ in this case). The l.u.b. of the (infinite) subset containing all rational numbers less than $\sqrt{2}$, for example, is not itself a rational number: thus the completion of this lattice requires the inclusion of the irrational numbers too. This suggests that the proof of the following theorem is non-trivial: in fact it involves constructing the required lattice by a method like that of Dedekind cuts for constructing the real numbers. (For proofs see, for example, [3] or [14].)

6.29. Theorem. Every partially ordered set may be embedded in a complete lattice.

6.30. Theorem. If, in the lattice D, $\bigsqcup X$ exists for all $X \subseteq D$, then D is complete. (That is to say, $\bigsqcap X$ also exists for all $X \subseteq D$. The proof is to show that $\bigsqcup\{a : a \sqsubseteq X\}$ is the required g.l.b. Notice that if $\bigsqcup X$ exists for all $X \subseteq D$, then in particular $\bigsqcup \emptyset$ exists, and hence $\bot$ exists: cf. 6.22.)

Products and Sums Having now introduced complete lattices, we next consider two ways of combining complete lattices to form new ones.

6.31. Definition. If $D_1, D_2, \ldots, D_n$ are complete lattices, then we take $D_1 \times D_2 \times \ldots \times D_n$ to be the set of elements of the form $\langle x_1, x_2, \ldots, x_n \rangle$ where $x_i \in D_i$ $(1 \leq i \leq n)$. We may partially order these elements by saying $\langle x_1, x_2, \ldots, x_n \rangle \sqsubseteq \langle y_1, y_2, \ldots, y_n \rangle$ if $x_i \sqsubseteq y_i$ for all i $(1 \leq i \leq n)$. Under this ordering the space is a complete lattice too.

6.32. Definition. If, as before, $D_1, D_2, \ldots, D_n$ are complete lattices, we take $D_1 + D_2 + \ldots + D_n$ to be the disjoint union of all the elements of $D_1, D_2, \ldots, D_n$, together with a new $\bot$ and $\top$. We order the elements as follows: $\bot \sqsubseteq x \sqsubseteq \top$ for all $x \in D_1 + D_2 + \ldots + D_n$, and if x is an element of the D_i summand and y an element of the D_j summand then $x \sqsubseteq y$ in $D_1 + D_2 + \ldots + D_n$ if and only if $i = j$ and $x \sqsubseteq y$ in D_i. This space is also a complete lattice.

This construction, with a new $\bot$ and $\top$ weaker and stronger, respectively, than all the elements of the component lattices, is called the *separated sum*. An alternative procedure is to make $\bot$ and $\top$ in the sum domain the images of $\bot$ and $\top$ of *each* of the component domains. This alternative construction is called the *coalesced sum*. A pictorial illustration of the alternatives is shown in Fig.6.7. The choice is to some extent a matter of taste, but using the coalesced sum can lead to some technical difficulties: consider, for example, the problems that arise if one of the summands is the one-element lattice. An intuitive way of thinking about the separated sum is that for the undefined element of a component lattice at least we know the component to which it belongs; so it does not correspond to the completely undefined element in the sum lattice.

Notice that it is not forbidden for the same lattice to appear as two distinct summands of a sum lattice: that is, for D_i to be the same lattice as D_j, for $j \neq i$. In this case each element of the component lattice appears twice in the sum lattice, as implied by the phrase "disjoint union" used above.

6.33. Definition. In any lattice, $\bot$ and $\top$ are called *improper elements*. All the other elements are called *proper*.

6.34. Notation. If x is an element of a product lattice, so that $x = \langle x_1,\ldots,x_n\rangle$, then $x{\downarrow}i$ denotes x_i if $1 \leqslant i \leqslant n$, and $\bot$ otherwise. This use of an explicit operator for selecting a component of an n-

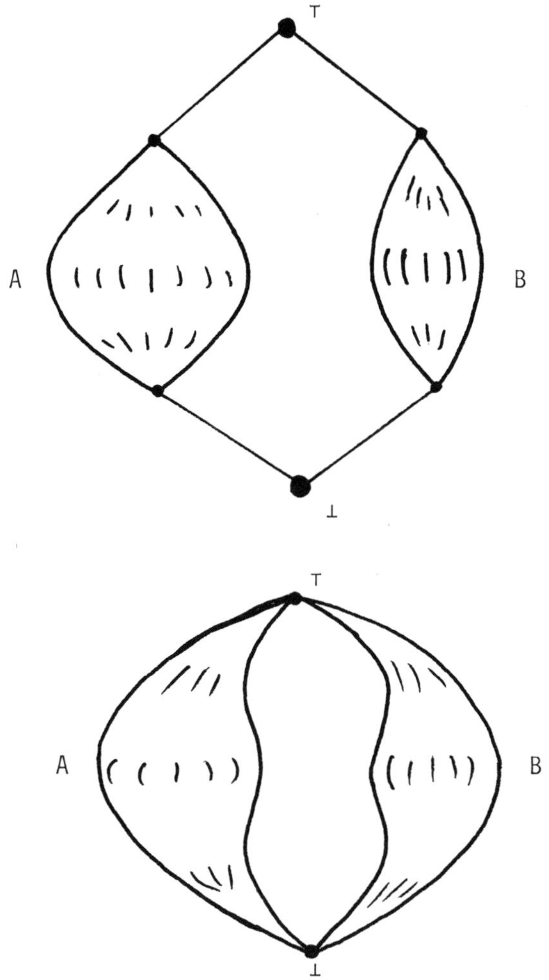

Fig. 6.7. Separated and coalesced sums.

tuple frees the subscript notation for other more informal use.

6.35. Notation. If $D = D_1 + D_2 + .. + D_n$ and $x_i \in D_i$ $(1 \leq i \leq n)$, then $(x_i \text{ in } D)$ denotes the corresponding element of the sum lattice D.

If $x \in D$ then $x|D_i$ denotes the following element of D_i:

if $x \equiv \bot_D$ then $(x|D_i) \equiv \bot_{D_i}$;

if $x \equiv \top_D$ then $(x|D_i) \equiv \top_{D_i}$;

if x corresponds to an element y of D_i then $(x|D_i) \equiv y$;

otherwise (if x corresponds to an element of some other summand lattice), $(x|D_i) \equiv \bot_{D_i}$.

(Note that here, and whenever there is danger of confusion, we decorate $\bot$ and $\top$ with subscripts to indicate the lattice to which they belong. We omit the subscripts if this information is implied by the context.)

If $D = D_1 + D_2 + ... + D_n$ and $x \in D$ then $x \mathsf{E} D_i$ denotes the following element of the truth value lattice T:

if $x \equiv \bot_D$ then $(x \mathsf{E} D_i) \equiv \bot_T$;

if $x \equiv \top_D$ then $(x \mathsf{E} D_i) \equiv \top_T$;

if x corresponds to some element of D_i then $(x \mathsf{E} D_i) \equiv$ *true*;

otherwise (if x corresponds to an element of some other summand), $(x \mathsf{E} D_i) \equiv$ *false*.

It must be admitted that the notation of 6.35, and even the machinery underlying it, is not entirely satisfactory. It rapidly becomes exceedingly tedious to be continually distinguishing between a value considered as an element of a sum domain and the *same* value considered as an element of a component lattice. Sometimes this leads workers to omit entirely these operations ("injection" into a sum lattice and "projection" into a component space), on the grounds that they may be deduced from the context if required. Such informality in turn leads to difficulties for people developing programs which accept denotational semantic definitions as input and process them in some way automatically (for example, Mosses [37]). This area is one which is likely to see some revision in the spirit of our remarks on notation in Chapter 3 above.

These two constructions, one to form tuples and the other to combine several types of value into one space, are two of the principal ways in which we require to form new lattices. We must now consider function spaces, which give us a third way of forming new lattices from old.

Functions on lattices.

We began this chapter with a discussion of several functions which were all solutions of a particular fixed point equation; then we motivated our introduction of partially ordered sets and lattices by saying that the solution we required was the weakest, or minimal, one. So it is natural to begin our discussion of functions by defining an ordering on them.

6.36. Definition. If f and g are functions from D to D′, where D and D′ are complete lattices, then $f \sqsubseteq g$ if $f(x) \sqsubseteq g(x)$ for all $x \in D$.

Note that, if D′ is a flat lattice such as the integers, and if the inconsistent value ⊤ does not arise, then $f \sqsubseteq g$ if g is defined for more values of the argument than f is (that is, if $g(x) \not\equiv \perp$ and $f(x) \equiv \perp$ for some x), and if the two functions always give equal results for those arguments for which both functions are defined. It may easily be checked that under this ordering the weakest function among these discussed at the start of this chapter was indeed the one we expected. The weakest function of all, of course, is the one which is undefined everywhere: that is, the function $\lambda x.\perp$.

Monotonicity. We have been ordering our value spaces according to the "information content" of the elements. This allows us immediately to impose some restriction on the functions we consider, for it is clearly reasonable to assume that if we know more information about the argument of a function we shall know more (or at any rate, no less) about the result. That is to say, functions must be *monotonic*.

6.37. Definition. A function $f : D \to D'$ is monotonic if $f(x) \sqsubseteq f(y)$ whenever $x \sqsubseteq y$.

Notice that another way of looking at the partial ordering given in Definition 6.36 above is that the operation of applying f to x is monotonic in f.

This property of monotonicity would be enough to

guarantee the existence of weakest fixed points, since a theorem of Tarski [60] states that every monotonic function on a complete lattice has a complete lattice of fixed points — and hence always has a minimal one. We shall not go into this theorem in any more detail here. Later on, in fact, we shall be able to give an explicit formula for the minimal fixed point of a function. Unfortunately, however, monotonicity is not a sufficient restriction for us to solve our other problem: that of constructing a space isomorphic with its own function space. We must therefore continue to search for a stronger condition, and so we now look in a little more detail at the general nature of the process of computation.

Continuity. In Chapter 4 we first mentioned the problems of computing with infinitary objects, which cannot be represented inside a finite computer. In particular, we were considering functions which depended on other functions. The essential idea was that we had to work with *approximations*: we were to build up an adequate approximation to the required result by using sufficiently good, but still finite, approximations to the functions on which it depended. This same idea is applicable to any process intended to compute an infinitary value; it derives from the finite nature of our computers. It does not mean that we can handle only finite objects; infinitary objects, though, can be treated only as the limit (or least upper bound) of some set of finite approximations. Moreover, we must be able to represent these approximations somehow inside our computer.

It is not necessary here to consider the exact details of how approximate elements of a particular value space might be represented. However, one thing we do know about any technique which represents values by finite strings of symbols drawn from some finite (or, indeed, countably infinite) alphabet is that it can only represent countably many values. The use of finite bit patterns is an example of such a technique. Any computer must employ representations subject to this same restriction. So we may reasonably demand of all the value spaces in which we hope to compute that they come equipped with a particular countable subset of elements from which all the other elements may be built up. That is, we demand that our domains be *countably based*. Notice that we are still not saying anything about which elements would be basis elements in any particular space: all this discussion is about the nature of computing in general.

6.38. Definition. A set $E \subseteq D$ is a *basis* of D if $x = \bigsqcup\{e \mid e \in E \text{ and } e \sqsubseteq x\}$ for all $x \in D$, and $\bigsqcup E' \in E$ for all finite $E' \subseteq E$. If the second condition were absent, the set E would be a *subbasis* of D.

From this definition, we see that elements of a value space which are not themselves basis elements will be approximated by an *infinite* set of basis elements. So since we cannot expect such a value to be computed in its entirety (any more than we can expect to have π written out completely), all we can hope for is that our computing process will generate the appropriate basis elements one by one, in such a way that any particular one will turn up sooner or later in a finite time. This will not be possible for all values: for some there will not exist methods of enumerating their particular subset of basis elements (that is, methods of generating the elements one by one). Such a value is *uncomputable*.

We next ask how this notion of computing a value by enumerating its basis elements affects our ideas about permissible functions. A function must produce an *enumeration* of the basis elements of its answer from an *enumeration* of those of its argument. Any particular basis element of the answer must be produced in finite time, when the function will have received only a finite part of the enumeration of the argument.

Now let D and D′ be complete lattices with bases $E \subseteq D$ and $E' \subseteq D'$, and consider a function $f : D \to D'$. Instead of elements of D we can equally well consider subsets of E (remember that each such subset has a l.u.b., since D is a complete lattice; conversely, each element of D is the l.u.b. of a subset of E, since E is a basis). So each $X \subseteq E$ defines a value $\bigsqcup X$, which f maps to $f(\bigsqcup X)$. We require, then, that for at least one subset $Y' \subseteq E'$ such that $\bigsqcup Y' = f(\bigsqcup X)$, each $y' \in Y'$ should be produced from only a *finite* subset of X. So we impose:

6.39. Condition. For all $X \subseteq E$ there exists a $Y' \subseteq E'$ such that $\bigsqcup Y' = f(\bigsqcup X)$, and for all $y' \in Y'$ $y' \sqsubseteq f(\bigsqcup X_f)$ for some finite $X_f \subseteq X$.

This condition is very close to Rogers' notion of

enumeration reducibility ([45], p.145). Let us examine its consequences: we shall see that it imposes a restriction both on the functions we allow, and on our value spaces. In the first place, since each basis element of the answer is produced by some finite set of basis elements of the argument, the whole answer must be included in the l.u.b. of the results obtained from all such finite sets. So we arrive at the following theorem:

6.40. Theorem. Condition 6.39 implies that for all $X \subseteq E$, $f(\bigsqcup X) \sqsubseteq \bigsqcup\{f(\bigsqcup X_f) \mid X_f \subseteq X$ and X_f finite$\}$.

Proof: Assuming Condition 6.39, if $y' \sqsubseteq f(\bigsqcup X_f)$ for some finite $X_f \subseteq X$, then
$y' \sqsubseteq \bigsqcup\{f(\bigsqcup X_f) \mid X_f \subseteq X$ and X_f finite$\}$. This holds for all $y' \in Y'$, so by 6.6
$\bigsqcup Y \sqsubseteq \quad \{f(\bigsqcup X_f) \mid X_f \subseteq X$ and X_f finite$\}$.

6.41. Theorem. If f is monotonic, then the condition given by Theorem 6.40 holds for all $X \subseteq E$ if and only if the same condition holds for all $X \subseteq D$.

Proof: Assume the condition holds for all $X \subseteq E$. Now, since E is a basis of D, for all $Z \subseteq D$

$$\begin{aligned} f(\bigsqcup Z) &= f(\bigsqcup\{z \mid z \in Z\}) \\ &= f(\bigsqcup\{\bigsqcup\{x \mid x \in E \text{ and } x \sqsubseteq z\} \mid z \in Z\}) \\ &= f(\bigsqcup X) \qquad \text{(by 6.17)} \end{aligned}$$

where $X = \{x \mid x \in E$ and $x \sqsubseteq z$ for some $z \in Z\}$.

So, by the condition we are assuming,

$f(\bigsqcup Z) \sqsubseteq \quad \{f(\bigsqcup X_f) \mid X_f \subseteq X$ and X_f finite$\}$.

Now, by the definition of X, for each finite $X_f \subseteq X$

there is a finite $Z_f \subseteq Z$ such that each $x \in X_f$ approximates some $z \in Z_f$. Then $\bigsqcup X_f \sqsubseteq \bigsqcup Z_f$, by an induction based on 6.16, and so, by monotonicity of f,

$$f(\bigsqcup X_f) \sqsubseteq f(\bigsqcup Z_f).$$

So, since including all the other Z_f's does no harm,

$$f(\bigsqcup Z) \sqsubseteq \quad \{f(\bigsqcup Z_f) \mid Z_f \subseteq Z \text{ and } Z_f \text{ finite}\},$$

for all $Z \subseteq D$. The reverse implication is trivial, since $E \subseteq D$.

This restriction we have just derived is a restriction on permissible functions, and it is couched in terms of finite subsets of a set of approximations. In later work it will often be more useful to have another version of the same restriction expressed instead in terms of the function's effect on the set of approximations as a whole. As we shall see, to consider the effect on *arbitrary* subsets $X \subseteq D$ would be too general; we confine our attention to sets of values which are, in a sense, tending towards a limit. A chain is an example of the kind of set we have in mind: it is a simple example of a *directed set*.

6.42. Definition. A set X is *directed* if every finite subset of X has an upper bound in X; that is, if $A \subseteq X$ is finite then there is a $b \in X$ such that $A \sqsubseteq b$. (Finite subsets of X need not have *least* upper bounds in X; nor, if X is a subset of a lattice D, need l.u.b.'s in D of finite subsets of X also be in X.)

6.43. Corollary. Every directed set is non-empty

(since the empty set is one of its finite subsets).

6.44. Corollary. If E is a basis of D then for all $x \in D$ the set $\{e \mid e \in E \text{ and } e \sqsubseteq x\}$ is directed (since l.u.b's of finite sets of basis elements are also basis elements).

These provide examples of directed sets with richer structure than the simple chains mentioned above. In each case the element x is the limit which the directed set is approaching: notice that x may or may not be a basis element itself.

6.45. Theorem. A non-empty set X is directed if and only if every pair of elements has an upper bound in X.

Proof: To show that all finite subsets have upper bounds if pairs do, use induction on the size of the subset. The reverse implication is trivial, since pairs are finite subsets.

We now use this concept of a directed set to define a restriction on functions.

6.46. Definition. A function $f : D \to D'$ is *continuous* if $f(\bigsqcup X) = \bigsqcup \{fx \mid x \in X\}$ for all directed $X \subseteq D$.

To get some insight into the effect of restricting functions to be continuous, let us introduce the following definitions.

6.47. Definition. A directed set is *interesting* if it does not contain its least upper bound; that is, if $\bigsqcup X \notin X$.

6.48. Corollary. No finite directed set is interesting (by 6.8, since the whole set is a finite subset of itself).

6.49. Corollary. If $f : D \to D'$ is monotonic then $f(\bigsqcup X) = \bigsqcup\{fx \mid x \in X\}$ for all uninteresting directed $X \subseteq D$.

6.50. Corollary. All monotonic functions on finite lattices are continuous.

6.51. Definition. A point $x \in D$ is a *limit point* if $x = \bigsqcup X$ for some *interesting* directed $X \subseteq D$.

Saying that some monotonic function is also continuous thus says something new only about that function's behaviour on limit points. We next relate this notion of continuity to our earlier ideas about computation, which led us to Theorem 6.41. In fact, as the next theorem shows, a function is continuous if and only if it is monotonic and the condition given by 6.41 is satisfied.

6.52. Theorem. A function $f : D \to D'$ is continuous if and only if it is monotonic and $f(\bigsqcup X) = \bigsqcup\{f(\bigsqcup X_f) \mid X_f \subseteq X \text{ and } X_f \text{ finite}\}$ for all $X \subseteq D$.

Proof. Let f be continuous. For $x,y \in D$, if $x \sqsubseteq y$ then $\{x,y\}$ is directed. So

$$\begin{aligned} f(y) &= f(x \sqcup y) \\ &= f(x) \sqcup f(y) && \text{(by continuity)} \\ &\sqsupseteq f(x) && \text{(definition of } \sqcup) \end{aligned}$$

and f is thus monotonic.

Now for any $X \subseteq D$, $S = \{\bigsqcup X_f \mid X_f \subseteq X \text{ and } X_f \text{ finite}\}$ is a directed set, since $\emptyset \in S$ so that S is non-empty, and for any $\bigsqcup X_1, \bigsqcup X_2 \in S$ their l.u.b., $\bigsqcup(X_1 \cup X_2)$ by 6.17 is also in X. Moreover,

$$\bigsqcup X = \bigsqcup\{\bigsqcup X_f \mid X_f \subset X \text{ and } X_f \text{ finite}\},$$

from which the required result follows by the continuity of f. Conversely, let f be monotonic and for all $X \subseteq D$ let $f(\bigsqcup X) \sqsubseteq \bigsqcup\{f(\bigsqcup X_f) \mid X_f \subseteq X \text{ and } X_f \text{ finite}\}$. Let $Y \subseteq D$ be directed; so for any finite $Y_f \subseteq Y$ there is a $y \in Y$ such that $\bigsqcup Y_f \sqsubseteq y$. Then by monotonicity $f(\bigsqcup Y_f) \sqsubseteq f(y)$ for some $y \in Y$; so by taking upper bounds on both sides we have:
$\bigsqcup\{f(\bigsqcup Y_f) \mid Y_f \subseteq Y \text{ and } Y_f \text{ finite}\} \sqsubseteq \bigsqcup\{f(y) \mid y \in Y\}$.
So, by assumption,

$$f(\bigsqcup Y) \sqsubseteq \bigsqcup\{f(y) \mid y \in Y\}.$$

But, again by monotonicity, $f(y) \sqsubseteq f(\bigsqcup Y)$ for all $y \in Y$, so that $\bigsqcup\{f(y) \mid y \in Y\} \sqsubseteq f(\bigsqcup Y)$. Hence $f(\bigsqcup Y) = \bigsqcup\{f(y) \mid y \in Y\}$ and so f is continuous as required.

Thus we have now shown that condition 6.39, obtained by considering the general nature of computation, implies that all our functions be not merely monotonic, but also continuous. The reader is urged to make sure that all the argument in this section on continuity is well understood, so that the reason for our insistence on continuity is properly appreciated.

Our definition of continuity in 6.46 is equivalent to the normal topological definition of continuity if our lattices are appropriately set up as topological spaces. The topological ramifications of our theory are, however, on the whole outside the scope of this book; readers who are interested are referred to Scott [48], [50] or [51].

We now give a couple of results about combinations of continuous functions.

6.53. Theorem. Let $f : D \to D'$ where $D = D_0 \times D_1$ (with partial orderings of D, D_0, D_1 related as in 6.31). Then f is continuous on D if and only if it is continuous on D_0 and D_1 separately.

6.54. Theorem. The composition of continuous functions is continuous. (Apart from checking that $\lambda x.f(g\ x)$ is continuous if f and g are, it is necessary also to look at functions of several variables, including cases where variables are shared, such as $\lambda x.f(x,x)$.)

Exercises.

1. If for some $f : D \to D'$, $f(\bigsqcup X) = \bigsqcup\{f(x) \mid x \in X\}$ for *all* $X \subseteq D$, not merely for directed $X \subseteq D$, then f would be said to be *additive*. Examine the previous arguments to check whether additivity of functions is necessarily implied by Condition 6.39.

2. Give a specific example of each of the following kinds of functions on complete lattices:

(a) one which is not monotonic;
(b) one which is monotonic but not continuous;
(c) one which is continuous but not additive (as defined above);
(d) one which is additive.

You may choose any complete lattices you like for the domains and ranges of these functions, but say what they are.

Continuous Lattices. Although the restriction to continuous functions is a necessary condition for 6.39 to hold, it is not sufficient. The chain of reasoning leading from Condition 6.39 to the requirement for continuous functions was made up of three theorems; and although the last two of these (6.41 and 6.52) were double implications (that is, "if and only if" statements), the first one (6.40) was only a single implication. Condition 6.39 implied that a certain other condition should hold, but not necessarily vice versa. It is therefore possible that we may have relaxed some requirement at that first stage. And in fact we did. Condition 6.39 states that each finite piece of information about the result should be obtainable from finite information about the argument; from this we correctly inferred that each finite piece of result information was weaker than the l.u.b. of *everything* obtainable from finite pieces of argument information. Thus we let in the pathological possibility that (in some "interesting" case) some finite piece of result information might be weaker than some l.u.b. itself, but not weaker than anything in some interesting directed set of approximations to that l.u.b. Removing this possibility amounts to a restriction on the lattices we allow as value spaces.

A naive first version of this new condition we seek to impose on a lattice D would be the following: for all $y \in D$ and directed $X \subseteq D$, $y \sqsubseteq \bigsqcup X$ if and only if $y \sqsubseteq x$ for some $x \in X$. But this would be too severe, as y itself might be a limit point: than we ought to require only that each *approximation* to y is weaker than some approximation to $\bigsqcup X$. So the correct formulation makes use of the following definition.

6.55. Definition. For $x,y \in D$, $x \ll y$ (read "x is well below y") if whenever $y \sqsubseteq \bigsqcup Z$ for some directed $Z \subseteq D$ then $x \sqsubseteq z$ for some $z \in Z$.

The idea here is that if $x \ll y$, then x is an *essential chunk* of the information in y: however we choose to build up a set of approximations to y (that is, for *any* directed Z such that $y \sqsubseteq \bigsqcup Z$), at least *one* of the approximations will either be x, or contain all the information in x.

6.56. Definition. A point $a \in D$ such that $a \ll a$ is said to be *isolated*.

Notice that an isolated point cannot be the limit point of any interesting directed set. Any set of approximations to an isolated point a must contain a itself: so a is an essential part of itself. An isolated point can thus only be reached if it is computed explicitly.

The final condition we now impose on our value spaces is that they are *continuous* complete lattices, where continuity is defined as follows.

6.57. Definition. A lattice D is *continuous* if for all $y \in D$, $y = \bigsqcup \{x \in D \mid x \ll y\}$.

Thus any element y is simply the join of all its essential parts, and contains nothing else. We know that any directed set of approximations to y contains each essential chunk, so this condition ensures that the limit point of a directed set contains only the information actually in the set itself: no other information "creeps in" by another route.

An example of the kind of situation this requirement excludes is illustrated in Fig.6.8. a is the l.u.b. of an interesting directed set A, and $b \sqsubseteq a$. But then by the continuity restriction b must be the l.u.b. of some set B such that each element of B approximates some element of A: the situation illustrated, where the greatest lower bound of the two sides is $\bot$, will not do. Here the only element which is *essential* for b is $\bot$, for apart from that there is a choice of two quite independent routes to get to b or beyond (that is, to a), one involving only elements of B and the other involving only elements of A. Of course if we *actually* ever got to a we would involve B, because $b \sqsubseteq a$; but that would take an infinite amount of computing. All we can do in finite time is produce an element of A which adequately approximates a; and that will not include any of the information in B. So, formally, $\bot \preccurlyeq b$, but for no $b' \in B$ do we have $b' \preccurlyeq b$. Thus, since $b \neq \bigsqcup\{x \mid x \preccurlyeq b\}$, the continuity restriction is broken. Notice that this difficulty would not arise if a were isolated (and hence A uninteresting); for then any set of approximations to a would include a, so that there would be no way of getting beyond b without including all the information in b. The arbitrary choice of "non-essential" information would be removed.

A further example of the effects of the continuity restriction is afforded by a lattice which we shall be using a lot in the next chapter. Let ω be the set of non-negative integers: that is $\omega = \{n \mid n \geq 0\}$. Then $P\omega$ is the power-set of ω, the set of all subsets

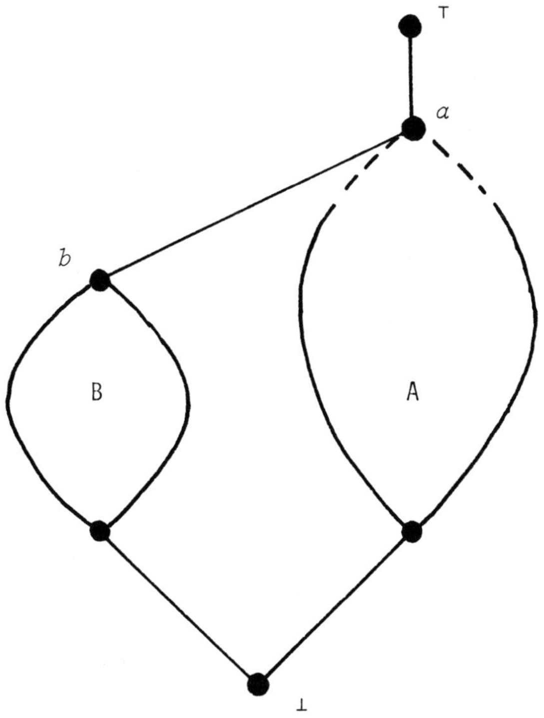

Fig. 6.8. A non-continuous lattice.

of ω. Under the set-inclusion ordering $P\omega$ becomes a complete, and indeed continuous, lattice; $\perp$ is the empty set $\emptyset$, and $\top$ is ω itself. Notice that $\top$ is not isolated: it is, for example, the limit of the interesting directed set $\{\{n \mid 0 \leqslant n \leqslant k\} \mid k \geqslant 0\}$. If now we form the *coalesced* sum of $P\omega$ with any other domain, such as some flat lattice or even another copy of $P\omega$ itself, the resulting sum domain will not be a complete lattice, and therefore not allowed. Notice that this problem is avoided if we form the *separated* sum instead, as the new $\top$ element is then safely isolated. Nor are we *always* prevented from using the coalesced sum, for very often the domains we seek to unite in this way themselves have isolated $\top$ elements; however, extra care has to be taken to check that this is so.

In order to show that restricting ourselves to continuous functions on continuous lattices is precisely equivalent to our original Condition 6.39, we shall finally prove the converse of Theorem 6.40. First we prove some lemmas.

6.58. Lemma. For all $y \in D$, $\{x \mid x \ll y\}$ is directed.

Proof: We know $\perp \ll y$, so the set is not empty; moreover it follows immediately from the definition of $x \ll y$ that if $w \ll y$ and $x \ll y$ then also $(w \sqcup x) \ll y$. The result follows by 6.45.

6.59. Corollary. In a continuous lattice every point that is not isolated is a limit point.

6.60. Lemma. If D is a continuous lattice with

basis E, then for all $x \in D$, $x = \bigsqcup\{e \mid e \in E \text{ and } e \ll x\}$.

Proof:

$$x = \bigsqcup\{y \mid y \in D \text{ and } y \ll x\} \qquad \text{(since D is continuous)}$$
$$= \bigsqcup\{\bigsqcup\{e \mid e \in E \text{ and } e \sqsubseteq y\} \mid y \ll x\}$$
$$\text{(since E is a basis)}$$
$$= \bigsqcup\{e \mid e \in E \text{ and } e \ll x\} \quad \text{(since } e \sqsubseteq y \ll x \text{ implies } e \ll x\text{)}.$$

6.61. Theorem. Let E, E′ be bases for continuous lattices D, D′, and let f be a function from D to D′. If, for all $X \subseteq E$,

$f(\bigsqcup X) \sqsubseteq \bigsqcup\{f(\bigsqcup X_f) \mid X_f \subseteq X \text{ and } X_f \text{ finite}\}$, then there is a $Y' \subseteq E'$ such that $\bigsqcup Y' = f(\bigsqcup X)$ and, for each $y' \in Y'$, $y' \sqsubseteq f(\bigsqcup X_f)$ for some finite $X_f \subseteq X$.

Proof: Let $y' = \{e' \mid e' \in E' \text{ and } e' \ll f(\bigsqcup X)\}$. Then by 6.60 the first condition is satisfied; and since for each $y' \in Y'$

$y' \ll f(\bigsqcup X) = \bigsqcup\{f(\bigsqcup X_f) \mid X_f \subseteq X \text{ and } X_f \text{ finite}\}$,

and since $\{f(\bigsqcup X_f) \mid X_f \subseteq X \text{ and } X_f \text{ finite}\}$ is directed, by 6.55 the second condition also holds.

6.62. Summary. Permissible value spaces (called *domains* from now on) are countably based, continuous complete lattices; and allowed functions on domains are continuous.

We should perhaps now check that the space of continuous functions on a domain is itself a domain, and that so are the spaces formed as the products or sums of domains (as defined in 6.31 and 6.32). We shall not bother to do this now, as it will be a natural consequence of our method of constructing domains, to be described later.

Finally in this chapter, before we proceed to

investigate the existence of the domains we require, we devote a little more attention to our other problem, which concerned the existence of fixed points.

A Fixed Point Operator

6.63. Definition. For any domain D, the function $fix : [D \to D] \to D$ is defined by $fix(f) = \bigsqcup_{n=0}^{\infty} f^n(\bot)$.

6.64. Theorem. If $f : [D \to D]$ is a continuous function, fix maps f to its minimal fixed point.

Proof: For some f let $p = fix(f) = \bigsqcup_{n=0}^{\infty} f^n(\bot)$.

Since $\bot \sqsubseteq f^n(\bot)$ for all $n \geq 0$,

$$p = \bigsqcup_{n=0}^{\infty} f^n(\bot)$$

$$= \bigsqcup_{n=0}^{\infty} f(f^n(\bot)).$$

But, since f is monotonic, by induction $f^n(\bot) \sqsubseteq f^{n+1}(\bot)$, so that $\{f^n(\bot) \mid n \geq 0\}$ is directed. Hence, since f is continuous,

$$p = f(\bigsqcup_{n=0}^{\infty} f^n(\bot)) = f(p).$$

So p is a fixed point of f. To show that it is minimal, we let a be an arbitrary fixed point and show that $p \sqsubseteq a$. Now $\bot \sqsubseteq a$ and, since f is monotonic, $f(\bot) \sqsubseteq f(a) = a$. Thus by induction, for all $n \geq 0$, $f^n(\bot) \sqsubseteq a$, and hence

$$p = \bigsqcup_{n=0}^{\infty} f^n(\bot) \sqsubseteq a.$$

Exercise

3. Show that fix is (a) monotonic and (b) continuous.

Chapter 7

REFLEXIVE DOMAINS

The Inverse Limit Construction.

There are two strategies for finding a suitable domain isomorphic with its own function space, as required for the λ-calculus. We can either attempt to construct such a domain explicitly, or we can examine the lattices we already know to see if there is a suitable candidate, in the sense that either it is the domain we want or that it contains such a domain as a subspace.

Explicit construction provided the earliest successful solution [52], and we now give a brief outline of the method.

We set up a hierarchy of domains D_n ($n \geq 0$). D_0 is a continuous lattice containing at least two elements, and D_{n+1} is the space of functions from D_n to D_n. Then we investigate the properties of the limit of this sequence of domains, which we call D_∞.

In Fig.7.1, for example, we show the first three domains in the sequence for the simplest possible case, starting with the two-element lattice. (If D_0 had only one element, then so would D_n for all n; and we would be constructing the trivial solution to our problem, mentioned and rejected earlier.) D_1 has three elements and D_2 has 10. D_3 is not shown, as it has 120549 elements.

Mappings are defined in both directions between adjacent domains in the sequence: these enable us to think of each domain as being embedded in its successor in a structure-preserving way. The mappings between the first three domains in our example

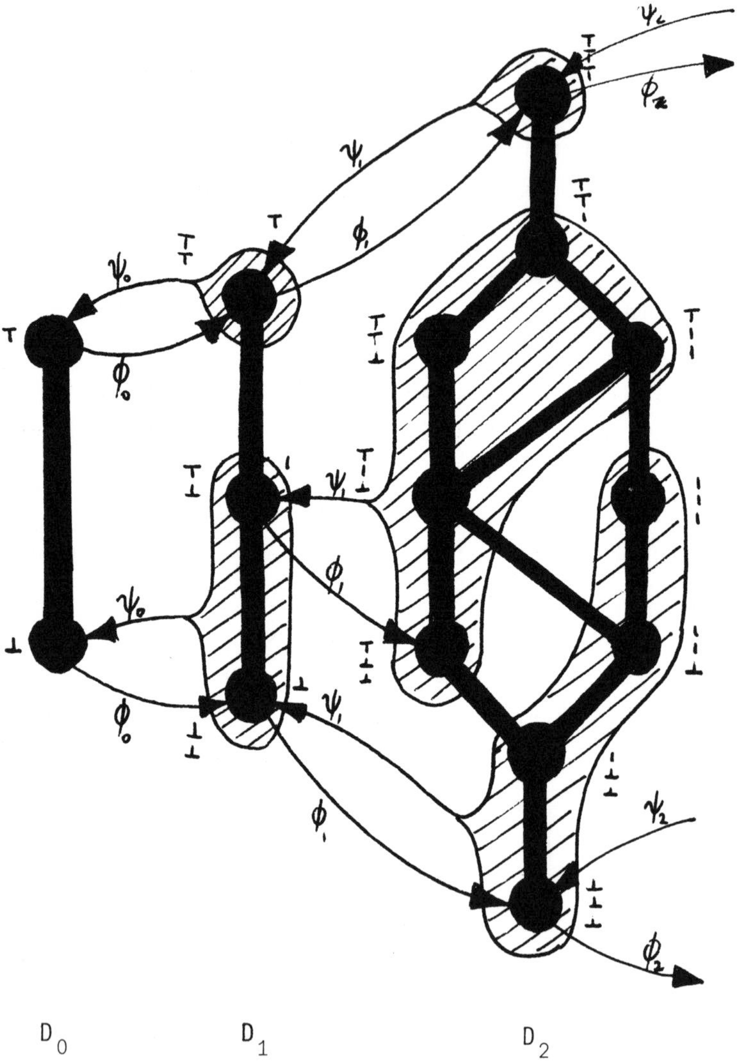

Fig. 7.1. First three domains in a hierarchy.

sequence are also shown in Fig.7.1.

The limit domain, D_∞, is then defined. Just as real numbers may be formally defined as sequences of better and better rational approximations, so an element of D_∞ is defined as a sequence of elements from each of the finite domains. Each member of one of these sequences is related to its predecessor by the appropriate mapping (the ψ mappings in Fig.7.1). and so the technique is known as an *inverse limit* construction. The method indeed leads to a satisfactory solution, though there is a fair amount of purely technical detail involved in showing that everything works out. The details are described by Sanderson [46] or (for those who prefer to use topological language) by Scott [50].

Exercise.

1. Write a program to check that the domain D_3, described above, has 120549 elements.

The $P\omega$ Model.

In the present treatment, however, we concentrate on the other approach, and cast around for a suitable complete lattice for our purposes. One possibility is $P\omega$, the power set of the non-negative integers (that is, the set of all sets of non-negative integers) ordered by the set inclusion relation $\subseteq$. As we mentioned in the previous chapter, this is a complete lattice; it is countably based (the finite sets of integers forming the basis); and it is continuous. So it is certainly worth looking at a little more closely.

$P\omega$, moreover, has an even more beguiling property.

All our domains must be countably based; that is, for each domain D there must be a countable set of basis elements $\{e_n \mid n \in \omega\}$ such that $x = \bigcup\{e_n \mid e_n \subseteq x\}$ for all $x \in D$. So we could easily define a mapping ε from any such D to $P\omega$: namely, for $x \in D$ $\varepsilon(x) = \{n \mid e_n \sqsubseteq_D x\}$. We see that $x \sqsubseteq y$ if and only if $\varepsilon(x) \subseteq \varepsilon(y)$, and that ε maps basis elements of D to basis elements of $P\omega$: in short, every domain can be embedded in $P\omega$ by such a mapping. So any domain in which we might be interested can be regarded as a subspace of $P\omega$. Further, every continuous function on such a subspace can be extended (because $P\omega$ is a continuous lattice) to a continuous function defined on the whole of $P\omega$. (This theorem will not be proved here. The proof, together with a much more detailed discussion of the $P\omega$ model, may be found in Scott [53], of which the present treatment is a much condensed version).

This suggests that if we can produce a suitable treatment for continuous functions on $P\omega$, and if we can discover a way to find any particular domain as a subspace, then we shall have a satisfactory model. This we shall now attempt to do.

To some this may all seem rather far-fetched; and this fiddling with sets of integers may appear to have little or no connection with real programming languages. So perhaps it is worth restating the object of this investigation. Our study of programming languages has led us to require domains which satisfy certain structural constraints, such as isomorphism with a space of functions satisfying the axiom of extensionality. Consideration of the nature of computation allowed us to impose further constraints, such as continuity. We are now asking whether any system satisfying all these requirements can possibly exist, or whether our demands are too severe. We could, of course, ignore this question, and go straight on in the blithe hope that everything was all right; but then there would always be the risk that we were talking nonsense. So our purpose is to demonstrate that a domain can be constructed which satisfies the formal requirements, to give us confidence that our theory is not vacuous. In this activity a certain artificiality does not matter: once we have demonstrated that our requirements are satisfiable we can safely return to thinking of our value domains in any more intuitively natural way we please.

Exercise.

2. Let the integer x be a solution of $x = x+1$. Prove that you are the Pope. Comment on the relevance of this proof to the subject of this chapter.

Functions on $P\omega$. In order to consider the possibility of $P\omega$ containing its own function space, we must find a way of associating particular continuous functions on $P\omega$ with particular elements in $P\omega$. Let f be such a function, and for some $x \in P\omega$ let $y = f(x)$. Now we have stated several times the characteristic property of continuous functions that every finite piece of information in the result is produced from some finite piece of information in the argument. Here, the finite pieces of information are the basis elements, or finite sets of integers

$e_n \in P\omega$. So we are saying that every $e_m \subseteq y$ is related to some $e_n \subseteq x$. The function f could therefore be characterized by the set of ordered pairs of integers

$$\{(n,m) \mid e_m \subseteq f(e_n)\}. \quad (7.1)$$

In fact we shall adopt a slight variant of this, purely for reasons of technical convenience, and use the set

$$\{(n,m) \mid m \in f(e_n)\}. \quad (7.2)$$

Since each e_m in the first case is a finite set of integers, the second formulation is no different in power from the first: one of the reasons it is more convenient is that the minimal function, which maps every argument to the empty set, is itself represented by the empty set.

Continuous functions may thus be represented by sets of ordered pairs of integers. But ordered pairs of integers are themselves enumerable, so that each ordered pair may be represented by a single integer and continuous functions may in this way be represented by sets of integers - elements of $P\omega$.

To put this idea into effect it remains for us to specify some actual enumerations for basis elements and for ordered pairs of integers. Those we are about to give are, of course, not the only ones possible: equally satisfactory models could be set up using other choices. But the object of the present exercise is simply to show that at least *one* suitable model exists, so it is quite proper to take arbitrary decisions when designing it.

For the finite sets of integers we shall use

n \ m	0	1	2	3	4	5	...
0	0	2	5	9	14	20	...
1	1	4	8	13	19	26	...
2	3	7	12	18	25	33	...
3	6	11	17	24	32	41	...
4	10	16	23	31	40	50	...
5	15	22	30	39	49	60	...
⋮	⋮	⋮	⋮	⋮	⋮	⋮	⋱

Fig. 7.2. An enumeration of ordered pairs $\langle n, m \rangle$.

the following enumeration: a set e will be assigned an integer as follows.

$$e \approx \sum_{i \in e} 2^{i} \tag{7.3}$$

That is to say, if we write the integer as a binary numeral, and count the digits from the right (starting at zero), then digit i will be set to 1 if and only if i is in the set e. Obviously this defines a 1-1 correspondence between finite sets and non-negative numerals.

For an ordered pair (n,m) we use a standard diagonal enumeration as illustrated in Fig.7.2. Specifically, the integer corresponding to a pair (n,m) is as follows:

$$(n,m) \approx \tfrac{1}{2}(n+m)(n+m+1)+m \tag{7.4}$$

This also defines a 1-1 correspondence.

We can now give the element of Pω corresponding to a continuous function f : P$\omega \to$ Pω, by means of the following definition.

7.5. Definition. $graph(f) = \{(n,m) \mid m \in f(e_n)\}$.

Notice that we are identifying an ordered pair with its index in the enumeration.

Conversely, the function determined by any set $u \in$ Pω is given by the following definition.

7.6. Definition.

$fun(u)(x) = \{m \mid \exists\, e_n \subseteq x \,.\, (n,m) \in u\}$.

7.7. Theorem. Every continuous function f is uniquely determined by its graph in the sense that

$$fun(graph(f)) = f.$$

Proof: Substituting the definitions of *fun* and

graph in the required result gives us

$$f(x) \quad = \quad \{m \mid \exists\, e_n \subseteq x \;.\; m \in f(e_n)\}.$$

This is simply a description of our continuity requirement, and therefore holds for all x.

However, not every element $u \in P\omega$ is the graph of a function. In particular, monotonicity requires that if the pair (n,m) is in u, then so must (k,m) for all k such that $e_n \subseteq e_k$. So the converse of the previous theorem is the following:

<u>*7.8. Theorem.*</u> For all $u \in P\omega$, $u \subseteq graph(fun(u))$, where equality holds only if $(k,m) \in u$ whenever $(n,m) \in u$ and $e_n \subseteq e_k$.

Proof: From the definitions we have

$$graph(fun(u)) \quad = \quad \{(n,m) \mid e_k \subseteq e_n \;.\; (k,m) \in u\}.$$

By considering the subset for which $k=n$ we see that $u \subseteq graph(fun(u))$, and it is also readily seen that the condition for equality is as stated.

The enumerations introduced in 7.3 and 7.4 satisfy the following property.

<u>*7.9. Lemma.*</u> If $(j,m) \in e_i$ then $e_i \not\subseteq e_j$.

Proof: Follows immediately from the following observations:

1. If $e_i \subseteq e_j$ then $i \leq j$.
2. If $n \in e_i$ then $n < i$.
3. If k corresponds to (j,m) then $j \leq k$.

A basis element, e_i, regarded as a function, in its ordered pairs explicitly specifies components of the result for a finite set of possible argument elements. Lemma 7.9 says that if any of these elements is comparable with e_i itself, it is strictly weaker: no basis element explicitly gives information about how it is itself mapped by the function (though some information may of course be derivable by monotonicity from information about weaker elements). This situation is somewhat reminiscent of the inverse limit construction mentioned above, in which the finite function elements were all defined on strictly smaller domains. It is a reasonable restriction for basis elements to satisfy, for cardinality considerations are such that only when we include the limit points may we expect to find functions being elements of their argument space. So any pair of enumerations must satisfy this property if it is to be a reasonable replacement for 7.3 and 7.4; otherwise anomalous results occur, particularly in situations, such as self application, where functions are identified with their arguments.

LAMBDA

We have now seen how elements of $P\omega$ can be treated as specifying continuous functions on $P\omega$. Our next step is to codify this by introducing some new notation. We call this new notation LAMBDA, and we could of course define it completely formally as a new language and give its formal semantics rather as we shall be doing later for the λ-calculus itself. However, we prefer to proceed a little more informally, and to regard LAMBDA as being merely some new notation (for one particular constant and some operations on elements of $P\omega$) to add to our existing repertoire of ordinary mathematics. The new notations with their meanings are given by the following six definitions;

in 7.9 to 7.13 x, y and z denote elements of $P\omega$.

$$0 = \{0\} \tag{7.10}$$

$$x+1 = \{n+1 \mid n \in x\} \tag{7.11}$$

$$x-1 = \{n \mid n+1 \in x\} \tag{7.12}$$

$$x \supset y,z = \{n \in y \mid 0 \in x\} \cup \{n \in z \mid \exists\, m.m+1 \in x\} \tag{7.13}$$

$$x(y) = \{m \mid \exists\, e_n \subseteq y.(n,m) \in x\} \tag{7.14}$$

$$\lambda x.E = \{(n,m) \mid m \in E[e_n/x]\} \tag{7.15}$$

In 7.14 x is a name and E is an expression (in LAMBDA notation); $E[e_n/x]$ denotes the value of E when x takes the value e_n; it should not be confused (though the resemblance is not coincidental) with the notation $[E_1/x]E$, which stands for the *expression* obtained by 'substituting' E_1 for x in E.

Now we have introduced yet another system involving the symbol λ, and so it may be useful to remind ourselves of the differences between the λ-notation, the λ-calculus and LAMBDA. We first introduced the λ-notation, as a convenient means of discussing functions we already knew about but could not express without some circumlocution. Then we glorified this notation into a calculus by stating that *any* expression satisfying the syntax was to be regarded as valid, and by giving conversion rules according to which they could be manipulated. We are at present seeking a model for this system, to see whether there is any set of values which may be assigned to the expressions and which behave according to the rules. The notation LAMBDA has now been introduced, and formally it describes certain operations on sets of integers. As we shall see, when considering some of these operations we have it in mind that these sets of integers can represent functions, and these values do indeed behave fairly much as the λ-calculus has taught us to expect. But we cannot say that Pω and the appropriate operations of LAMBDA together provide a model for the λ-calculus itself: in particular, η-conversion is invalid, for not *every* element of Pω is the graph of a function. So we must still continue our search. When we succeed we shall give the formal semantics of the λ-calculus by a set of equations which assign a value to each expression of the λ-calculus; to write these equations we shall use LAMBDA.

In the meantime, however, we must explain the LAMBDA notation itself; in doing so we shall give several different "meanings" to elements of Pω. In the first place, ∅ and ω, the minimal and maximal elements of Pω, will take the place of ⊥ and ⊤ in our earlier discussion of lattices, and we shall frequently write them as such. We also choose to regard the singleton sets to represent the integers themselves: so $\{n\}$ will represent n. Notice that these singleton sets together with ⊤ and ⊥, if regarded as a subspace of Pω, form the usual flat lattice of (non-negative) integers. Moreover, equations 7.10 to 7.12 provide the primitives we need to operate on these representations of integers. Note that since negative integers are not in Pω, we expect 0-1 to be undefined; sure enough, its value is ⊥.

One way of regarding the remaining elements of Pω is as "multi-valued" integers, for example the results of multivalued functions. The arithmetic operations, x+1 and x-1, are in accord with this view, as they operate on each value in the set x.

Equation 7.13 defines a notation for a conditional expression. In this we use {0} as a representation for *true*, and any set containing only non-zero elements ({1}, for example) as representing *false*. A set containing both zero and non-zero elements is regarded as the "contradictory" truth-value: according to 7.13 this results in the union of the two arms of the conditional. As we shall see a little below, other definitions of the conditional operator are also possible, giving different results in the contradictory case. Of course, we could still be regarding the elements of $P\omega$ as representing arithmetic quantities, whether single- or multivalued: then equation 7.13 would simply be defining a test for zero.

In the next equation the element called x is understood as representing a function (by the mechanism already described); there is nothing in particular implied about how the argument y is to be interpreted. The equation merely spells out the operation of functional application as implied in our definition of *fun* above. The final equation provides us with functional abstraction; the result is again to be understood as (the graph of) a function.

Properties of LAMBDA. Let us now investigate some of the properties of expressions in this new notation, to check if they are well-behaved.

7.16. Theorem. LAMBDA-expressions denote continuous functions of their free variables.

Proof: Equations 7.10 to 7.14 define functions which

are obviously continuous, and by Theorem 6.54 any composition of them is also continuous. To bring in abstraction, we must also prove that if some expression is continuous in its free variables then an abstraction formed from it is continuous in the remaining variables; this amounts to showing that if $f(x,y)$ is continuous in both its variables then $\lambda x.f(x,y)$ is continuous in y. From equation 7.15 we have

$$\begin{aligned}\lambda x.f(x,y) &= \{(n,m) \mid m\in f(e_n,y)\}\\ &= \{(n,m) \mid \exists\, e_k\subseteq y \,.\, m\in f(e_n,e_k)\}\\ &= \bigcup\{\{(n,m) \mid m\in f(e_n,e_k)\} \mid e_k\subseteq y\}\\ &= \bigcup\{\lambda x.f(x,e_k) \mid e_k\subseteq y\}\end{aligned}$$

thus showing that $\lambda x.f(x,y)$ is indeed continuous in y.

7.17. Theorem. $(\lambda x.\mathrm{E})(y) = \mathrm{E}[y/x]$

Proof: Let E define (in LAMBDA) a function f of x. Then $f(x) = \mathrm{E}$ and $\lambda x.\mathrm{E} = graph(f)$. Now since $fun(graph(f)) = f$ we have $fun(graph(f))(y) = f(y)$. But for any u, $fun(u)(y)$ is, in LAMBDA-notation, simply $u(y)$; and $f(y)$ is, by definition of f, $\mathrm{E}[y/x]$. So $(\lambda x.\mathrm{E})(y) = \mathrm{E}[y/x]$ as required.

This theorem justifies our use of the usual techniques for evaluating expressions involving functional application. Since our new LAMBDA-notation does not contain anything which goes against the normal referentially transparent use of names in mathematics, the value $\mathrm{E}[y/x]$ is just the same as the value of $[y/x]\mathrm{E}$; so Theorem 7.17 corresponds to the β-conversion rule in the λ-calculus. (If we had bothered to give a formal semantics for LAMBDA, we would have been able to prove the remarks in the previous sentence explicitly: we shall in fact be doing this for the λ-calculus itself in Chapter 8.) The normal treatment of names in mathematics also allows us to use α-conversion; as we have remarked, however, η-conversion is invalid.

7.18. Theorem. Any continuous function f of n variables can be written as

$$f(x_1,x_2,\ldots,x_n) \quad = \quad u(x_1)(x_2)\ldots(x_n)$$

where u is an element of $P\omega$.

Proof: We simply iterate the process of forming the graph of a continuous function; as we have shown (Theorem 7.16), at each stage the function remains continuous. Finally

$$u \quad = \quad \lambda x_1.\lambda x_2.\ldots.\lambda x_n.f(x_1,x_2,\ldots,x_n).$$

Note that this argument does not imply that u is necessarily definable in LAMBDA, but merely that it exists. The theorem allows us to curry functions freely.

7.19. Theorem. The LAMBDA-expression

$$Y \quad = \quad \lambda f.(\lambda x.f(x(x)))(\lambda x.f(x(x)))$$

denotes the minimal fixpoint function; that is, $Y(u)$ denotes the minimal fixed point (in $P\omega$) of the continuous function denoted by u.

Proof: By a calculation exactly similar to that in Chapter 5 we know that $Y(u) = u(Y(u))$; so $Y(u)$ is a fixed point of u. We now have to show it is the least fixed point. So let a be any other fixed point of u, and let $d = \lambda x.u(x(x))$. We have to show that $d(d) \subseteq a$; for this it is enough to show that if $e_i \subseteq d$ then $e_i(e_i) \subseteq a$, because by continuity

$$d(d) = \bigcup_j \bigcup_k \{\{e_j(e_k) \mid e_k \subseteq d\} \mid e_j \subseteq d\}$$

$$= \{e_i(e_i) \mid e_i \subseteq d\}.$$

We proceed by induction, and assume for all $e_n \subset e_i$ that $e_n \subseteq d$ implies $e_n(e_n) \subseteq a$; then let $e_i \subseteq d$ and $m \in e_i(e_i)$. We wish to show that $m \in a$. Now since $m \in e_i(e_i)$ there must exist some n such that $(n,m) \in e_i$ and $e_n \subseteq e_i$. But since by Lemma 7.9 $e_i \not\subseteq e_j$, $e_n \subset e_i$; and moreover $e_n \subseteq d$; so by the inductive hypothesis $e_n(e_n) \subseteq a$; and therefore by monotonicity $u(e_n(e_n)) \subseteq u(a)$; so $u(e_n(e_n)) \subseteq a$. But, since $(n,m) \in d$, we know that $m \in d(e_n)$; and $d(e_n) = u(e_n(e_n))$. So $m \in a$ as required, and the proof is complete.

Notice that since Y involves self-application this was one of the situations where we expected to have to rely on Lemma 7.9, which restricted our choice of particular enumerations for setting up our encodings of functions.

Examples of LAMBDA-definable values.

$\perp$. There are, of course, many expressions whose values are totally undefined. One we have already encountered gives us:

$$\perp = 0-1. \tag{7.20}$$

Another is

$$\perp = (\lambda x.x(x))(\lambda x.x(x)). \tag{7.21}$$

To check this, notice that the right hand side may be obtained from $Y(\lambda y.y)$, and so it is the least fixed point of the identity function.

Union. To define $x \cup y$ we must use something of a trick. We notice that according to our particular encodings $\lambda z.0$, considered as a set, contains both 0 (corresponding to (0,0)) and also infinitely many non-zero elements. So we can write

$$x \cup y \quad = \quad (\lambda z.0) \supset x, y. \tag{7.22}$$

Thus this definition embodies a pun by which we define our element as a function and use it as a truth value. We could avoid this dependence on the details of the Pω model by providing union as a primitive in LAMBDA; it is required for some later completeness results.

$\top$. We can immediately use the previous definition in defining $\top$ as follows:

$$\top \quad = \quad Y(\lambda x.0 \cup (x+1)). \tag{7.23}$$

Tuples. We incorporate tuples into our notation by the following series of definitions:

$$\langle\rangle \quad = \quad \bot \tag{7.24}$$

$$\langle x\rangle \quad = \quad \lambda z.(z-1) \supset x, \bot \tag{7.25}$$

$$\langle x_1, x_2\rangle \quad = \quad \lambda z.(z-1) \supset x_1, ((z-1)-1) \supset x_2, \bot \tag{7.26}$$

$$\langle x_1, x_2, \ldots, x_n\rangle \quad = \quad \lambda z.(z-1) \supset x, \langle x_2, \ldots, x_n\rangle (z-1) \tag{7.27}$$

For selection of an element from a tuple we introduce the following notation:

$$u{\downarrow}i \quad = \quad u(i). \tag{7.28}$$

Then these definitions imply that

$$\langle x_1, x_2, \ldots, x_n\rangle {\downarrow} i = \begin{cases} x_i & (1 \le i \le n) \\ \bot & (i > n) \end{cases} \tag{7.29}$$

A stronger form of conditional. It will be convenient to have a stronger form of the conditional expression than the one in LAMBDA itself. According to this new form the value of the expression is $\top$ in the contradictory case, rather than the union of the two arms. It is defined as follows:

$$z \mathrel{\overline{\supset}} x,y \quad = \quad z \supset (z \supset x,\top),(z \supset \top,y). \tag{7.30}$$

Computability. In this section we briefly consider what it means for some element of $P\omega$ to be computable. As we remarked in the previous chapter, the best we can expect for an element which is infinite is some method of generating any finite part of it (that is, any basis element approximating it) within a finite time. That is to say, we require an algorithmic method which will sooner or later generate any particular integer in the set.

In logic the usual way to formalise this idea of having an algorithm which will generate any particular element of some set within a finite time is to use the concept of *recursive enumerability.* For an introduction to this notion the reader is referred, for example, to Hartley Roger's book [45]. Every non-empty r.e. (recursively enumerable) set is the range of a primitive recursive function. Using this fact, we now outline a proof that an element of $P\omega$ is recursively enumerable if and only if it is LAMBDA-definable.

Our strategy is as follows. For any primitive recursive function p we shall define in LAMBDA a function $\hat{p}$ whose values on our representations of integers (the singleton sets) are as specified by p.

Moreover, $\hat{p}$ will be a *distributive* function; that is to say, it will satisfy the following equations

$$\hat{p}(\bot) = \bot$$

$$\hat{p}(x \cup y) = \hat{p}(x) \cup \hat{p}(y). \qquad (7.31)$$

Hence $\hat{p}(\top)$ will give us the set which is the range of our original p; so we shall have a way of defining in LAMBDA any r.e. set by making use of its associated primitive recursive function.

Specifically, we first define a function \$ which maps any function u into one which gives the same results as u when applied to the singleton sets and is otherwise distributive; so

$$\$(u) = \lambda x.\bigcup\{u(\{i\}) \mid i \in x\}. \qquad (7.32)$$

In LAMBDA, \$ may be defined as follows:

$$\$ = Y(\lambda s \lambda u \lambda z.z \supset u(0), s(\lambda t.u(t+1))(z-1)). \qquad (7.33)$$

The reader is invited to check that this definition behaves as expected.

Now any primitive recursive function p may be defined as follows (as a function from ω to $P\omega$):

$$p(0) = a$$

$$p(n+1) = f(n)(p(n))$$

where $a \in P\omega$ and f is some (continuous) function. Now let

$$\hat{p} = Y(\lambda u.\$(\lambda n.n \supset a, f(n-1)(u(n-1)))). \qquad (7.34)$$

It will be seen that $\hat{p}$ is the required distributive function whose values on the representations of integers are as specified by p. So the range of p, given by $\hat{p}(\top)$, is LAMBDA-definable if $\hat{p}$ is (notice that this is where we needed the union operation

(7.22), in order to define τ in LAMBDA). With this in mind, we can see, by comparing the definition scheme for primitive recursive functions (page 6 of Rogers [45]) with the definition of LAMBDA notation (equations 7.10 to 7.15 above) that a distributive function like $\hat{p}$ above *can* be defined in LAMBDA for every primitive recursive function, and hence that every recursively enumerable set is LAMBDA-definable. On the other hand, an examination of equations 7.10 to 7.15 also shows that every LAMBDA-definable element of $P\omega$ is recursively enumerable.

It is reasonable to adopt this criterion, that an element x of $P\omega$ be recursively enumerable, as a definition of computability of x. Other criteria we might invent, such as that the set $\{n \mid e_n \sqsubseteq x\}$ be recursively enumerable, are equivalent, and it accords with the intuitions about computing which motivated our theory based on continuity. So, taking this as our definition, we have outlined a proof of the following:

7.34. Theorem. An element of $P\omega$ is computable if and only if it is LAMBDA-definable.

A partial recursive function of the usual kind (see Rogers [45] page 26) can be thought of as a mapping to the singleton sets together with $\bot$ (which, as usual, stands for "undefined"). To say that a singleton set is recursively enumerable is to say that an algorithm exists which in some finite time will generate the sole element. It may thus be seen that our definition of computability is simply a generalisation of the usual one.

Retracts

We have now completed our examination of the properties of $P\omega$ itself, and we have developed a theory of continuous functions on $P\omega$, each of them associated with a particular element of $P\omega$, in a way which might well be satisfactory for our purposes. We also mentioned, when introducing this model, how every suitable value domain could be regarded as a subspace of $P\omega$. It remains for us to discuss how to pick out particular subspaces that interest us (such as a domain isomorphic with its function space), and how to arrange that, when discussing various functions and operators, we can confine our attention to their behaviour on some particular subspace. Among other things, this will enable us to handle in a convenient way the whole important matter of data types in programming languages, as will be apparent in some of our later examples.

The way we pick out the subspaces we require is by means of *retracts*. A retract is a continuous function on $P\omega$ (and so can also be regarded as an element of $P\omega$). The range of any such function is a subspace of $P\omega$, so in that sense *any* function defines some particular subspace. But a retract has the further property that it is the identity function on its range. That is to say, its range and its fixed point set coincide, and it is therefore idempotent: applying it more than once makes no difference. So we have the formal definition:

7.35. Definition. An element $a \in P\omega$ is a *retract* if it satisfies the equation

$$a = a \circ a$$

where, as usual, $f \circ g = \lambda x.f(g(x))$.

Before we go on to look at some examples of retracts, we ought to check that the subspaces they define are suitable for our purposes. In fact the use of a retract, rather than an arbitrary function, ensures that the subspace it defines is indeed a continuous lattice, as required. To show this, since $P\omega$ is itself a continuous lattice, it is enough to prove the following theorem.

7.36. Theorem. The range of any retract of a continuous lattice is also a continuous lattice.

Proof: Let L be a continuous lattice, and $j : L \to L$ a retract. Since j is monotonic, by Tarski's theorem its fixed point set is a complete lattice, so we have merely to prove that this lattice is also continuous. Now since L is continuous, for all $y \in L$,

$$y = \bigsqcup\{x \mid x \ll_L y\}$$

So for all $y \in j(L)$,

$$\begin{aligned} y = j(y) &= j(\bigsqcup\{x \mid x \ll_L y\}) \\ &= \bigsqcup\{j(x) \mid x \ll_L y\} \text{ (since } \{x \mid x \ll_L y\} \text{ is directed).} \end{aligned}$$

Now any directed $S \subseteq j(L)$ is also a directed subset of L, and $\bigsqcup S$ is the same in both lattices since $j(\bigsqcup_L S) = \bigsqcup_L S$. So if $y \sqsubseteq \bigsqcup S$ and $x \ll_L y$ then for some $z \in S$ $x \sqsubseteq z$. Hence by monotonicity $j(x) \sqsubseteq j(z) = z$. Thus $x \ll_L y$ implies $j(x) \ll_{j(L)} y$, so that

$$\{j(x) \mid x \ll_L y\} \subseteq \{j(x) \mid j(x) \ll_{j(L)} y,\ x \in L\}$$
$$= \{z \mid z \ll_{j(L)} y,\ z \in j(L)\}.$$

Hence

$$y \sqsubseteq \bigsqcup\{z \mid z \ll_{j(L)} y\}.$$

But since $z \ll y$ implies $z \sqsubseteq y$,

$$y \sqsupseteq \bigsqcup\{z \mid z \ll_{j(L)} y\},$$

and so $j(L)$ is a continuous lattice.

In future we shall use the word "retract" indiscriminately for the function and the domain it defines (in fact strictly the function is a *retraction*, its range the retract). Note, however, that two quite different functions may yet have the same range.

Examples of retracts. Let us consider some examples of how retracts are used. Our first defines the lattice of truth values.

$$bool \quad = \quad \lambda u.u \supset 0,1. \tag{7.37}$$

It can easily be seen that the only four values which this function can give are $\bot$, $\top$, 0 and 1, and that these values are fixed points of *bool*. So *bool* represents simply the idea of being a boolean value.

As a second example, consider the following:

$$fun \quad = \quad \lambda u.\lambda x.u(x) \tag{7.38}$$

When this is applied to an element $u \in P\omega$, whatever the value of u, the result is a function. If u is itself a function, then $fun(u) = u$. So *fun* represents the idea of a continuous function from $P\omega$ into $P\omega$.

Similarly, pairs of elements of $P\omega$ may be characterised by the following retract:

$$pair \;=\; \lambda u.\langle u{\downarrow}1, u{\downarrow}2\rangle. \tag{7.39}$$

The integers are given by the following:

$$int \;=\; \lambda u.u \sqsupset 0,(int(u-1) \sqsupset u,u) \tag{7.40}$$

Exercise

3. Show that *int* is a retract, and that its range is isomorphic with the usual flat lattice of integers.

This flat lattice may also be used to model other sets of basic values besides the non-negative integers. Its elements may readily be put in 1-1 correspondence with all the integers, or with characters, or (as we shall see later) with locations in an abstract computer store, to give but a few examples.

7.41. Definition. If a is a retract, we write

$u{:}a$ for $u = a(u)$, and

$\lambda u{:}a.\mathrm{E}$ for $\lambda u.[a(u)/u]\mathrm{E}$.

The first of these notations expresses the fact that u is in the subspace characterised by the retract a. The other notation states that the function is restricted to the range of a, and that we need be concerned only with its behaviour on that subspace. In particular, two expressions $\lambda x{:}a.\mathrm{E}_1$ and $\lambda y{:}a.\mathrm{E}_2$ denote the same function if and only if they give equal results when applied to each element in the range of a.

Methods of Combining Retracts. As well as the basic spaces of values, such as those given by *bool* and *int*, we need ways of defining new spaces in terms of old ones. The three principal ways are provided by the operators we now define, for product spaces, separated sum domains and function spaces respectively.

7.42. Definition.

$a \otimes b \;=\; \lambda u.\langle a(u{\downarrow}1), b(u{\downarrow}2)\rangle$

$a \oplus b \;=\; \lambda u.u{\downarrow}1 \;\bar{\supset}\; \langle 0, a(u{\downarrow}2)\rangle, \langle 1, b(u{\downarrow}2)\rangle$

$a \multimap b \;=\; \lambda u.b \circ u \circ a.$

7.43. Theorem. If a and b are retracts, then so are $a \otimes b$, $a \oplus b$ and $a \multimap b$.

Proof: By simple calculation; for example

$$(a \multimap b)\circ(a \multimap b) = \lambda u.b\circ(b\circ u\circ a)\circ a$$
$$= \lambda u.b\circ u\circ a$$
$$= a \multimap b.$$

7.44. Theorem. $u : a \otimes b$ if and only if $u = \langle u_1, u_2\rangle$ and $u_1 : a$ and $u_2 : b$.

This theorem shows that if A and B are the domains given by the retracts a and b respectively, then $a \otimes b$ gives a domain isomorphic to A×B.

7.45. Theorem. $u : a \oplus b$ if and only if $u = \bot$ or $u = \top$ or $u = \langle 0, u_1\rangle$ and $u_1 : a$ or $u = \langle 1, u_2\rangle$ and $u_2 : b$.

Hence the domain specified by $a \oplus b$ is isomorphic to the separated sum A+B of the domains A and B specified by the retracts a and b.

7.46. Theorem. $u : a \multimap b$ if and only if $u = \lambda x{:}a.u(x)$ and if for all x such that $x : a$, $u(x) : b$. Hence the domain specified by $a \multimap b$ is isomorphic with the space of continuous functions from the domain specified by a to the domain specified by b.

7.47. Remark. The definitions of $\otimes$ and $\oplus$ can be extended in an obvious way to combine more than two retracts together. We shall not bother to give the explicit formulae, but if we use expressions such as $a \otimes b \oplus c$ we shall be implying this extended meaning rather than $(a \otimes b) \otimes c$ or $a \otimes (b \otimes c)$.

With this machinery we are able to construct many of the domains we need in our discussions of the semantics of programming languages. For example, if the truth-value domain T is given by *bool* and the integers N by *int*, then a domain

$$V = T+N+[N \to N] \tag{7.48}$$

containing the truth values, the integers and the functions from integers to integers, would simply be given by the retract

$bool \oplus int \oplus (int \circ\!\!\to int)$.

Reflexive Domains

We are left with the problem of constructing domains which contain themselves; that is, domains which are defined circularly. These are known as *reflexive domains*. Let us consider a particular example, a value domain which contains integers and functions, where the functions are assumed to be defined on all the values. So we want

$$E = N+[E \to E]. \tag{7.49}$$

Rephrasing this in terms of retracts, we are seeking a retract e such that

$e = int \oplus (e \multimap e).$

e is, of course, an element of $P\omega$ corresponding to a continuous function, so as usual we can write the solution to this equation as a fixed point expression as follows

$$fix(\lambda e. int \oplus (e \multimap e)). \tag{7.50}$$

To check that this defines a retract as required, we need the following theorem.

7.51. Theorem. If F is a continuous function mapping retracts to retracts, then $fix\ F$ is also a retract.

Proof: $\perp$ is a retract; so, by a trivial induction $F^n(\perp)$ is a retract for all n. Then

$$\begin{aligned}(fix\ F)\circ(fix\ F) &= \bigcup_{n=0}^{\infty}\{F^n(\perp)\} \circ \bigcup_{m=0}^{\infty}\{F^m(\perp)\}\\ &= \bigcup_{n=0}^{\infty}\bigcup_{m=0}^{\infty}\{F^n(\perp)\circ F^m(\perp)\} \text{ (by continuity)}\\ &= \bigcup_{j=0}^{\infty}\{F^j(\perp)\circ F^j(\perp)\}\\ &\qquad \text{(by monotonicity, since } F^n(\perp)\circ F^m(\perp) \subseteq F^j(\perp)\circ F^j \text{ where } j \text{ is the greater of } m \text{ and } n)\\ &= \bigcup_{j=0}^{\infty}\{F^j(\perp)\} \text{(since } F^j(\perp) \text{ is a retract)}\\ &= fix\ F.\end{aligned}$$

Note that the sequence of retracts $F^n(\perp)$ in our example (7.50) gives rise to the following sequence of domains.

$D_0 = \{\perp\}$

$D_1 = N+\{\perp\}$

$$D_2 = N+[D_1 \to D_1]$$

$$D_3 = N+[D_2 \to D_2].$$

This is the same sequence that would have been used if we had constructed our required reflexive domain by means of the inverse limit construction which we mentioned earlier. In that case, however, we should have had to define explicit embeddings of each domain in its successor and to go through a somewhat tedious demonstration that the limit domain existed and had the required structure. Now the fixed point operator *fix* gives the required retract at once, and the fixed point property together with the definitions of ⊗, ⊕ and ⊶ allows us to check that its structure is as we wish.

As a further example, consider the domain

$$V = N+[V \times V]. \tag{7.52}$$

The retract specifying this domain is, of course,

$$fix(\ v.int \oplus (v \otimes v)). \tag{7.53}$$

This is the domain of binary trees with a flat lattice of atoms for the ends of the branches. It could be used as a semantic value domain for pure LISP [31]. Notice that it contains not only all the finite trees, but also many infinite ones, such as x where

$$x = \langle 1, x \rangle$$

so that

$$x = \langle 1, \langle 1, \langle 1, \ldots \rangle \rangle \rangle .$$

We now have all we need to demonstrate the existence of suitable domains for (almost) all purposes in our theory of semantics. When domain equations (such as 7.48, 7.49 and 7.50 above) are given, appropriate retract definitions may always be constructed to define a suitable subspace of $P\omega$ to model the required domain.

A model for the λ-calculus. Unfortunately, one particular case where the method breaks down is the one which prompted this entire discussion: a model for the λ-calculus with full η-conversion, in which every value is therefore required to be a function. The domain we seek is isomorphic with its function space, and so is described by the equation

$$E = [E \to E]. \qquad (7.54)$$

If we employ our usual technique we obtain the retract

$$fix(\lambda e.e \hookrightarrow e). \qquad (7.55)$$

Unfortunately, the value of this is ⊥; that is to say, this method constructs the trivial one-element solution of the equation, mentioned and rejected earlier.

This problem does not arise in more complicated cases, where the presence of other summands in the required value space eliminates any possibility of a trivial solution.

To solve the problem in this particular case we slightly doctor the retract definition (7.55) above so as to avoid the trivial solution. We try instead

$$fix(\lambda e.I \cup (e \hookrightarrow e)) \qquad (7.56)$$

where I is the identity function. It is easy to see that ⊥ is not a fixed point of $(\lambda e.I \cup (e \hookrightarrow e))$; we now embark on a series of results to show that 7.56

does give the domain we require.

7.57. Lemma. $I \subseteq I \hookrightarrow I$.

Proof: By Theorem 7.8, $u \subseteq graph(fun(u))$; this, written in LAMBDA, is $u \subseteq \lambda x.u(x)$. So $\lambda u.u \subseteq \lambda u.\lambda x.u(x)$. But $\lambda u \lambda x.u(x) = \lambda u.\lambda x.I(u(I(x))) = \lambda u.I \circ u \circ I$. So $I \subseteq I \hookrightarrow I$ as required.

7.58. Lemma. For all $n \geq 0$, $I \subseteq (\lambda e.e \hookrightarrow e)^n I$.

Proof: The result holds for $n=0$ and (by Lemma 7.57) for $n=1$. For $n>1$ we use induction on n, so assume the result holds for $n=m$. Then

$$
\begin{aligned}
(\lambda e.e \hookrightarrow e)^{m+1} I &= (\lambda e.e \hookrightarrow e)^m ((\lambda e.e \hookrightarrow e) I) \\
&= (\lambda e.e \hookrightarrow e)^m (I \hookrightarrow I) \\
&\supseteq (\lambda e.e \hookrightarrow e)^m I \quad \text{(by Lemma 7.57 and monotonicity)} \\
&\supseteq I \quad \text{(inductive hypothesis)}
\end{aligned}
$$

So the result holds for all n.

7.59. Lemma. For all $n \geq 0$, $(\lambda e.I \cup (e \hookrightarrow e))^n I = (\lambda e.e \hookrightarrow e)^n I$.

Proof: Again by induction on n, so assume the result for $n=m$.

$$
\begin{aligned}
&(\lambda e.I \cup (e \hookrightarrow e))^{m+1} I \\
&= (\lambda e.I \cup (e \hookrightarrow e))((\lambda e.I \cup (e \hookrightarrow e))^m I) \\
&= (\lambda e.I \cup (e \hookrightarrow e))((\lambda e.e \hookrightarrow e)^m I) \quad \text{(inductive hypothesis)} \\
&= I \cup (\lambda e.e \hookrightarrow e)^{m+1} I \\
&= (\lambda e.e \hookrightarrow e)^{m+1} I. \quad \text{(Lemma 7.58)}
\end{aligned}
$$

But the result holds trivially for $n=0$; so it holds for all n.

7.60. *Theorem.* Let $d = fix(\lambda e. I \cup (e \multimap e))$; then d is a retract and $d = d \multimap d$.

Proof:

$$\begin{aligned} d &= \bigcup_{n=0}^{\infty} (\lambda e. I \cup (e \multimap e))^n \bot \\ &= \bot \cup \bigcup_{n=1}^{\infty} (\lambda e. I \cup (e \multimap e))^{n-1} I \\ &= \bigcup_{n=0}^{\infty} (\lambda e. (e \multimap e))^n I \qquad \text{(Lemma 7.59)} \end{aligned}$$

So, by an argument precisely similar to that in the proof of Theorem 7.51, d is a retract. Moreover,

$$\begin{aligned} d &= (\lambda e. e \multimap e)(\bigcup_{n=0}^{\infty} (\lambda e. e \multimap e)^n I) \quad \text{(by continuity, since the l.u.b. is taken over a chain)} \\ &= d \multimap d. \end{aligned}$$

So d is a retract giving a domain isomorphic with its own function space. Moreover, the domain it gives is not the one element space, for it may easily be checked that $\bot$ and $\top$ are both fixed points of d. Thus we have at last found a non-trivial domain suit able as a model for the λ-calculus.

The retracts which are stronger than the identity function (such as the ones treated in this section) form a special class, known as the *closure operations*. These have several interesting properties; for example, together they comprise a retract domain which is itself the range of a closure operation. If we had gone to the trouble of proving these and one or two more facts about closure operations, we could have obtained our required domain a little more easily, simply by restricting our attention to the domain of closure operations. In fact, if V is the retract for closure operations, our required retract would be

$$fix(\lambda e{:}V.e \circ\!\!\rightarrow e). \tag{7.61}$$

Further details about closure operations, and the properties of the lattices they produce, may be found in Scott [53], which also contains much more information about the ramifications of the $P\omega$ model and LAMBDA. For us, however, it is time to leave these theoretical foundations, and to return to the formal semantics of the λ-calculus. The reader should make sure, when studying the later chapters, that he appreciates which parts of the preceding theory will be underpinning the machinery we shall be describing.

The Domains in our Semantic Definitions: Error Elements

When in the following chapters we define semantic domains by means of equations such as 7.48 or 7.49 above, we shall be automatically invoking the retract techniques we have just discussed. However, we shall also make the following extra assumption, and shall do so tacitly all the time, without explicit fuss. When required, any domain may come equipped with an extra element, an "*error*" element, denoted by ?. ? will be incomparable with all the other elements of the domain except $\perp$ and $\top$, so that there will be a continuous test for equality between any element and ?.

More specifically, we assume that each of the basic domains (which are almost invariably flat lattices) comes with an extra error element, and that the retracts produced by the operators $\oplus$, $\otimes$ and $\circ\!\!\rightarrow$ also specify domains with an extra error element appropriately in their structure. The projection and injection mappings between sum domains and their components map error element to error element. To specify this machinery in complete detail would be excessively tedious without adding anything of new interest: we leave it to any reader with sufficient concern and enthusiasm to do for himself.

This provision, of course, gives us a natural value to use as the result of computations which go wrong. The structure is arranged so that to test whether some value is the error element is continuous and computable, which allows our semantic definitions to specify without embarrassment that errors be detected and appropriate action taken. We shall not give any specific examples now, but simply invite the reader to notice the use of ? in subsequent definitions.

Chapter 8

FORMAL SEMANTICS OF THE λ-CALCULUS

From now on we shall be able to take the theory of the previous chapter for granted most (but not all) of the time. Just occasionally we shall have to refer to it explicitly, when, for example, we use an argument based on continuity. We are now fully equipped to give the formal semantics of the λ-calculus in the same style as we used for the binary numerals.

Syntax

Syntactic Categories

$I \in$ Ide	(the "usual" identifiers)
$E \in$ Exp	(λ-expressions)

Syntax

$E ::= I \mid \lambda I.E \mid E_0 E_1$

There are two kinds of syntactic object in this language, identifiers and expressions. Ide is the set of "usual" identifiers, defined a little vaguely so as to avoid going into irrelevant details about their particular microsyntax. All we require is that we can tell whether two identifiers are the same.

In the syntax, the symbol 'λ' (here and always) stands for itself. All the Greek capital letters (I and E here) are syntactic variables, like N in the earlier example. The production E_0E_1 says that an expression can consist of two expressions juxtaposed; the subscripts are introduced to allow us to refer to the components separately.

Digression on Syntax

This use of subscripts indicates that our form of syntax description is being used as both generative and analytic syntax. *Generative* syntax tells how expressions may be *constructed* from their components; our description here corresponds with our generative syntax for the λ-calculus given in Definition 5.4 (pp.57-58) (we ignore the final clause, bracketed expressions, for now, but will mention them later). On the other hand, *analytic* syntax or, as McCarthy [30] called it, *abstract syntax*, tells how to *analyse* a given expression, to say what kind of expression it is and to extract the components.

According to McCarthy, abstract syntax involves a set of predicate functions and selector functions. In our present case these would be the following:

Predicates	Corresponding selectors
IsIdentifier(*s*)	*Ident*(*s*)
IsAbstraction(*s*)	*BoundVariable*(*s*), *Body*(*s*)
IsApplication(*s*)	*Rator*(*s*), *Rand*(*s*)
IsExpression(*s*)	

The domain of the predicates is all finite strings over the alphabet containing the identifiers and the symbols 'λ', '.', and possibly parentheses. IsExpression is defined by

$$IsExpression(s) = IsIdentifier(s) \vee IsAbstraction(s) \vee IsApplication(s).$$

However, everything is not altogether plain

sailing, because we generally assume that the selector functions are not defined over all strings, but only on that subset characterised by the corresponding predicate. So we cannot simply write definitions like:

$$IsApplication(s) = IsExpression(Rator(s)) \wedge IsExpression(Rand(s))$$

because *Rator* and *Rand* are not defined over all strings. The job of devising effective algorithms for these predicates and selectors is therefore non-trivial (it is called writing a parser). We shall ignore all these problems and merely assume, when giving the syntax as above, that a parser exists, and that we can with propriety mention the components of the productions.

Nowadays it is often found convenient to model these systems of predicates and selectors by means of *parse trees*. Each production in a language corresponds to a particular kind of node. Which kind a given node is can be determined from a special label attached to the node. The components of the production are represented by branches from the node, each with appropriate selector names. These trees provide the same information as McCarthy's functions; in this model the parser is the program which maps strings in the language to the appropriate tree. If desired, our syntax description may be thought of as specifying the structure of such trees. Thus, an expression node is one of three possible kinds, called 'I', 'λI.E' and 'E_0E_1'. The first kind has one branch, with selector 'I', leading to an identifier node; the second has two branches, with selectors 'I' and 'E', leading to an identifier and an expression node respectively; the third has two branches, with selectors 'E_0' and 'E_1', both leading to expression nodes. But again we mention this possible mechanism merely in order to take it for granted, and, on the whole, ignore it.

Another problem we may ignore is ambiguity. If the syntax we have given is taken to be the actual grammar of the language, it is ambiguous: the expression $\ulcorner E_1E_2E_3 \urcorner$, for example, has two possible parses. For a viable concrete language, we could disambiguate the grammar by changing the final production to $\ulcorner E_0(E_1) \urcorner$ or $\ulcorner (E_0E_1) \urcorner$; for more complicated languages these matters would be taken care of by precedence and association rules, parentheses and so on. Here we continue with our somewhat idealized form of syntax, ignoring problems of ambiguity and suchlike, and shall simply assume that all this has been sorted out by the time the parser presents us with the fruit of its labours.

So our language has two syntactic categories, Ide and Exp. We could say

$$\text{Ide} \subset \text{Exp} \subset \{\text{strings over alphabet}\}$$

but in practice (as indicated by the tree model) some formal type distinctions help. Thus, instead of saying Ide ⊂ Exp we prefer to say that one possible kind of expression has an identifier as its sole component.

We must now give some semantics to these syntactic objects.

Semantics

The semantics of our language will define mappings from its syntactic categories into a domain of values. So our first task is to define the domain of values of expressions. Here we have a choice, between a domain including some primitive atomic values and one containing only functions. That is to say, we must choose between domains given by the equations

$$E = A + [E \to E]$$

and

$$E = [E \to E]$$

where A is a domain of primitive values. The first of these is more like the value domains of ordinary programming languages, which certainly include primitive values (such as numbers) as well as functions, procedures etc. And the first equation avoids the extra problems we encountered at the end of Chapter 7. However, our syntax at present provides us with no regular way of *expressing* any values other than functions, so it is perhaps a little pointless to include them in the semantics. We shall therefore adopt the second equation for the present, and discuss possible extensions later. (Notice, though, that this is an independent decision. We *could* have a semantics with primitive values *and* the present syntax, relying on reserved identifiers to denote some of the elements of A.) That the value domain exists is guaranteed by the previous chapter.

The value of any expression depends on its *environment*, which tells what the identifiers mean in the expression: that is, it says what values the identifiers *denote*. So an environment may be specified by a function from Ide to a domain D of denotable values (which are called somewhat loosely "denotations" for short). For the present language D is the same as E, the domain of expression values, though this is by no means true for all languages. Thus our second semantic domain, the domain of all possible environments, is given by $U = [\mathrm{Ide} \to E]$.

We shall use the variable ε to take values in E, and ρ to denote environments in U. So we may write:

Value Domains

$\varepsilon \in E = [E \to E]$	Value of expressions
$\rho \in U = [\mathrm{Ide} \to E]$	Environments.

We shall write $\rho[\![I]\!]$ for the value denoted by I in the environment ρ.

As Strachey [58] points out, when we have defined its value domain we have already said a considerable amount about a language.

Now we must define the semantic functions, which relate the syntactic and semantic domains.

Semantic Functions We first define a function, which will be used in all our language definitions, for producing new environments. A characteristic of the λ-calculus, and of many other languages, is that the value denoted by an identifier depends on its context, and is determined by scope rules. We formalise this by giving each different scope a separate ρ. We form new environments out of old by the notation

$\rho[\delta/I]$.

The environment $\rho[\delta/I]$ differs from ρ only insofar as it maps I to δ (whether or not ρ mapped I to any proper value at all). Our more formal description of this makes use of the conditional expression, which we now define.

8.1. Definition. For $b \in T$ (the domain of truth-values) and $x,y \in D$, the expression

$$b \to x,y \quad \text{has value} \quad \begin{cases} x \text{ if } b \text{ is } \mathit{true} \\ y \text{ if } b \text{ is } \mathit{false} \\ \bot_D, \top_D \text{ or } ?_D \\ \quad \text{if } b \text{ is } \bot_D,\ \top_D \text{ or } ?_D. \end{cases}$$

This function is continuous in all its arguments; we shall consider it in more detail later.

8.2. Definition. The environment $\rho[\delta/I]$ is defined by the following equation:

$$(\rho[\delta/I])[\![I']\!] \equiv (I' = I) \to \delta,\ \rho[\![I']\!]$$

where $=$ is a continuous version (which in this case simply means a monotonic version) of the equality operator.

It should be remembered that '$\rho[\delta/I]$' is a mathematical notation: it is *not* a command and neither destroys nor updates ρ, which continues to denote the same environment as before. $\rho[\delta/I]$ simply denotes *another* environment, in general different from ρ.

The notation '$\rho[\delta/I]$' is reminiscent of that for the substitution operation in the λ-calculus. As we shall see, the similarity is not accidental, but the two operations should not be confused. The notation

$[M/x]X$ denotes an expression, defined in terms of the expression X by purely syntactic transformation. $\rho[\delta/I]$, on the other hand, denotes an environment mapping, defined abstractly in terms of the environment ρ (by means of the conditional function).

We may now define the semantic function we call $\mathscr{E}$, which is to relate expressions to their values. But in general the value of an expression will depend on the values of its free variables: that is to say, the expression must be evaluated in an environment (the exception is the pure combinators — λ-expressions with no free variables — whose value is the same in any environment). So:

$$\mathscr{E} : [\text{Exp} \to [U \to E]]$$

and we write $\mathscr{E}[\![E]\!]\rho$ to denote the value of the expression E in the environment ρ.

We define $\mathscr{E}$ by cases which match the syntactic description of Exp, just as we did with $\mathscr{N}$ for the numerals.

$$\mathscr{E}[\![I]\!]\rho \quad = \quad \rho[\![I]\!] \qquad (8.3)$$

$$\mathscr{E}[\![\lambda I.E]\!]\rho \quad = \quad \lambda\varepsilon.\mathscr{E}[\![E]\!](\rho[\varepsilon/I]) \qquad (8.4)$$

$$\mathscr{E}[\![E_0E_1]\!]\rho \quad = \quad (\mathscr{E}[\![E_0]\!]\rho)(\mathscr{E}[\![E_1]\!]\rho) \qquad (8.5)$$

In these equations, as usual, the $[\![\,]\!]$ brackets enclose syntactic objects in the language; $\rho[\varepsilon/I]$ is a mixed notation, however, as the I denotes a syntactic object, and the others denote semantic values. As required, the right hand side of each equation specifies a value in E: in 8.4, for example, the right hand side denotes a function. When such a function is applied (as in 8.5), the operation invoked is understood to be application in the reflexive domain E, as defined in the previous chapter using the Pω model and LAMBDA.

If we wished to consider the abstract syntax representation more explicitly, we can think of the right hand sides of these equations as arms of a conditional expression, where the appropriate arm for an expression is selected by means of predicates (such as *IsAbstraction*) or tests on the type label of the expression's parse tree. If none of the tests is satisfied the default value would be the error value $?_E$, though if the parser successfully rejects all syntactically illegal strings this should never occur.

It is important to avoid confusion between the language being defined and the notation used to define it: in this example such confusion is easy because of the similarity between the two. The expressions within the ⟦⟧ brackets are in the *defined* language: we are giving their semantics with sufficient formality that we shall be able (for example) to prove the validity of the conversion rules for that language. All other expressions (even including λ-expressions) are in the *defining* notation, which is based on LAMBDA and must be explicated using the mathematics of the previous chapter. Thus we use the LAMBDA notation to define the semantics of the λ-calculus language. This danger of confusion will become less when we define less similar languages.

Note that by simply using the appropriate Greek letters we are, for conciseness' sake, avoiding some formality with the retract machinery. For example, the right hand side of equation 8.4 ought to be $\lambda\varepsilon{:}\mathbf{E}.\mathscr{E}[\![E]\!](\rho[\varepsilon/I])$. We shall tacitly do this kind of thing all the time, and take the machinery for granted.

The details of the semantic definition are summarised in Table 8.1.

Table 8.1: The λ-Calculus

Syntactic Categories

$I \in \mathbf{Ide}$	(the usual identifiers)
$E \in \mathbf{Exp}$	(λ-expressions)

Syntax

$E ::= I \mid \lambda I.E \mid E_0 E_1$

Value Domains

$\varepsilon \in \mathbf{E} = [\mathbf{E}\to\mathbf{E}]$	(values of expressions)
$\rho \in \mathbf{U} = [\mathbf{Ide}\to\mathbf{E}]$	(environments)

Semantic Functions

$\mathscr{E} : [\mathbf{Exp}\to[\mathbf{U}\to\mathbf{E}]]$

$$\mathscr{E}[\![I]\!]\rho = \rho[\![I]\!] \tag{8.3}$$

$$\mathscr{E}[\![\lambda I.E]\!]\rho = \lambda\varepsilon.\mathscr{E}[\![E]\!](\rho[\varepsilon/I]) \tag{8.4}$$

$$\mathscr{E}[\![E_0 E_1]\!]\rho = (\mathscr{E}[\![E_0]\!]\rho)(\mathscr{E}[\![E_1]\!]\rho) \tag{8.5}$$

Possible Extensions

Including Primitive Values in E. Let us now look at how this semantics changes if we make the other choice for the expression value domain and set

$$E = A + [E \to E]$$

where A is some domain of primitive values. Since this domain now has more than one component, equations 8.4 and 8.5 have to be altered by the insertion of the appropriate injection and projection operations. If, too, we wish to have some way of actually expressing values from A, then we may add a new syntactic category of constants:

$K \in \text{Con}$ (constants)

a new production to the syntax of expressions:

$$E ::= K$$

a new semantic function $\mathscr{K}: \text{Con} \to E$ and a new semantic equation in the definition of $\mathscr{E}$:

$$\mathscr{E}[\![K]\!]\rho = \mathscr{K}[\![K]\!] \ .$$

The semantic definition that results is shown in Table 8.2. More details can of course be given: they might involve, for example, the definition given earlier for numerals. Note that the value of a constant is not necessarily restricted to the A component of E: this allows the atoms to come equipped with their own primitive functions. If A contained the integers, for example, presumably at least the successor function would be available as a constant, and probably other functions too.

Table 8.2: The λ-Calculus with atoms

Syntactic Categories

I ∈ Ide	(the usual identifiers)
K ∈ Con	(constants)
E ∈ Exp	(expressions)

Syntax

$E :: \; I \mid K \mid \lambda I.E \mid E_0 E_1$

(Syntax of Con omitted.)

Value Domains

A	(some primitive values)
$\varepsilon \in E = A + [E \to E]$	(values of expressions)
$\rho \in U = [Ide \to E]$	(environments)

Semantic Functions

$\mathscr{K} : [Con \to E]$

(Detailed definition omitted)

$\mathscr{E} : [Exp \to [U \to E]]$

$$\mathscr{E}[\![I]\!]\rho \equiv \rho[\![I]\!] \qquad (8.3)$$

$$\mathscr{E}[\![K]\!]\rho \equiv \mathscr{K}[\![K]\!] \qquad (8.6)$$

$$\mathscr{E}[\![\lambda I.E]\!]\rho \equiv (\lambda\varepsilon.\mathscr{E}[\![E]\!]\,(\rho[\varepsilon/I]))\text{ in }E \qquad (8.7)$$

$$\mathscr{E}[\![E_0E_1]\!]\rho \equiv (\mathscr{E}[\![E_0]\!]\rho \mid [E\to E])(\mathscr{E}[\![E_1]\!]\rho) \qquad (8.8)$$

Parenthesized Expressions If desired, the syntax may be augmented by a production:

E ::= (E)

and the semantics by a corresponding new equation:

$\mathscr{E}[\![(E)]\!]\rho = \mathscr{E}[\![E]\!]\rho.$

This would allow our syntax to serve as a concrete syntax in which it is possible, by using sufficient parentheses, to write any expression unambiguously. This is not necessary if our syntax is regarded as defining an abstract syntax.

To avoid clutter, we shall ignore these extensions in most of the ensuing discussion. Readers who wish to do so will find little difficulty in carrying them through.

Implementation: Conversion Rules

We are regarding the conversion rules of the λ-calculus as part of a possible implementation of the language, and we now embark on a proof that such an implementation would be correct: that is to say, we show that no allowable conversion will alter the value denoted by an expression. More formally, we prove

$$E_0 \text{ cnv } E_1 \Rightarrow (\mathscr{E}[\![E_0]\!]\rho \equiv \mathscr{E}[\![E_1]\!]\rho \quad \text{for all } \rho).$$

Note that if $A\rho \equiv B\rho$ for all ρ then, by extensionality, $A \equiv B$.

8.9. Definition. $E_0 \equiv E_1$ means $\mathscr{E}[\![E_0]\!] \equiv \mathscr{E}[\![E_1]\!]$.

So what we are proving is that

8.10. Theorem. $E_0 \text{ cnv } E_1 \Rightarrow E_0 \equiv E_1$.

We recall our explicit conversion rules:

(α) $\lambda x.X$ cnv $\lambda y.[y/x]X$ (y not free in X)

(β) $(\lambda x.M)N$ cnv $[N/x]M$

(η) $\lambda x.Mx$ cnv M (x not free in M).

Two expressions E_0 and E_1 are convertible if either:

(1) one may be transformed into the other by direct application of one of the explicit rules;

(2) one may be transformed into the other by application of a rule to one of its subcomponents;

(3) one may be transformed into the other by a finite sequence of permissible conversions.

We must show that in all three cases $E_0 \equiv E_1$.

Proof: We first note that ≡, like cnv, is an equivalence relation: that is, it is reflexive, symmetric and transitive. This immediately deals with case (3) above: if equivalence is preserved by each step singly then it is preserved by the whole sequence. It remains for us to prove the validity of each single step.

The proof for case (2) provides a simple introduction to the important technique of *structural induction*. The principle behind this is as follows. If we have a set of finite structured objects (such as expressions) and wish to prove that a certain property holds for every object in the set, all we need do is show that the property holds for *any* object in the set *assuming* that it holds for any and all proper subcomponents of that object. Some objects in the set, of course, will have no subcomponents (they will be atomic); for these the inductive assumption is trivial and the desired property will have to be proved for them from scratch. Notice that this principle is valid only for *finite* structures; when we dissect such objects, sooner or later we come to atomic objects, and so the induction stops.

In the present case we use induction on the structure of the expressions E_0 and E_1. We consider each possible structure for expressions separately. Since the result is trivial for simple identifiers, we must prove:

(i) if E cnv E' then $\ulcorner \lambda I.E \urcorner \equiv \ulcorner \lambda I.E' \urcorner$; and

(ii) if E_2 cnv E_2' and E_3 cnv E_3' then $\ulcorner E_2 E_3 \urcorner \equiv \ulcorner E_2' E_3' \urcorner$.

(Note the use of quasi-quotation, which we explained in Chapter 2.) The proofs are straightforward.

(i) By induction we may assume $E \equiv E'$.

So $\mathscr{E}[\![E]\!]\rho = \mathscr{E}[\![E']\!]\rho$ (all ρ).

In particular $\mathscr{E}[\![E]\!](\rho[\varepsilon/I]) = \mathscr{E}[\![E']\!](\rho[\varepsilon/I])$ (all ε,ρ)
So, by extensionality,

$$\lambda\varepsilon.\mathscr{E}[\![E]\!](\rho[\varepsilon/I]) = \lambda\varepsilon.\mathscr{E}[\![E']\!](\rho[\varepsilon/I]) \qquad \text{(all } \rho)$$

So, by 8.4, $\mathscr{E}[\![\lambda I.E]\!]\rho = \mathscr{E}[\![\lambda I.E']\!]\rho$ (all ρ)

i.e. $\ulcorner \lambda I.E \urcorner \equiv \ulcorner \lambda I.E' \urcorner$.

(ii) Similarly, assuming by induction that $E_2 \equiv E_2'$ and $E_3 \equiv E_3'$, we have

$$(\mathscr{E}[\![E_2]\!]\rho)(\mathscr{E}[\![E_3]\!]\rho) = (\mathscr{E}[\![E_2']\!]\rho)(\mathscr{E}[\![E_3']\!]\rho) \qquad \text{(all } \rho)$$

So, by 8.5 $\mathscr{E}[\![E_2 E_3]\!]\rho = \mathscr{E}[\![E_2' E_3']\!]\rho$ (all ρ)

i.e. $\ulcorner E_2 E_3 \urcorner \equiv \ulcorner E_2' E_3' \urcorner$.

In fact this structural induction is slightly atypical,

for its basis occurs either when the corresponding components are identical (and therefore both convertible and equivalent) or when one is convertible to the other by one of the explicit rules. Finally, therefore, we must show that the explicit rules preserve equivalence; i.e. we are left with case (1).

For this we need two lemmas. The first will cause us no trouble, but the proof of the second is long.

8.11. Lemma. If I is not free in E, then

$$\mathscr{E}[\![E]\!](\rho[\delta/I]) = \mathscr{E}[\![E]\!]\rho \qquad \text{(for all } \rho,\delta).$$

That is, if I does not occur free in some expression, the value I denotes in the expressions's environment is irrelevant. The proof is also a simple structural induction on the structure of E.

Exercise.

1. Prove Lemma 8.11.

8.12. Substitution Lemma. For all ρ,

$$\mathscr{E}[\![[E_1/I]E_0]\!]\rho = \mathscr{E}[\![E_0]\!](\rho[\mathscr{E}[\![E_1]\!]\rho/I]).$$

This states that the result of evaluating a substituted expression in some environment is the same as evaluating the original expression in a modified environment. Let us define

$$E_0' \text{ to mean } [E_1/I]E_0 \qquad (8.13)$$

and

$$\rho' \text{ to mean } \rho[\mathscr{E}[\![E_1]\!]\rho/I] \qquad (8.14)$$

So E_0' refers to the modified expression, formed by substitution, and ρ' refers to the modified environment. So we must prove

$\mathscr{E}[\![E_0']\!]\rho \equiv \mathscr{E}[\![E_0]\!]\rho'$

and we shall call the sides of this assertion *L* and *R* respectively.

Proof: The proof is another structural induction, on the structure of E_0; it is again by cases, based on the definition of substitution (Definition 5.7). (As might be imagined, it is tedious. Readers who are prepared to take it on trust may skip, when they get bored, to page 166.)

According to Definition 5.7, the expression E_0', or $[E_1/I]X$, is definined as follows:

1. E_0 is a variable:
   - 1.1. If $E_0 \equiv I$ then $E_0' \equiv E_1$.
   - 1.2. If $E_0 \not\equiv I$ then $E_0' \equiv E_0$.
2. E_0 is an application E_2E_3:
   $E_0' \equiv ([E_1/I]E_2)([E_1/I]E_3)$.
3. E_0 is an abstraction $\lambda I_1.E_2$:
   - 3.1. If $I_1 \equiv I$ then $E_0' \equiv E_0$.
   - 3.2. If $I_1 \not\equiv I$ then
     - 3.2.1. If I does not occur free in E_2 or I_1 does not occur free in E_1 then $E_0' \equiv \lambda I_1.[E_1/I]E_2$;
     - 3.2.2. Otherwise $E_0' \equiv \lambda I_2.[E_1/I]([I_2/I_1]E_2)$ where I_2 is a new variable which does not occur free in E_1 or E_2.

1. E_0 is a variable.

1.1. If E_0 is I then E_0' is E_1.

So $L = \mathscr{E}[\![E_1]\!]\rho$.

$$
\begin{aligned}
R &= \mathscr{E}[\![I]\!]\rho' \\
&= \rho'[\![I]\!] && \text{(by 8.3)} \\
&= (\rho[\mathscr{E}[\![E_1]\!]\rho/I])[\![I]\!] && \text{(definition of } \rho'\text{)} \\
&= \mathscr{E}[\![E_1]\!]\rho. && \text{(by 8.2)}
\end{aligned}
$$

So $L = R$.

1.2. If E_0 is I_1, not I, then E_0' is E_0, or I_1.

$$L = \mathscr{E}[\![I_1]\!]\rho = \rho[\![I_1]\!]. \qquad \text{(by 8.3)}$$

$$
\begin{aligned}
R &= \mathscr{E}[\![I_1]\!]\rho' = \rho'[\![I_1]\!] \\
&= (\rho[\mathscr{E}[\![E_1]\!]\rho/I])[\![I_1]\!] \\
&= \rho[\![I_1]\!]. && \text{(by 8.2, since } I \not\equiv I_1\text{)}
\end{aligned}
$$

So $L = R$.

2. E_0 is $\ulcorner E_2E_3 \urcorner$.

Then E_0' is $\ulcorner E_2'E_3' \urcorner$ where E_2' is $[E_1/I]E_2$
and E_3' is $[E_1/I]E_3$.

$$
\begin{aligned}
L &= \mathscr{E}[\![E_2'E_3']\!]\rho \\
&= (\mathscr{E}[\![E_2']\!]\rho)(\mathscr{E}[\![E_3']\!]\rho) && \text{(by 8.5)} \\
&= (\mathscr{E}[\![E_2]\!]\rho')(\mathscr{E}[\![E_3]\!]\rho') \\
& && \text{(by the inductive hypothesis)} \\
&= \mathscr{E}[\![E_2E_3]\!]\rho' \\
&= R.
\end{aligned}
$$

3. E_0 is $\ulcorner \lambda I_1.E \urcorner$.

So $R = \mathscr{E}[\![\lambda I_1.E]\!]\rho'$

$= \lambda\varepsilon.\mathscr{E}[\![E]\!](\rho'[\varepsilon/I_1])$ (by 8.4)

3.1. If I_1 is I then E_0' is E_0.

So $L = \mathscr{E}[\![\lambda I.E]\!]\rho$

$= \lambda\varepsilon.\mathscr{E}[\![E]\!](\rho[\varepsilon/I])$ (by 8.4)

and $R = \lambda\varepsilon.\mathscr{E}[\![E]\!](\rho'[\varepsilon/I])$ (since I_1 is I)

But $\rho'[\varepsilon/I] = \rho[\mathscr{E}[\![E_1]\!]\rho/I][\varepsilon/I]$ (definition of ρ')

$= \rho[\varepsilon/I]$. (from 8.2)

So $L = R$.

3.2. If I_1 is not I then E_0' is $\ulcorner \lambda I_2.[E_1/I][I_2/I_1]E \urcorner$ where I_2 will be specified below.

Let $E_2 = [I_2/I_1]E$, so that E_0' is $\ulcorner \lambda I_2.[E_1/I]E_2 \urcorner$.

Then $L = \mathscr{E}[\![\lambda I_2.[E_1/I]E_2]\!]\rho$

$= \lambda\varepsilon.\mathscr{E}[\![[E_1/I]E_2]\!](\rho[\varepsilon/I_2])$ (by 8.4)

$= \lambda\varepsilon.\mathscr{E}[\![E_2]\!]\rho_\varepsilon''$ (by hypothesis)

where $\rho_\varepsilon'' = \rho[\varepsilon/I_2][\mathscr{E}[\![E_1]\!](\rho[\varepsilon/I_2])/I]$.

So, substituting the definition of E_2,

$L = \lambda\varepsilon.\mathscr{E}[\![[I_2/I_1]E]\!]\rho_\varepsilon''$

$= \lambda\varepsilon.\mathscr{E}[\![E]\!](\rho_\varepsilon''[\mathscr{E}[\![I_2]\!]\rho_\varepsilon''/I_1])$ (by hypothesis)

$= \lambda\varepsilon.\mathscr{E}[\![E]\!](\rho_\varepsilon''[\rho_\varepsilon''[\![I_2]\!]/I_1])$ (by 8.3)

and we also have

$R = \lambda\varepsilon.\mathscr{E}[\![E]\!](\rho'[\varepsilon/I_1])$. (by 8.4)

To proceed we need to know what I_2 is.

3.2.1. If I is not free in E or if I_1 is not free in E_1 then I_2 is I_1.

In both cases $\rho''_\varepsilon = \rho[\varepsilon/I_1](\mathscr{E}[\![E_1]\!](\rho[\varepsilon/I_1])/I]$.

So $\rho''_\varepsilon[\![I_2]\!] = \rho''_\varepsilon[\![I_1]\!] = \varepsilon$ (by 8.2, since $I \neq I_1$).

So $L = \lambda\varepsilon.\mathscr{E}[\![E]\!](\rho''_\varepsilon[\varepsilon/I_1])$ (substituting for $\rho''_\varepsilon[\![I_2]\!]$)

$= \lambda\varepsilon.\mathscr{E}[\![E]\!]\rho''_\varepsilon$ (since $\rho''_\varepsilon[\![I_1]\!] = \varepsilon$).

Now *EITHER* I is not free in E, in which case

$\mathscr{E}[\![E]\!]\rho''_\varepsilon = \mathscr{E}[\![E]\!](\rho[\varepsilon/I_1])$

and $\mathscr{E}[\![E]\!](\rho'[\varepsilon/I_1]) = \mathscr{E}[\![E]\!](\rho[\varepsilon/I_1])$

and hence $L = R$;

OR I_1 is not free in E_1, and then

$\mathscr{E}[\![E_1]\!](\rho[\varepsilon/I_1]) = \mathscr{E}[\![E_1]\!]\rho$

so that $\rho''_\varepsilon = \rho[\varepsilon/I_1][\mathscr{E}[\![E_1]\!]\rho/I]$
(from the previous equation for ρ''_ε)

$= \rho'[\varepsilon/I_1]$ (for, since $I_1 \neq I$, the two postfixes commute).

So $L = \lambda\varepsilon.\mathscr{E}[\![E]\!]\rho''_\varepsilon$

$= \lambda\varepsilon.\mathscr{E}[\![E]\!](\rho'[\varepsilon/I_1])$

$= R$.

3.2.2. Finally, if I is free in E and I_1 is free in E_1, then I_2 is a new identifier which is not free in E or E_1.

So $\rho''_\varepsilon = \rho[\varepsilon/I_2][\mathscr{E}[\![E_1]\!](\rho[\varepsilon/I_2])/I]$ (definition)

$= \rho[\varepsilon/I_2][\mathscr{E}[\![E_1]\!]\rho/I]$ (by 8.11, as I_2 is not free in E_1).

So $\rho''_\varepsilon[\![I_2]\!] = \varepsilon$ (as I_2 is not I) and $\rho''_\varepsilon[\rho''_\varepsilon[\![I_2]\!]/I_1] \;=\; \rho''_\varepsilon[\varepsilon/I_1]$

$= \rho[\varepsilon/I_2][\mathscr{E}[\![E_1]\!]\rho/I][\varepsilon/I_1].$

So $L \;=\; \lambda\varepsilon.\mathscr{E}[\![E]\!](\rho[\varepsilon/I_2][\mathscr{E}[\![E_1]\!]\rho/I][\varepsilon/I_1])$

$= \lambda\varepsilon.\mathscr{E}[\![E]\!](\rho[\mathscr{E}[\![E_1]\!]\rho/I][\varepsilon/I_1])$ (by 8.11, as I_2 is not free in E)

$= \lambda\varepsilon.\mathscr{E}[\![E]\!](\rho'[\varepsilon/I_1])$ (definition of ρ')

$= R.$

So we have now exhausted all the cases (not to mention anyone who has been following the details); so the proof of Lemma 8.12 is completed.

Proof of Theorem 8.10 (concluded): We now complete the proof of the conversion rules. We have to show E_0 cnv $E_1 \Rightarrow E_0 \equiv E_1$ for α-, β- and η- conversion.

α-conversion.

$E_0 \;\equiv\; \ulcorner\lambda I.E\urcorner$

$E_1 \;\equiv\; \ulcorner\lambda I'.[I'/I]E\urcorner$ where I' is not free in E.

Then $\mathscr{E}[\![E_1]\!]\rho \;\equiv\; \lambda\varepsilon.\mathscr{E}[\![[I'/I]E]\!](\rho[\varepsilon/I'])$ (by 8.4)

$\equiv \lambda\varepsilon.\mathscr{E}[\![E]\!](\rho[\varepsilon/I'][\mathscr{E}[\![I']\!](\rho[\varepsilon/I'])/I])$ (by Lemma 8.12)

$\equiv \lambda\varepsilon.\mathscr{E}[\![E]\!](\rho[\varepsilon/I'][\varepsilon/I])$ (by 8.3)

$\equiv \lambda\varepsilon.\mathscr{E}[\![E]\!](\rho[\varepsilon/I])$ (Lemma 8.11 and 8.2, as I' is not free in E.)

$\equiv \mathscr{E}[\![E_0]\!]\rho$. (by 8.4)

This holds for all ρ, so $E_0 \equiv E_1$.

β-conversion.

$E_0 \;\equiv\; \ulcorner(\lambda I.E)E'\urcorner$

$E_1 \;\equiv\; [E'/I]E.$

Then $\mathscr{E}[\![E_0]\!]\rho \equiv (\mathscr{E}[\![\lambda I.E]\!]\rho)(\mathscr{E}[\![E']\!]\rho)$ (by 8.5)

$\equiv (\lambda\varepsilon.\mathscr{E}[\![E]\!](\rho[\varepsilon/I]))(\mathscr{E}[\![E']\!]\rho)$ (by 8.4)

$\equiv \mathscr{E}[\![E]\!](\rho[\mathscr{E}[\![E']\!]\rho/I])$ (by 7.17)

$\equiv \mathscr{E}[\![[E'/I]E]\!]\rho$ (Lemma 8.12)

$\equiv \mathscr{E}[\![E_1]\!]\rho$.

This holds for all ρ, so $E_0 \equiv E_1$.

η-conversion.

$E_0 \equiv \ulcorner\lambda I.E(I)\urcorner$ where I is not free in E,
$E_1 \equiv E$.

Then $\mathscr{E}[\![E_0]\!]\rho \equiv \lambda\varepsilon.\mathscr{E}[\![E(I)]\!](\rho[\varepsilon/I])$ (by 8.4)

$\equiv \lambda\varepsilon.(\mathscr{E}[\![E]\!](\rho[\varepsilon/I]))(\mathscr{E}[\![I]\!](\rho[\varepsilon/I]))$ (by 8.5)

$\equiv \lambda\varepsilon.(\mathscr{E}[\![E]\!]\rho)(\varepsilon)$
(Lemma 8.11, as I not free in E).(*)

So for all ε',

$(\mathscr{E}[\![E_0]\!]\rho)\varepsilon' \equiv (\lambda\varepsilon.(\mathscr{E}[\![E]\!]\rho)(\varepsilon))\varepsilon'$

$\equiv (\mathscr{E}[\![E]\!]\rho)\varepsilon'$

$\equiv (\mathscr{E}[\![E_1]\!]\rho)\varepsilon'$

So, by extensionality (5.3), $E_0 \equiv E_1$.

Thus our proof of Theorem 8.10 is complete.

If we use instead the semantics given in Table 8.2, the last part of the proof of Theorem 8.10 is no longer valid. The equation marked (*) above becomes

$\mathscr{E}[\![E_0]\!]\rho \equiv \lambda\varepsilon.(\mathscr{E}[\![E]\!]\rho|[E\to E])(\varepsilon)$ in E

and the argument which follows it is valid only if we can assume that $\mathscr{E}[\![E]\!]\rho$ is in the $[E\to E]$ subdomain of

E. Otherwise $\mathscr{E}[\![E_0]\!]\rho \equiv ?$ and E_0 and E_1 are not equivalent. So if we are working with functions and other values too, we must check before using η-conversion that what we are applying is indeed a function: the rule is not universally valid. Of course the following restricted conversion always does hold:

$$\ulcorner \lambda I.(\lambda I'.E)I \urcorner \text{ cnv } \ulcorner \lambda I'.E \urcorner \quad \text{(if I is not free in E)}$$

but this is merely a consequence of the α- and β-rules.

<u>Equivalence of Nonconvertible Expressions.</u>

We have shown that

$$E_0 \text{ cnv } E_1 \Rightarrow E_0 \equiv E_1$$

and we now consider the converse question. That is, if two expressions are equivalent, are they necessarily convertible? We consider two cases.

<u>*First Case: E_0 and E_1 have normal forms.*</u> In this case we can prove that

$$E_0 \text{ c}\not\text{nv } E_1 \Rightarrow E_0 \not\equiv E_1.$$

This follows from a theorem of Böhm in the formal λ-calculus (i.e. in the purely syntactic system, not this semantic model). Of course we cannot say in the formal λ-calculus whether $E_0 \equiv E_1$, because this would assert that the values of E_0 and E_1 are equal in all environments, and in the purely syntactic system even the concept of environment is unknown. To get the idea of what is actually proved, we first consider the special case where this causes no problem, which is when the values of E_0 and E_1 are independent of the environment: that is, if they are both pure combinators, with no free varisbles. Then the theorem is as follows.

8.13. Theorem. If E_0 and E_1 are λ-expressions with no free variables, having distinct normal forms, then there exists a sequence of combinators $G_1 G_2 \ldots, G_s$ such that

$$E_0 G_1 G_2 \ldots G_s X_0 X_1 \quad \text{cnv} \quad X_0$$

$$E_1 G_1 G_2 \ldots G_s X_0 X_1 \quad \text{cnv} \quad X_1$$

for any X_0, X_1.

This implies that

$$E_0 G_1 G_2 \ldots G_s \equiv K, \text{ and}$$

$$E_1 G_1 G_2 \ldots G_s \equiv KI.$$

But K and KI are unequal in the space E for all ρ, and hence by extensionality so are E_0 and E_1.

The theorem is actually proved as a corollary of the more general case, where E_0 and E_1 *may* have free variables. To show that $E_0 \not\equiv E_1$ what we would really like to say is "there exists an environment in which $E_0 \not\equiv E_1$". But in the λ-calculus we have to say it in the following form, which by our substitution lemma (8.12) is equivalent: "there exists a substitution for some or all the free variables such that then $E_0 \not\equiv E_1$". More formally:

8.14. Theorem. Let E_0 and E_1 be λ-expressions in normal form, not convertible, and let $I_1, I_2, \ldots, I_t$ include all the free variables in E_0 and E_1. Then there exist sequences $U_1, U_2, \ldots, U_t$ and $H_1, H_2, \ldots, H_s$, where each U_j is either I_j or some combinator, and each H_k is either a combinator or some variable not otherwise occurring, such that, for

$$E_i' = [U_1/I_1][U_2/I_2]...[U_t/I_t]E_i \qquad (i=0,1)$$

we have

$$E_i'H_1H_2...H_sX_0X_1 = X_i \qquad (i=0,1)$$

where X_0 and X_1 are two variables not otherwise occurring. This theorem, which will not be proved here (but see Böhm [4]), is all that is necessary to show that, if E_0 and E_1 have normal forms, then

$$E_0 \text{ cnv } E_1 \Leftrightarrow E_0 \equiv E_1.$$

Second Case: E_0 and E_1 do not have normal forms. In this case the above statement is not true. We shall demonstrate this by exhibiting an example of two expressions which are nonconvertible, but yet are equivalent.

In developing this example, which was anticipated long ago in the exercises of Chapter 5, we shall use upper case letters to denote λ-expressions, i.e. elements of Exp, including individual variables. Later we shall use the corresponding lower case letters to denote the values of those expressions in some environment ρ.

Consider the following expressions:

$$G \equiv \lambda Y.\lambda F.F(YF)$$

$$Y_1 \equiv \lambda F.(\lambda X.F(XX))(\lambda X.F(XX))$$

$$Y_2 \equiv Y_1G.$$

Note that all these expressions are pure combinators, so their values are independent of their environment.

8.15. Definition. (In the λ-calculus) A fixed point of a λ-expression F is any X such that

$F(X)$ cnv X.

8.16. Definition. A fixed point operator is any Z such that for all F, ZF is a fixed point of F; i.e.

$F(ZF)$ cnv ZF for all $F \in$ Exp.

8.17. Lemma. All fixed points of G are fixed point operators.

Proof: Let X be a fixed point of G, so that X cnv GX. Then, for all F,

$$
\begin{aligned}
XF &\text{ cnv } GXF \\
&\equiv (\lambda Y.\lambda F.F(YF))XF \quad \text{(definition of G)} \\
&\text{cnv}_\beta\ F(XF).
\end{aligned}
$$

Exercise.

2. Prove that all fixed point operators are fixed points of G. [You will have to use η-conversion for this exercise. Even if we are using the semantics for which this does not in general hold, you can show that it is valid for this particular case.]

8.18. Lemma. Y_1 is a fixed point operator.

Proof: Exercise 9(i) of chapter 5; note that the Y_1 here is convertible to $\lambda F.\Delta(F \circ \Delta)$ as defined there.

8.19. Lemma. Y_2 is a fixed point operator

Proof: Exercise 9(iii) of chapter 5; or, more simply:

Y_1 is a fixed point operator; (lemma 8.18)

so $Y_2 \equiv Y_1 G$ is a fixed point of G;

so Y_2 is a fixed point operator. (lemma 8.17)

8.20. Theorem. Y_1 c$\not\!\!$v Y_2.
Proof: Exercise 10 of Chapter 5.

We now consider the images of Y_1, Y_2 and G in the value space E, using y_1, y_2 and g to denote them. We can show that, for any ρ,

$$\mathscr{E}[\![G]\!]\rho = g = \lambda y.\lambda f.f(yf)$$

$$\mathscr{E}[\![Y_1]\!]\rho = y_1 = \lambda f.(\lambda x.f(xx))(\lambda x.f(xx))$$

$$\mathscr{E}[\![Y_2]\!]\rho = y_2 = y_1 g.$$

8.21. Lemma. if $x = gx$ then $xf = f(xf)$ for all $f \in E$.

Proof: $xf \equiv gxf \equiv (\lambda y.\lambda f.f(yf))xf \equiv f(xf)$. (Compare this with proposition 1, above.)

8.22. Remark. y_1 is the *minimal* fixed point operator (this was Theorem 7.19). That is:

(1) if $x = fx$, then $y_1 f \sqsubseteq x$;

(2) if y is a fixed point operator, i.e. if $yf = f(yf)$ for all $f \in E$, then $y_1 \sqsubseteq y$.

8.23. Theorem. $y_1 \equiv y_2$.

Proof: y_1 is a fixed point of g (analogue of Exercise 9(ii) of Chapter 5). So $y_1 g \sqsubseteq y_1$ (by 8.22(1)). But $y_1 g = y_2$, and so $y_2 \sqsubseteq y_1$. On the other hand, because y_1 is a fixed point operator, y_2 is a fixed point of g; so y_2 is a fixed point operator by 8.21 and hence $y_1 \sqsubseteq y_2$. (by 8.22(2)). So $y_1 \equiv y_2$.

8.24. Corollary. $Y_1 \equiv Y_2$, even though Y_1 c$\not\!\!$v Y_2.

To summarise: convertible expressions are equivalent; non-convertible expressions are non-equivalent if both have normal forms, but not necessarily otherwise.

For a fuller discussion of the relationship between semantic equivalence and the conversion rules, we refer the reader to papers by Christopher Wadsworth [65] [66], who gives in fact a completely syntactic characterisation (based on *head-normal form*, a weaker analogue of normal form) of semantic equivalence, for a λ-calculus with full η-conversion (so that $E = [E \to E]$). In particular, too, he considers the case we have omitted, where one expression has a normal form and the other does not. The result in this case depends on which of our two semantic definitions we choose (the previous cases were independent of this choice). In the λ-calculus with atoms (Table 8.2), no expression with a normal form is equivalent to any expression without. On the other hand, in the λ-calculus without atoms and therefore with full η-conversion (Table 8.1) the expressions $\ulcorner \lambda x.x \urcorner$ and $\ulcorner (\lambda f.(\lambda x.f(xx))(\lambda x.f(xx)))(\lambda f \lambda x \lambda y.x(fy)) \urcorner$ are equivalent (they both denote the identity function). Many more details are given in Wadsworth's papers.

The Power of Various Implementations: Order of Evaluation.

We have proved the validity of the conversion rules; this means that any mechanical evaluator for the λ-calculus that uses these rules will never give a wrong answer. However, sometimes such an interpreter may not produce an answer at all. For example, a normal order interpreter, which terminates only when it reduces an expression to normal form, will not terminate on either of the following expressions:

(a) $(\lambda x.xx)(\lambda x.xx)$ (Example 5.11)

(b) $\lambda f.(\lambda x.f(xx))(\lambda x.f(xx))$ (cf. Exercise 7 of Chapter 5)

The value of expression (a) is ⊥, so we would not expect an interpreter to terminate (it would be quite unreasonable to expect the interpreter to type the symbol '⊥' whenever it was presented with an expression whose value was ⊥, for this would be equivalent to a solution of the Halting Problem). But expression (b) denotes a proper value, the minimal fixed point function.

Exercise

3. Prove that the value of $(\lambda x.xx)(\lambda x.xx)$ in any environment is ⊥.

So a particular interpreter may be less than completely potent, for it may fail to find an answer in certain cases when one does exist. In this particular case we could patch matters up by having the evaluator terminate whenever it reached normal form or whenever it reached an abstraction (so our example (b) above would terminate immediately). There will of course still be expressions (such as our example (a)) for which such an interpreter would not terminate. The penalty for this patch is that we can no longer use the Church-Rosser Theorem (5.14) to tell immediately whether two possible answers are distinct and therefore (by the last section's result) unequal, for the answers are no longer necessarily in normal form. Thus, for example, we would no longer be able sensibly to use the representation for the integers given in Exercise 4 of Chapter 5. This might not worry us, particularly if our value space included atoms which with their primitive functions were sufficiently rich and if there existed a canonical representation for the output of such values. If the atoms formed a flat lattice with a countable number of elements, it should certainly be possible to devise a suitable output syntax (such as the numerals for the numbers); then we might be satisfied with an interpreter which for atomic values produced the canonical output, for functions output some equivalent expression, and for the other values produced an error stop or failed to terminate. Our patched normal order interpreter, augmented with suitable machinery for the atoms, would successfully meet this specification.

A note on Improper Values.

Consider the function

$\lambda y.(\lambda x.xx)(\lambda x.xx)$.

This function gives $\bot$ for all arguments, and its value is therefore $\bot_{[E\to E]}$. In the semantics with atoms this does not correspond to $\bot_E$, as we are using separated sums, and our patched interpreter handles it correctly: it immediately terminates.

Unfortunately, however, the same thing would happen if we tried the same patch on our normal order interpreter for the semantics without atoms. This interpreter, too, would immediately terminate on the above expression, though in this case $\bot_{[E\to E]}$ *is* $\bot_E$, and so we would expect non-termination.

If we really wish to provide the semantics of

this interpreter, therefore, we must distinguish between $\perp_E$ and $\perp_{[E \to E]}$. We can do this in effect by defining a sum domain with only one component domain. Using notation suggested by Robert Milne [33], for any domain D we write D° for the sum domain with D as its sole component. The structure of D° is like that of D except that new maximal, minimal and error elements are adjoined (see Fig. 8.1). Then the value space for our λ-calculus without atoms would be given by

$$E \quad = \quad [E \to E]^{\circ}$$

and the semantic equations (8.3 - 8.5) would have to include the appropriate projection and injection functions as in Table 8.2. We mention this device, however, as no more than a curiosity: when concerned with the behaviour of algorithmic interpreters we are almost invariably dealing with a semantics involving other values as well as functions - where, as we have seen, the problem does not arise.

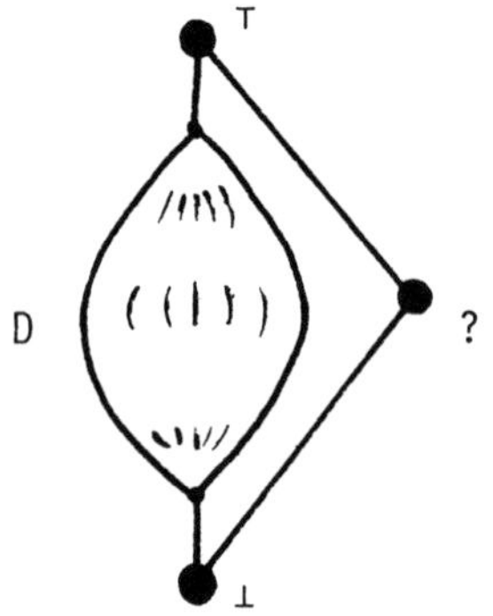

Fig. 8.1. A sum domain with one component.

Call by Value

Except, perhaps, for the device just mentioned, the particular interpreters we have considered have not caused any change to the semantics of the language. The λ-expressions exhibit the correct behaviour when applied to other expressions: our problems have really only concerned the selection of an appropriate representation of the value for purposes of output. A full analysis of these problems would require our getting down to details of the (lattices of) inputs and outputs, the representations which our interpreter transforms and perhaps also the structure of the atom subdomain. We do not propose to go into these areas further here (though we shall discuss syntactic lattices before the end of this chapter). The situation is somewhat analogous (though the analogy should not be pressed too hard) to events like integer overflow causing a program to fail: this is sometimes best thought of as a failure in the way the implementation is representing integers, rather than a property of the semantics of the integers themselves.

Changes of a more profound nature are also possible in the specification of an order of interpretation. One in particular we prefer to regard as causing a change in the semantics of the language. This is partly because it corresponds closely to the behaviour of many existing languages, and also because some languages even offer a choice explicitly within the language.

We are referring to *call by value*. In this mode of evaluation the operator and operand of an application are evaluated *before* the application itself is performed. So an expression like

$(\lambda y.0)((\lambda x.xx)(\lambda x.xx))$

which the normal order interpreter would evaluate to 0, fails to terminate under call by value.

Gordon Plotkin has suggested how this change to the semantics of the λ-calculus may be explained as follows in terms of *strict functions* (see, too, for example, Reynolds [43]).

8.25. Definition. A function f is *strict* if $f\bot \equiv \bot$; it is *doubly* strict if in addition $f\top \equiv \top$; and *completely* strict if $f? \equiv ?$ as well.

8.26. Definition. The function *strict*: $[E \to E] \to [E \to E]$ is such that for all $x \in E$,

$$strict\ f\ x \equiv \begin{cases} \bot, \top \text{ or } ? \text{ if } x \text{ is } \bot, \top \text{ or } ? \\ f\ x \text{ otherwise} \end{cases}$$

That is, *strict* maps a function f into the corresponding completely strict function. Then to achieve call-by-value semantics, we redefine equation 8.7 in Table 8.2 as follows

$$\mathscr{E}[\![\lambda I.E]\!]\rho = [strict(\lambda\varepsilon.\mathscr{E}[\![E]\!](\rho[\varepsilon/I]))] \text{ in } E. \quad (8.27)$$

This small change has far-reaching consequences. One is that in the absence of atoms it becomes rather more important to distinguish between $\bot_E$ and $\bot_{[E\to E]}$, and so to use the modified domain $E = [E\to E]°$. Another is to introduce restrictions on β-conversions, which will become apparent if the reader tries to reprove the validity of this rule in the new semantics. The properties of recursively defined functions are also somewhat altered (though we have not studied them extensively in this example language). Y_λ, indeed, ceases to be a minimal fixed point operator, and is instead a function whose result is always $\perp_E$. These extra complications have prompted some theoreticians to call for the replacement of the call by value rule in our languages - even though the hardware required to implement call by name efficiently would be a little more complicated. We, however, merely identify the controversy and refrain from joining in.

Notice that here, too, an interpreter which insists on a normal form for its operators and operands before application will be yet weaker than the revised semantics. As before, analysis of this requires discussion of representations.

If we were to summarise these two sections into one concept, it would be the idea that various implementations of the same language may differ in effectiveness. Such differences are often best not confused with the semantics of the language, though this is not always so.

Definitional Interpreters

This is an appropriate place to contrast our approach to semantic definition with another to which it is superficially similar. We have seen how our semantic equations may be recast, with the help of a conditional expression, into a single function definition. We could regard such a definition as being an interpreter for the defined language written in the defining language, and itself intended for mechanical evaluation, at least in principle. Our defining language would be a variant of the λ-calculus, and our approach would closely resemble that of Peter Landin several years ago [24], who defined a subset of Algol 60 in terms of the λ-calculus, implemented with his SECD machine [25].

A problem with this way of looking at things is that assumptions made about the defining language are automatically carried over to the defined language, without explicit mention. In our example, if the defining language had normal order semantics then so would the defined language; if the defining language were call by value (as the SECD implementation is) then so would be the defined language. Other assumptions are also implicitly transmitted. The danger is, of course, that someone who has the wrong idea about the defining language will never know that he also has the wrong idea about the defined language. In a useful paper [42], however, John Reynolds describes how by increasing the convolutedness of the interpreter the order of evaluation in the defined language can be specified explicitly, independently of the order of evaluation in the defining language (this paper will probably be more approachable after we have reached our Chapter 11).

Such a way of looking at our method reduces it to just another method of mechanistic definition, with all the problems such methods bring. This was not our intention. Our "defining language" was not to be regarded as intended for mechanical evaluation, but rather as describing various relationships which hold in some value space. The fact that the expressions of these relationships are susceptible to manipulation according to rules is an uncovenanted extra; and when in a particular case some such method fails to terminate, we do not say that the value of that particular expression is *ipso facto* undefined, but rather that the method we tried does not work in this case and we must look around for some other way to do it. It is sometimes stated that the semantics given by Scott's model for the λ-calculus is a "normal order", or "call-by-name" semantics. While it is true that normal order or call-by-name evaluation more reliably produces the value specified by the model than other methods, nevertheless the statement is misleading: in the semantic model syntactic matters, like the order of applying conversion rules, are irrelevant.

Before leaving the subject of interpreters, we briefly consider the special case where the defined language and the defining language are one and the same (since our defining language uses λ-notation our semantic definition could easily be turned into an example of this kind of interpreter). Such interpreters are called *metacircular*. The first and most famous example was that given by McCarthy [31] for the language LISP 1.5. These interpreters have a self-contained look, and it is easy to conclude that they provide, on their own, a complete definition of the semantics. This is not true: McCarthy himself pointed out that the reader must have independent knowledge of the semantics at least of one particular program in the language - the interpreter itself (he suggested that this was easier than learning the whole language). The semantics of the language may be thought of as a "fixed point" of the metacircular interpreter - and it is quite true that if the reader has a fairly good knowledge of the semantics the interpreter may enable him to converge (in an informal kind of way) on the correct solution. The trouble is that the solution is not unique, so that it is possible, by starting with incorrect assumptions about the language, to reach another fixed point, which will only confirm one's misconceptions. Perhaps one of the most insidious examples is the call-by-name/call-by-value distinction. Unless special precautions are taken (such as those suggested by Reynolds in the paper we have mentioned), a language with either one of these modes of evaluation will be a fixed point of the same metacircular interpreter, and there will be no way of telling which one is correct. But there are also simpler examples: consider the language in which the value of *every* expression is the number 27. Such a language has a certain lack of expressive power, but it would be a solution of the metacircular interpreter formed from our semantic definition, and of the LISP interpreter, and others. The truth is that the *minimal* fixed point of the interpreter will be the language in which the value of every expression is undefined: so that the interpreter cannot really be thought of as *defining* anything at all.

Syntactic Lattices

We shall soon finish our study of the λ-calculus and

turn to languages which more closely resemble those in common use. But first we shall consider just one more aspect, which has to do with syntax.

Our syntax definition was

$$E ::= I|\lambda I.E|E_0E_1$$

which said that an expression consisted of *either* an identifier *or* an identifier with an expression *or* two expressions, the extra symbols, such as 'λ', being in a sense noise.

Now suppose the identifiers are elements of a flat lattice Id (like the lattice N of integers). Then we could regard the λ-expressions as being elements of a reflexive domain Ex, where
$Ex = Id + [Id \times Ex] + [Ex \times Ex]$. In this domain the second subcomponent contains the abstraction expressions, and the third the application expressions. Note carefully that all this is syntax, not semantics: a point in Ex is an *expression*, not the *value* of an expression. There are no environments involved; in fact there is no interpretation of the expressions at all.

If now we put

$$Ex_1 = Id$$
$$Ex_2 = [Id \times Ex]$$
$$Ex_3 = [Ex \times Ex]$$

then the predicates of McCarthy's abstract syntax become $IsEx_1$, $IsEx_2$ and $IsEx_3$. (Using a notation we introduced earlier (6.35), we can write $IsEx_1(x)$ as $(x \in Ex_1)$ and so on.) His selectors are simply the appropriate projection functions; so, for example,

$Body(E) \; = \; (E|\mathsf{Ex}_2)\downarrow 2$

$Rator(E) \; = \; (E|\mathsf{Ex}_3)\downarrow 1.$

Here the (|) notation projects into the appropriate subdomain, and the ↓ selects the appropriate element from a pair. Note that both these functions may be slightly redefined, in the spirit of the end of Chapter 7, so as to give the error value ?, instead of ⊥, for proper but invalid arguments.

The syntax analyser is now that function which maps strings over some alphabet into elements of Ex. Illegal strings are mapped to ?, and all the strings specified by our earlier syntax definition to be elements of Exp are mapped to corresponding values in Ex.

However, Exp by definition contained only finite expressions, whereas Ex is a very much richer domain. Ex certainly contains elements corresponding to all the finite expressions in Exp, but it also contains limit points which can only be represented by infinite expressions (many of which are uncomputable). If any system deserves to be called "abstract syntax", this does.

To illustrate this, we permit ourselves slightly more informality of notation. Instead of writing

$\mathsf{Ex} \; = \; \mathsf{Id} + [\mathsf{Id} \times \mathsf{Ex}] + [\mathsf{Ex} \times \mathsf{Ex}]$

let us write

$\mathsf{Ex} \; = \; \mathsf{Id} + \lambda\mathsf{Id}.\mathsf{Ex} + \mathsf{Ex}(\mathsf{Ex})$

and if we write, for example,

$x \; = \; \ulcorner a(b) \urcorner$

for x, a, b, ∈ Ex, we shall mean that x is that

element, in the [Ex × Ex] subdomain of Ex, which is the pair whose first element is a and the second b.

Now, for x, e ∈ Ex, consider the equation

$$e = \ulcorner x(e) \urcorner.$$

This has a solution in Ex, and this solution is the fixed point of the function x′ where

$$x' = \lambda y{:}Ex.\ulcorner x\ (y)\urcorner.$$

(Speaking very informally indeed, we could say that the solution is the fixed point of x.) This solution can only be represented by the infinite expression:

x(x(x(x(...(x(...   ...))...))))

or perhaps [11]:

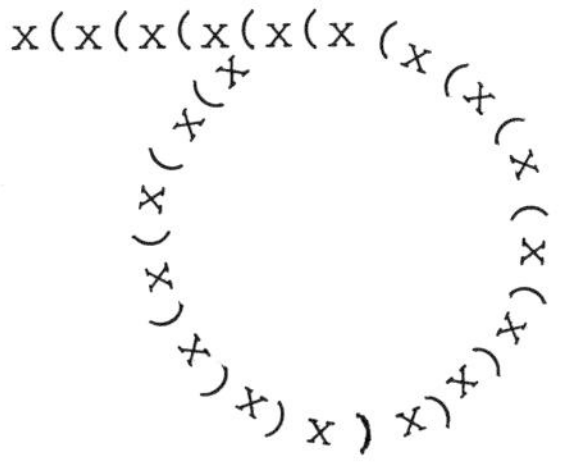

It is fix_{Ex} (x'), where, as usual,

$$fix_{Ex} f = \bigsqcup_{n=0}^{\infty} f^{n}(\bot_{Ex}).$$

<u>*Semantics for elements of* Ex</u> We can now define a semantic function, which we shall call $\mathcal{V}$, which gives the value in E of expressions in Ex, evaluated in a particular environment. So

$$\mathcal{V} : [Ex \to [U \to E]]$$

where, as before, ρ ∈ U = [Id→E] and ε ∈ E = [E→E].

$\mathcal{V}$ is defined as follows (in this definition we still for old times' sake, use ⟦⟧ brackets to surround syntactic elements, now elements of Ex; since we now have functions, such as *Rator*, whose arguments and results are all in Ex, these brackets may now be nested):

$$\begin{aligned}\mathcal{V}[\![E]\!]\rho \;=\; & (E\in Id) \rightarrow \rho[\![\mathit{Ident}[\![E]\!]]\!],\\ & (E\in\lambda Id.Ex) \rightarrow (\lambda\varepsilon{:}E.\mathcal{V}[\![\mathit{Body}[\![E]\!]]\!](\rho[\varepsilon/\mathit{BndVar}[\![E]\!]])),\\ & (E\in Ex(Ex)) \rightarrow (\mathcal{V}[\![\mathit{Rator}[\![E]\!]]\!]\rho)(\mathcal{V}[\![\mathit{Rand}[\![E]\!]]\!]\rho),\\ & ?_E\end{aligned}$$

where $\mathit{Ident}[\![E]\!] = (E|Id), \mathit{Body}[\![E]\!] = (E|\lambda Id.Ex)\downarrow 2$
etc.

This is recognisably the same definition as we had before for $\mathcal{E}$; but it is now defined over all Ex, not merely the subset of Ex corresponding to Exp.

Or is it?

The elements of Exp were all finite expressions, so if we had cared to do so we could have used a structural induction argument to prove that $\mathcal{E}$ was well defined for all elements of Exp: this would have been analogous to Exercise 1 of Chapter 3, which did the same for the earlier function $\mathcal{N}$ and Nml. But now Ex contains infinite expressions; it is, therefore, not a well-founded set; so proofs by induction are inapplicable, and things are more complicated.

However, $\mathcal{V}$ is a continuous function. (If we chose, we could write it

$$\mathcal{V} \;=\; \lambda E\lambda\rho.[\;\ldots\;].$$

This would be a recursive definition.) As usual, we may define the function Ξ:

$\Xi \;=\; \lambda\mathcal{V}\lambda E\lambda\rho.[\;\ldots\;]$

and the function $\mathcal{V}$ is a fixed point of Ξ. So

$$\mathcal{V} \;=\; \mathit{fix}\,\Xi \;=\; \bigsqcup_{n=0}^{\infty} \Xi^{n}(\bot).$$

Of course, the functionality of $\mathcal{V}$ is given by

$\mathcal{V}$: [Ex→[[Id→E]→E]

where E = [E→E] and Ex = Id +[Id × Ex]+[Ex × Ex], and so Ξ is an element of the domain

[[Ex→[[Id→E]→E]]→[Ex→[[Id→E]→E]]]

and the particular fixed point operator *fix* that we want is an element of the domain

[[[Ex→[[Id→E]→E]]→[Ex→[[Id→E]→E]]]→[Ex→[[Id→E]→E]]]

which, as Scott says somewhere [49], is a domain somewhat removed from everyday experience. But all the domains we have written are continuous lattices, familiar or otherwise, and therefore retracts of Pω and the functions are all continuous. So the theory guarantees that a minimal fixed point of Ξ exists, and that *fix*Ξ is it.

Syntactic Recursion Consider the equation $E = \ulcorner E_1(E) \urcorner$ where now E_1 can be any element of Ex, not necessarily an identifier. As we have already stated, $E = \mathit{fix}_{Ex}(x)$ where $x = \lambda u.\ulcorner E_1(u) \urcorner$. What can be said about the *semantic* value of E?

Obviously

$$\mathcal{V}[\![E]\!]\rho \;\equiv\; \mathcal{V}[\![\mathit{fix}_{Ex}(x)]\!]\rho.$$

We would like to show that this is the same as

$$\mathit{fix}_{E}(\mathcal{V}[\![E_1]\!]\rho).$$

So we wish to prove:

8.29. Theorem.

$\mathscr{V}[\![fix_{Ex}(\lambda u{:}Ex.\ulcorner E_1(u)\urcorner)]\!]\rho \equiv fix_E(\mathscr{V}[\![E_1]\!]\rho)$.

Proof:

$$\text{LHS} \equiv \mathscr{V}[\![\bigsqcup_{n=0}^{\infty}(\lambda u{:}Ex.\ulcorner E_1(u)\urcorner)^n[\![\bot_{Ex}]\!]]\!]\rho$$

$$\equiv \mathscr{V}[\![\bigsqcup_{n=0}^{\infty}\ulcorner E_1{}^n(\bot_{Ex})\urcorner]\!]\rho.$$

Now $\mathscr{V}$ is continuous; and, since $(\lambda u{:}Ex.\ulcorner E_1(u)\urcorner)$ is monotonic, the set $\{\ulcorner E_1{}^n(\bot_{Ex})\urcorner | n\geq 0\}$ is directed; so

$$\text{LHS} \equiv (\bigsqcup_{n=0}^{\infty}\mathscr{V}[\![E_1{}^n(\bot_{Ex})]\!])\rho$$

$$\equiv \bigsqcup_{n=0}^{\infty}(\mathscr{V}[\![E_1{}^n(\bot_{Ex})]\!]\rho)$$

since application is continuous in both variables and $\{\mathscr{V}[\![E_1{}^n(\bot_{Ex})]\!] | n\geq 0\}$ is directed; and

$$\text{RHS} \equiv \bigsqcup_{n=0}^{\infty}(\mathscr{V}[\![E]\!]\rho)^n(\bot_E).$$

We shall now prove that corresponding terms in these two series are equal, by induction on n.

The basis step, for $n=0$, follows immediately from the definition of $\mathscr{V}$:

$$\mathscr{V}[\![\bot_{Ex}]\!]\rho = \bot_E.$$

Now assume

$$\mathscr{V}[\![E_1{}^m(\bot_{Ex})]\!]\rho = (\mathscr{V}[\![E_1]\!]\rho)^m(\bot_E).$$

Then

$$\mathcal{V}[\![E_1{}^{m+1}(\bot_{Ex})]\!]\rho \equiv \mathcal{V}[\![E_1(E_1{}^{m}(\bot_{Ex}))]\!]\rho$$

$$\equiv (\mathcal{V}[\![E_1]\!]\rho)(\mathcal{V}[\![E_1{}^{m}(\bot_{Ex})]\!]\rho) \qquad \text{(by 8.28)}$$

$$\equiv (\mathcal{V}[\![E_1]\!]\rho)((\mathcal{V}[\![E_1]\!]\rho)^{m}(\bot_E)) \qquad \text{(hypothesis)}$$

$$\equiv (\mathcal{V}[\![E_1]\!]\rho)^{m+1}(\bot_E).$$

So, by induction, all corresponding terms in the two series are equal, and the l.u.b.'s are therefore also equal.

This theorem justifies the "rewriting rule" for evaluating fixed points, which is often used to evaluate recursive functions by hand. This says that we can obtain an arbitrarily good approximation to the value of an expression (if the value is an element of a flat lattice such as N this means that we can get the correct answer) by writing out sufficient of the infinite expression for the fixed point in the *expression* domain Ex. For example, we can evaluate *fact* 2, where *fact* is the fixed point of

$$\lambda\, fact.\lambda n.n=0 \to 1,\ n \times fact(n-1)$$

by the expression

$$(\lambda n.n=0\to 1, n\times(\lambda n.n=0\to 1, n\times(\lambda n.n=0\to 1, n\times(\bot_{Ex})(n-1))(n-1))(n-1))(2).$$

This is the "syntactic" way of doing fixed points. It works because if we choose the degree of approximation right in any particular case the $\bot_{Ex}$ disappears from the computation before we have to work with it. We have proved this way equivalent to the semantic method - that is, finding the fixed point in the *value* domain E of the single (finite) expression E_1 when we interpret it as a function in

$[E \to E]$.

(For a more formally syntactic approach to this matter, see Stephen Ward's presentation of *-conversion [67]. His * is our $\perp_{Ex}$.)

A Comment on Referential Transparency

The language we have studied in this chapter has pleasantly regular properties. A simple structural induction suffices to show, for example, that all the occurrences of a variable denote the same value (that is, for $\ulcorner \lambda I.E \urcorner$ all free occurrences of I in E denote the same value). Since the conversion rules are valid, we may introduce new variables to help in our analysis (since $\ulcorner E \text{ where } I = E_1 \urcorner$ is synonymous with $\ulcorner (\lambda I.E)E_1 \urcorner$, and λ-abstraction is freely allowed by the validity of the β-conversion rule). The λ-calculus, in fact, exhibits all the properties we group together under the name "referential transparency". (These properties are compromised, though not to the point of uselessness, if we adopt the call-by-value form of the equation for abstraction, given in 8.27.) This kind of language is very convenient for the purposes of mathematical argument and proofs - as witness the fact that we have used a very similar language (LAMBDA) as our own metalanguage.

We are now about to turn to consideration of languages in which this property (if it is exhibited at all) is less obvious. We shall later have to consider the effect of this on mathematical argument with these languages, such as when we try to prove the correctness of programs written in them.

Chapter 9

A SIMPLE ALGEBRAIC LANGUAGE OF FLOW DIAGRAMS

Languages with State

We now move on to consider languages in which there is some concept of a machine *state* which is altered by *commands*. The paradigm of such commands is of course the assignment statement, and we shall be considering the semantics of that in some detail later on. For the present, however, we shall not be concerned with details of how the state changes. All we shall assume is, firstly, that the state may change and, secondly, that such a change may affect the "value" of some expressions. This gives a kind of flowchart language, though we shall not go into details about what would be in the boxes in the flowchart. Nor shall we allow the full generality of control structure that may be expressed in such a flowchart: in fact at the start we shall not even have any loops.

These restrictions will be relaxed later. Our strategy in this discussion will be like that adopted by many devotees of Meccano:* we start with a very simple system, which we gradually augment by means of "accessory kits" as we become more ambitious.

Our first system will not even have any programmer-defined names. This means that we can dispense with the apparatus of environments for a while. What we do have are some primitive commands $\Phi \in \mathsf{Pri}$ and some primitive predicates $\Pi \in \mathsf{Pre}$. For now we

---

* The English and Canadian name for a children's construction kit. The Americans have something very similar, which they call "Erector Set".

shall assume that expressions do not have side effects: that is to say, the evaluation of an expression does not produce any change in the state. (Later on we shall extend our formalism to deal with side effects.)

The effect of executing a command is to change the state, and the appropriate "value" of a command is therefore a state transformation function. So if S is a set of states (whose precise nature we at present leave unspecified) then a command value γ will be an element of $[S \to S]$.

An expression will have a result (which initially we confine to T, the truth-value domain), and this result depends on the state. So in general an expression value ω is an element of $[S \to T]$: that is, an expression denotes a *function* which maps a state to a result.

We can fairly quickly specify the syntax and the value domains of our language:

Syntactic Categories

$\Gamma \in$ Cmd	(commands)
$E \in$ Exp	(expressions)
$\Phi \in$ Pri	(some primitive commands)
$\Pi \in$ Pre	(some primitive predicates)

Syntax

$\Gamma ::= \Phi \mid \texttt{dummy} \mid \texttt{if}\ E\ \texttt{then}\ \Gamma_0\ \texttt{else}\ \Gamma_1 \mid \Gamma_0;\Gamma_1$

$E ::= \Pi \mid \texttt{true} \mid \texttt{false} \mid \texttt{if}\ E_0\ \texttt{then}\ E_1\ \texttt{else}\ E_2$

Here, $\ulcorner \Gamma_0;\Gamma_1 \urcorner$ is to be used for sequencing; $\ulcorner \texttt{if}\ E\ \texttt{then}\ \Gamma_0\ \texttt{else}\ \Gamma_1 \urcorner$ is the conditional command;

⌜if E_0 then E_1 else E_2⌝ is the conditional expression.

Value Domains

$\beta \in T$ (truth values)

(Note that *true* and *false* are the values in T corresponding to true and false in the programming language.)

$\sigma \in S$ (machine states)

We also use

$\gamma \in [S \to S]$ (command values)

$\omega \in [S \to T]$ (expression values)

Before we give the semantic functions, we define the conditional operator as follows.

9.1. Definition. For $x \in E$, where E is a domain containing T as a summand, and $y, z \in D$,

$$x \to y,z \quad \text{has value} \begin{cases} y \text{ if } (x|T) \equiv \mathit{true} \\ z \text{ if } (x|T) \equiv \mathit{false} \\ \bot_D,\ \top_D \text{ or } ?_D \text{ if } (x|T) \equiv \bot_T,\ \top_T \\ \text{or } ?_T \text{ respectively.} \end{cases}$$

(If $x \in T$ the same definition applies, with x replacing occurrences of $(x|T)$.)

Note that this is the "completely strict" version of the conditional operator, corresponding to the $\bar{\supset}$ operator in Chapter 7. We shall consider a possible alternative definition, related more to LAMBDA's $\supset$, later.

Semantic Functions. We can now give the semantic functions for our language. There are two functions: one for commands and one for expressions.

$\mathscr{C}$: [Cmd → [S→S]]

$\mathscr{C}[\![\Phi]\!]$ = a given completely strict γ associated with Φ (9.2)

$\mathscr{C}[\![\text{dummy}]\!] = I$ (9.3)

$\mathscr{C}[\![\text{if E then } \Gamma_0 \text{ else } \Gamma_1]\!] = \lambda\sigma.\mathscr{E}[\![E]\!]\sigma \to \mathscr{C}[\![\Gamma_0]\!]\sigma, \mathscr{C}[\![\Gamma_1]\!]\sigma$ (9.4)

$\mathscr{C}[\![\Gamma_0;\Gamma_1]\!] = \mathscr{C}[\![\Gamma_1]\!] \circ \mathscr{C}[\![\Gamma_0]\!]$ (9.5)

Remember that application, denoted by juxtaposition, associates to the left, and takes precedence over all other operators. The right hand sides of these equations denote elements in [S→S]. 9.2 deals with the primitive commands: they all denote particular state transformations, which we do not explore further. 9.3 says that the dummy command changes nothing. 9.4 is for the conditional command: we explain it by considering what happens when the function it describes is applied to a state σ.

$\mathscr{C}[\![\text{if E then } \Gamma_0 \text{ else } \Gamma_1]\!]\sigma = \mathscr{E}[\![E]\!]\sigma \to \mathscr{C}[\![\Gamma_0]\!]\sigma, \mathscr{C}[\![\Gamma_1]\!]\sigma.$

$\mathscr{E}[\![E]\!]$ is applied to σ, and the result is used to determine whether $\mathscr{C}[\![\Gamma_0]\!]\sigma$ or $\mathscr{C}[\![\Gamma_1]\!]\sigma$, or some improper value, is the overall result. (We shall see later that it is unusual to have several occurrences of the same σ in one equation, because of the impracticality of remembering a complete state for use more than once; here, however, there is no problem, as the evaluation of the expression E does not change the state.)

9.5, which describes a sequence of commands, uses functional composition; so

$\mathscr{C}[\![\Gamma_0;\Gamma_1]\!]\sigma \;=\; (\mathscr{C}[\![\Gamma_1]\!]\circ\mathscr{C}[\![\Gamma_0]\!])\sigma \;=\; \mathscr{C}[\![\Gamma_1]\!](\mathscr{C}[\![\Gamma_0]\!]\sigma)$

The expressions have a similar function definition:

$\mathscr{E}$: [Exp → [S→T]]

$\mathscr{E}[\![\Pi]\!]$ = a given completely strict ω associated with Π (9.6)

$\mathscr{E}[\![\text{true}]\!]$ = $strict(\lambda\sigma.true)$ (9.7)

$\mathscr{E}[\![\text{false}]\!]$ = $strict(\lambda\sigma.false)$ (9.8)

$\mathscr{E}[\![\text{if } E_0 \text{ then } E_1 \text{ else } E_2]\!]$ =
$\lambda\sigma.\,\mathscr{E}[\![E_0]\!]\sigma\rightarrow\mathscr{E}[\![E_1]\!]\sigma,\mathscr{E}[\![E_2]\!]\sigma.$ (9.9)

The right hand sides define elements of [S→T]. 9.6 deals with the primitive predicates, whatever they may be. 9.7 and 9.8 are for the boolean constants, and give the appropriate truth value, provided that the state is proper; in these equations the function *strict* is as defined in 8.26 above. So, for example, if σ is proper,

$\mathscr{E}[\![\text{true}]\!]\sigma$ = *true*.

9.9 describes the conditional expression and is very similar to 9.4 except that the overall value is now a truth value rather than a state.

As usual, we present the complete definition of the language as a table (Table 9.1).

An Alternative Definition of the Conditional Operator

(In this section, for simplicity's sake, we shall assume that our domains do *not* contain an error element ?.)

We have adopted the "completely strict" conditional, for which $\top \rightarrow p,q \equiv \top$ and $\bot \rightarrow p,q \equiv \bot$. This

Table 9.1: Simple Algebraic Language of Flow Diagrams

Syntactic Categories

$\Gamma \in$ Cmd	(commands
$E \in$ Exp	(expressions)
$\Phi \in$ Pri	(some primitive commands)
$\Pi \in$ Pre	(some primitive predicates)

Syntax

Γ ::= Φ | dummy | if E then Γ_0 else Γ_1 | $\Gamma_0;\Gamma_1$

E ::= Π | true | false | if E_0 then E_1 else E_2

Value Domains

$\beta \in$ T	(truth values; *true*, *false* $\in$ T)
$\sigma \in$ S	(machine states)
$\gamma \in$ [S→S]	(command values)
$\omega \in$ [S→T]	(expression values)

Semantic Functions

$\mathscr{C}$: [Cmd → [S→S]]

$\mathscr{C}[\![\Phi]\!]$ = a given completely strict γ associated with Φ (9.2)

$\mathscr{C}[\![\text{dummy}]\!]$ I (9.3)

$\mathscr{C}[\![\text{if E then }\Gamma_0\text{ else }\Gamma_1]\!] = \lambda\sigma.\mathscr{E}[\![E]\!]\sigma \rightarrow \mathscr{C}[\![\Gamma_0]\!]\sigma, \mathscr{C}[\![\Gamma_1]\!]\sigma$ (9.4)

$\mathscr{C}[\![\Gamma_0;\Gamma_1]\!] = \mathscr{C}[\![\Gamma_1]\!] \circ \mathscr{C}[\![\Gamma_0]\!]$ (9.5)

$\mathscr{E}$: [Exp → [S→T]]

$\mathscr{E}[\![\Pi]\!]$ = a given completely strict ω associated with Π (9.6)

$\mathscr{E}[\![\text{true}]\!] = strict(\lambda\sigma.true)$ (9.7)

$\mathscr{E}[\![\text{false}]\!] = strict(\lambda\sigma.false)$ (9.8)

$\mathscr{E}[\![\text{if }E_0\text{ then }E_1\text{ else }E_2]\!] =$
$\lambda\sigma.\mathscr{E}[\![E_0]\!]\sigma \rightarrow \mathscr{E}[\![E_1]\!]\sigma, \mathscr{E}[\![E_2]\!]\sigma.$ (9.9)

definition is usually simple to work with, though it does imply that $x \to p,p \not\equiv p$ if x is not proper. Other definitions are also possible, for example one for which $\top \to p,q \equiv p \sqcup q$. In this case, $\lambda p.\lambda x.x \to p,p$ behaves much more like the combinator K (see Exercise 2 of Chapter 5) though still $(\lambda p.\lambda x.x \to p,p)(\bot) \equiv \bot$. With the completely strict definition, $\lambda p.\lambda x.x \to p,p$ behaves like a "completely strict K", K′, such that

$$\text{K}'ab = \begin{cases} a \text{ if } b \text{ is proper} \\ b \text{ otherwise.} \end{cases}$$

The completely strict definition is satisfactory for our languages and, as it is the simpler to use, we shall adopt it. The other form (the so-called "additive conditional") might, however, be more suitable for other kinds of language. There are several domains of basic values, such as the truth values or the integers - the kind of values which we expect to get printed out as answers, and from which all our other domains are constructed - and for our languages these are all flat lattices. Once we have one answer, to get another one too amounts to a contradiction. But this would not be so if we were allowed multi-valued answers - sets of valid answers, such as we introduced in our discussion of LAMBDA and Pω (page 124) - for then to produce another answer would, of course, simply be to increase the amount of information without leading to inconsistency.

Let us look a little more closely at this issue by considering an example discussed by Stephen Ward [67]. Consider the family of functions f_n such that

$$f_n(x) = \begin{cases} 0 \text{ if } x=n \\ \bot \text{ otherwise.} \end{cases}$$

We may define a function *Whichf*(f) such that

$Whichf(f_n) = n$.

That is to say, *Whichf*(f) seeks a value of x for which $f(x)$ terminates. It does so by initiating evaluations of $f(x)$ for various values of x, using parallel processing or some simulation of parallelism, such as time-slicing, until one such evaluation terminates.

Such a function is of course computable, though it is not definable in the λ-calculus. (According to our Theorem 7.34, though, it ought to be LAMBDA-definable. One possible definition is

$\lambda f.(Y(\lambda h.\lambda x.(f(x) \supset x,\bot) \cup h(x+1)))(0).$)

Now consider the function g where

$$g(x) = \begin{cases} 0 \text{ if } x=3 \text{ or } x=4 \\ \bot \text{ otherwise.} \end{cases}$$

What happens if *Whichf* is applied to g? According to our informal definition of *Whichf* above, the answer given may be 3 or it may be 4. Which answer is given depends on the details of the multiprocessing scheduler or other mechanisms which would not be specified in the semantics of the language in which *Whichf* was defined.

As the LAMBDA-definition suggests, this state of affairs is accommodated in our theory by saying that the proper answer to *Whichf*(g) is $3 \sqcup 4$. The fact that in most implementations the computation terminates after just *one* of the two integers is found may be thought of as just another example of the approximate nature of most implementations. It is a fairly important approximation, however, as otherwise many more computations would continue forever.

In this kind of situation the additive conditional might well be very much more the natural candidate. For example, if we had the expression ⌜if *Whichf*(*g*) = 3 then *p* else *q*⌝, in which the result of the test would be ⊤ (since 3 and 4 are both valid solutions of *Whichf*(*g*)), we probably would require its value to be $p \sqcup q$ rather than ⊤; if so, this would lead us to use the additive conditional.

Corresponding with this choice of possible definitions for the conditional, there are also alternative definitions for the truth-value functions. Table 9.2 shows two truth-table definitions of the logical *or* function ∨. The first is the doubly strict version which we would adopt with our usual interpretation of ⊤; the second is the additive version. There is some choice in the completely strict version over the values in parentheses. We have chosen values which do not require parallel processing in the implementation.

The additive or embodies the notion that the result is *true* if one of the operands is *true*, regardless of what the other is. The result is *false* only if both operands are *false*. (We alluded to this notion in our introduction of McCarthy's abstract syntax in Chapter 8). There is also the basic assumption that either of the operand values is susceptible to sub-

$\vee$	$\bot$	*false*	*true*	$\top$
$\bot$	$\bot$	$\bot$	$\bot$	$(\bot)$
false	$\bot$	*false*	*true*	$\top$
true	$\bot$	*true*	*true*	$\top$
$\top$	$(\bot)$	$\top$	$\top$	$\top$

Doubly Strict or

$\vee$	$\bot$	*false*	*true*	$\top$
$\bot$	$\bot$	$\bot$	*true*	*true*
false	$\bot$	*false*	*true*	$\top$
true	*true*	*true*	*true*	*true*
$\top$	*true*	$\top$	*true*	$\top$

Additive or

Table 9.2. Definitions of or.

sequent refinement to a stronger value. $\top$, the value that is both *true* and *false*, arises if one of the operands "has second thoughts" about its value. However, since the value of x is irrelevant to that of $x \vee$ *true*, we still put $\top \vee$ *true* = *true*. The other values for improper operands, including the initially surprising $\bot \vee \top =$ *true*, follow from monotonicity.

In this fairly simple situation we have been considering computations for which the required answers are sets, and we have been regarding implementations which non-deterministically produce just one element from the required set as merely approximations to a full implementation. Notice that this is quite different from seeking to treat non-determinism explicitly. For this, every domain required in expressing the outcome of a non-deterministic computation - whether a domain of basic values, or functions, or states or whatever - has to be replaced by a *powerdomain* (so called because they have the same sort of relationship to domains as powersets have to sets). Each element of a powerdomain is a set of elements of the domain from which it is formed, and the idea is that in any particular execution of the non-deterministic computation just *one* element of this set will be arbitrarily chosen. The construction of a powerdomain therefore becomes another way of constructing new domains out of old (like the formation of sums, products and function spaces), and it becomes necessary to use it in recursive domain equations just like the others. Ensuring that this is possible, however, enormously complicates the theory, and we shall not consider powerdomains further in this course.

Interested readers are referred to a paper [39] by Gordon Plotkin, who originated the idea, or to an alternative exposition by Michael Smyth [55]. In any case, more work still needs to be done on the semantics of systems involving parallelism and non-determinism before the techniques are really applicable in practice.

Exercise

1. In the absence of side effects, an Algol 60 boolean procedure with one boolean parameter can be regarded as specifying a function from truth values to truth values. Draw the lattice [T→T], where T is the four-element lattice of truth values (that is, ignoring ?). Which of the 36 elements of [T→T] can be written as Algol 60 procedures? Take the alternative interpretation of ⊤ described in this section, and assume that there is a random generator of booleans available which will serve (in the light of our comments above) as an approximate implementation of ⊤. [Hints: remember that ⊥ is interpreted as the result of a non-terminating computation, and that call-by-name may be used to ignore a parameter completely.]

(In this section we have been interpreting $\top_T$ as a valid result, stronger than both *true* and *false*. So we must not simply introduce an error element ? between ⊥ and this ⊤, for we do not want *true* ⊔ *false* to be comparable with ?. To incorporate an error element into this scheme of things, therefore, we must also introduce a new maximal element. We shall fortunately avoid all these complications by sticking to our original plan and using the completely strict conditional.)

Two Important Properties

We can prove the following two theorems about our language; in both cases the proofs are simple structural inductions.

The first theorem concerns $\top$ which we have decided to treat in as simple a way as possible (for example by adopting the completely strict conditional). As we remarked earlier, some workers prefer to leave $\top$ out of their domains altogether, but we decided not to do this, as we preferred to develop the theory in the "classical" way using lattices, in particular $P\omega$. In applying the theory to ordinary programming languages (that is, those not involving the extra complications to deal with parallelism and nondeterminism) the choice is largely a matter of taste, for in practice the need to treat $\top$ never arises.

9.10. Theorem. Provided that the initial state to which a program is applied is not $\top$, and provided none of the primitive commands and predicates maps any proper state to $\top$, the value $\top$ never arises in the analysis of any program in the language.

The second theorem simply states that once something has failed to terminate nothing more can be done, and that once an error has happened it has happened. This is, therefore, an essential property of any sensible semantics.

9.11. Theorem. All commands and expressions in the language are completely strict.

We shall rely on these properties, and we shall assume that these theorems are proved again every time we add an extension to the language.

Commutativity and Idempotence

9.12. Commutativity Two commands γ_0 and γ_1 *commute* if $\gamma_0 \circ \gamma_1 \equiv \gamma_1 \circ \gamma_0$.

A command γ and an expression ω commute if $\omega \equiv \omega \circ \gamma$; that is, the expression has the same value before or after the command.

Two expressions always commute, since the evaluation of one cannot affect the other (this will change when we allow side effects).

We use the infix com to express commutativity.

9.13. Idempotence A command γ is *idempotent* if $\gamma \circ \gamma \equiv \gamma$. That is, something is idempotent if evaluating, or executing, it more than once causes no further change.

Properties of Conditionals

In this section we list some simple properties of the conditional operator. All may be simply proved, by cases of the possible values of the test part. In this section b denotes a truth value; other Italic letters may be elements of any appropriate domain; in particular they might be in $[S \to S]$ (for conditional commands) or in $[S \to T]$ (for conditional expressions). We assume that all commands and expression values are completely strict.

(Left factorisation:)

$$f \circ (b \to \gamma_1, \gamma_2) \equiv b \to f \circ \gamma_1, f \circ \gamma_2. \tag{9.13}$$

If γ commutes with ω then

$$(\lambda\sigma.\omega\sigma \to p\sigma, q\sigma) \circ \gamma \equiv (\lambda\sigma.\omega\sigma \to (p \circ \gamma)\sigma, (q \circ \gamma)\sigma). \tag{9.14}$$

$$b \to (b \to p\ q)\ (b \to r\ s)$$
$$\equiv\ b \to p,(b \to r,s)$$
$$\equiv\ b \to (b \to p,q),s$$
$$\equiv\ b \to r,s \qquad (9.15)$$

If ω commutes with γ_1 and γ_2,

$$(\lambda\sigma.\omega\sigma{\to}p\sigma,q\sigma)\circ(\lambda\sigma.\omega\sigma{\to}\gamma_1\sigma,\gamma_2\sigma)$$
$$\equiv (\lambda\sigma.\omega\sigma{\to}(p\circ\gamma_1)\sigma,(q\circ\gamma_2)\sigma) \qquad (9.16)$$

If ω_0 and ω_1 have proper values on σ_0,

$$\omega_1\sigma_0{\to}(\lambda\sigma.\omega_0\sigma{\to}p\sigma,q\sigma),(\lambda\sigma.\omega_0\sigma{\to}r\sigma,s\sigma)$$
$$\equiv \omega_0\sigma_0{\to}(\lambda\sigma.\omega_1\sigma{\to}p\sigma,r\sigma),(\lambda\sigma.\omega_1\sigma{\to}q\sigma,s\sigma) \qquad (9.17)$$

9.15 gives a simplification rule for nested conditionals; 9.16 gives a rule for allowing two conditionals to be collapsed into one; and 9.17 says when nested conditionals may be turned inside-out.

The while-loop

We come now to the first "accessory kit" by which we extend our language. We wish to add a command of the form

⌜while E do Γ⌝.

We want this to be such that ⌜while E do Γ⌝ means the same as ⌜if E then (Γ;while E do Γ) else dummy⌝. So if $\gamma' = \mathscr{C}[\![\text{while E do }\Gamma]\!]$, we want

$$\gamma' \equiv \lambda\sigma.\mathscr{E}[\![E]\!]\sigma{\to}\mathscr{C}[\![\Gamma;\text{while E do }\Gamma]\!]\sigma,I\sigma \quad \text{(by 9.3,9.4)}$$
$$\equiv \lambda\sigma.\mathscr{E}[\![E]\!]\sigma{\to}(\gamma'\circ\mathscr{C}[\![\Gamma]\!])\sigma,\sigma\ . \quad \text{(by 9.5)}$$

Now if we regard the right hand side of this equation as a function H of γ so that

$$H(\gamma) \equiv \lambda\sigma.\mathscr{E}[\![E]\!]\sigma{\to}(\gamma\circ\mathscr{C}[\![\Gamma]\!])\sigma,\sigma$$

then we need

$$\gamma' = H(\gamma').$$

Thus γ' is a fixed point of H; as our earlier discussions about fixed points have indicated, it is the *minimal* fixed point that we require, so we use our minimal fixed point operator *fix*:

$$\gamma' = \mathit{fix}\ H\ .$$

We therefore add to the *syntax*:

Γ ::= while E do Γ

and a new clause to the definition of the *semantic function* $\mathscr{C}$:

$$\mathscr{C}[\![\text{while E do }\Gamma]\!] = \mathit{fix}(\lambda\gamma.\lambda\sigma.\mathscr{E}[\![E]\!]\sigma\rightarrow(\gamma\circ\mathscr{C}[\![\Gamma]\!])\sigma,\sigma) \quad (9.18)$$

(Notice that to show that Theorem 9.10 still applies with this extension we need $\top$ to be an *isolated* element of S.) We shall examine the properties of this extension in a little while. First we extend a little further.

Auxiliary Equations and Syntactic Sugar

It is often desirable to add features to a language not so as to increase the semantic power, but simply to make the facilities that already exist easier to use. For example, for the λ-calculus we mentioned (in passing) the expression $\ulcorner$E where I = $E_1\urcorner$, which meant exactly the same as $\ulcorner(\lambda I.E)(E_1)\urcorner$ but whose meaning was sometimes more obvious, and therefore easier, for the user. Such additions are called "syntactic sugar". (The term was first used by Peter Landin. There is no generally accepted phrase for the opposite sort of construction; but a graduate student who had gone out to work in industry once wrote me a letter complaining of his experiences with "syntactic alum", which seems as good a term as any.)

There are two possible ways to add syntactic sugar to a language. We can add a new production to the syntax and a corresponding new semantic equation. This formally extends the language and, of course, complicates the kind of proof that scans the equations one by one. The alternative is to leave the "core language" quite alone, and to introduce the sugar by auxiliary syntactic equations. These specify how a program may be "desugared", by purely syntactic transformation, to give a program in the core language. We shall, from time to time, adopt either method. Indeed, sometimes we shall use both methods, giving both kinds of definition and proving them equivalent. This will enable us to have the best of both worlds: the semantics of the new construct will be available in an explicit semantic equation, but this equation need not be considered in any proof about the language, as every occurrence of the construct can be translated into an alternative version in which it does not appear.

As an example of an auxiliary equation, let us define the operator ~.

9.19. Definition. $\ulcorner\sim E\urcorner \equiv \ulcorner \text{if } E \text{ then false else true}\urcorner$.
With this definition, let us prove

$$\ulcorner \text{if } \sim E_0 \text{ then } E_1 \text{ else } E_2\urcorner \equiv \ulcorner \text{if } E_0 \text{ then } E_2 \text{ else } E_1\urcorner$$

Proof: Let $\omega = \mathscr{E}[\![\text{if } \sim E_0 \text{ then } E_1 \text{ else } E_2]\!]$ and, for $r = 0,1,2$, let $\omega_r = \mathscr{E}[\![E_r]\!]$. We wish to prove that

$\omega = \lambda\sigma.\omega_0\sigma \to \omega_2\sigma, \omega_1\sigma$

Now $\omega \equiv \lambda\sigma.\mathscr{E}[\![\sim E_0]\!]\sigma \to \omega_1\sigma, \omega_2\sigma$ (by 9.9)

$\equiv \lambda\sigma.\mathscr{E}[\![\texttt{if } E_0 \texttt{ then false else true}]\!]\sigma \to \omega_1\sigma, \omega_2\sigma$ (by 9.19)

$\equiv \lambda\sigma.(\omega_0\sigma \to \mathit{strict}(\lambda\sigma.\mathit{false})\sigma, \mathit{strict}(\lambda\sigma.\mathit{true})\sigma) \to \omega_1\sigma, \omega_2\sigma$ (by 9.7 and 9.8)

So apply both sides to some arbitrary σ. If this σ is improper, we may easily check that equal values are obtained; if σ is proper, we proceed by cases depending on the value of $\omega_0\sigma$. For example, if $\omega_0\sigma \equiv \mathit{true}$,

$\omega\sigma \equiv (\mathit{true} \to \mathit{strict}(\lambda\sigma.\mathit{false})\sigma\ \mathit{strict}(\lambda\sigma.\mathit{true})\sigma) \to \omega_1\sigma, \omega_2\sigma$

$\equiv \mathit{false} \to \omega_1\sigma, \omega_2\sigma$ (since σ is proper)

$\equiv \omega_2\sigma$

$\equiv \lambda\sigma.\omega_0\sigma \to \omega_2\sigma, \omega_1\sigma.$

The remaining cases are similar.

Exercise

2. Prove that $\ulcorner \sim(\sim E) \urcorner \equiv \ulcorner E \urcorner$.

The until command.

We define this extension as a further example of an auxiliary equation.

9.20. Definition. $\ulcorner \texttt{until } E \texttt{ do } \Gamma \urcorner \equiv \ulcorner \texttt{while } \sim E \texttt{ do } \Gamma \urcorner$

Exercise

3. Prove that the above definition is equivalent to the following alternative:

$\mathscr{C}[\![\texttt{until } E \texttt{ do } \Gamma]\!] \equiv \mathit{fix}(\lambda\gamma.\lambda\sigma.\mathscr{E}[\![E]\!]\sigma \to \sigma, (\gamma \circ \mathscr{C}[\![\Gamma]\!])\sigma).$

The repeatwhile Loop

The repeatwhile loop is very similar to the while loop, the semantic difference being that the body is executed once before the test expression is first evaluated. We may add to the syntax the production

Γ ::= Γ repeatwhile E

and, by an argument similar to the one we used for the while-loop, we concoct the following semantic equation.

$$\mathscr{C}[\![\Gamma \text{ repeatwhile } E]\!] = fix(\lambda\gamma.(\lambda\sigma.\mathscr{E}[\![E]\!]\sigma \to \gamma\sigma, \sigma) \circ \mathscr{C}[\![\Gamma]\!]) \tag{9.21}$$

We now state two theorems, the first of which could serve as an alternative definition by auxiliary equation.

9.22. Theorem. $\ulcorner\Gamma$ repeatwhile E$\urcorner \equiv \ulcorner\Gamma$;while E do $\Gamma\urcorner$.

9.23. Theorem.

$\ulcorner$while E do $\Gamma\urcorner \equiv \ulcorner$if E then($\Gamma$ repeatwhile E)else dummy$\urcorner$.

The proof of those two theorems will provide an example for the first of three general methods of proof which we can use to attack this kind of problem, and which we will now consider. In describing these methods, we shall in general use primes to decorate minimal fixed points.

First Proof Method - Fixed Point Properties

The general scheme of the first method is as follows. Let $\gamma_0' = fix(H_0)$ and $\gamma_1' = fix(H_1)$, and suppose we wish to show that $\gamma_0' \equiv \gamma_1'$. The idea is to show that each side is also a fixed point of the other side's kernel: that is, that each γ is a fixed point of the other H.

So we try to show, firstly, that

$\gamma_1' = H_0(\gamma_1')$

for then γ_1 is a fixed point of H_0, and so $\gamma_0' \sqsubseteq \gamma_1'$.

We then show

$\gamma_0' = H_1(\gamma_0')$

for then, similarly, $\gamma_1' \sqsubseteq \gamma_0'$; and hence $\gamma_0' \equiv \gamma_1'$.

Simple Example Suppose we have $f : [D_1 \to D_2]$ and $g : [D_2 \to D_1]$.

To prove $fix(f \circ g) = f(fix(g \circ f))$.

Proof: Let $u = fix(f \circ g)$ and $v = fix(g \circ f)$, so that we must prove $u = fv$.

$$\begin{aligned}(f \circ g)(fv) &\equiv f(g(f(v))) \\ &\equiv f((g \circ f)(v)) \\ &\equiv fv \text{ (since } v \text{ is a fixed point of } (g \circ f)).\end{aligned}$$

So fv is a fixed point of $(f \circ g)$, and hence $u \sqsubseteq fv$. Similarly $v \sqsubseteq gu$, and hence by monotonicity, $fv \sqsubseteq f(gu)$. But $f(gu) = (f \circ g)u = u$, since u is a fixed point of $(f \circ g)$, and so $fv \sqsubseteq u$.

Thus from these two inequalities, $fv \equiv u$ as required.

Proof of Theorems 9.22 and 9.23. We now use this method to prove the Theorems 9.22 and 9.23.

Let $\gamma = \mathscr{C}[\![\Gamma]\!]$ and $\omega = \mathscr{E}[\![E]\!]$. Also let

$H_0(\gamma_0) = (\lambda\sigma.\omega\sigma \to (\gamma_0 \circ \gamma)\sigma, \sigma)$ and $H_1(\gamma_1) = (\lambda\sigma.\omega\sigma \to \gamma_1\sigma, \sigma) \circ \gamma$.

So

$fix(H_0) = \mathscr{C}[\![\texttt{while E do } \Gamma]\!]$

$fix(H_1) = \mathscr{C}[\![\Gamma \texttt{ repeatwhile E}]\!]$.

Let $\gamma_0' = \mathit{fix}(H_0)$ and $\gamma_1' = \mathit{fix}(H_1)$, and let $\gamma_2 = \lambda\sigma.\omega\sigma\to\gamma_1'\sigma,\sigma$. So our theorems now become:

$$\gamma_1' = \gamma_0'\circ\gamma \tag{9.24}$$

$$\gamma_0' = \gamma_2. \tag{9.25}$$

Proof:

$\gamma_1' = H_1(\gamma_1')$ (fixed point of H_1)

$\quad = (\lambda\sigma.\omega\sigma\to\gamma_1\sigma,\sigma)\circ\gamma_1'.$ (definition of H_1)

So $\gamma_1' = \gamma_2\circ\gamma.$ (definition of γ_2) (9.26)

$H_0(\gamma_2) = \lambda\sigma.\omega\sigma\to(\gamma_2\circ\gamma)\sigma,\sigma$ (definition of H_0)

$\quad = \lambda\sigma.\omega\sigma\to\gamma_1'\sigma,\sigma$ (by 9.26)

$\quad = \gamma_2.$ (definition of γ_2)

So γ_2 is a fixed point of H_0; so $\gamma_0' \sqsubseteq \gamma_2.$ (9.27)

This result half proves 9.25. Now we turn our attention back to 9.24.

$H_1(\gamma_0'\circ\gamma)$ $(\lambda\sigma.\omega\sigma\to(\gamma_0'\circ\gamma)\sigma\ \sigma)\circ\gamma$ (definition of H_1)

$H_0(\gamma_0')\circ\gamma$ (definition of H_0)

$\gamma_0'\circ\gamma.$ (fixed point of H_0)

So $\gamma_0'\circ\gamma$ is a fixed point of H_1; so $\gamma_1' \sqsubseteq \gamma_0'\circ\gamma.$ (9.28)

Now we take a slight shortcut:

$\gamma_2 = \lambda\sigma.\omega\sigma\to\gamma_1'\sigma,\sigma$ (definition of γ_2)

$\quad \sqsubseteq \lambda\sigma.\omega\sigma\to(\gamma_0'\circ\gamma)\sigma,\sigma$ (9.28 and monotonicity)

$\quad = H_0(\gamma_0')$ (definition of H_0)

$\quad = \gamma_0'.$ (fixed point of H_0)

So $\gamma_2 \sqsubseteq \gamma_0'.$ (9.29)

So, from 9.27 and 9.29, we have $\gamma_2 \equiv \gamma_0'$, which proves 9.25.

Hence $\gamma_2 \circ \gamma \equiv \gamma_0' \circ \gamma$, and so by 9.26 we have $\gamma_1' \equiv \gamma_0' \circ \gamma$, which is 9.24.

Comparison with Recursion Induction The method we have just described is somewhat similar to McCarthy's technique of *Recursion Induction* [32]. Our method proves $fix(H_0) \equiv fix(H_1)$ by showing that each side is a fixed point of the function on the other. Recursion Induction (as expressed in our notation) proves $\gamma_1' \equiv \gamma_2'$ by the following method:

Find H such that

1. γ_1' is a fixed point of H;
2. γ_2' is a fixed point of H;
3. $fix(H)$ is "total": that is, for all x, $fix(H)(x) \neq \bot$.

(Establishing point (3) requires a proof by induction.) This technique relies on the domain of the arguments and results of γ_1', γ_2' and $fix(H)$ being a flat lattice, and also assumes that the value $\top$ can never arise. For then (3) implies that $fix(H)$ is as strong as it could "possibly" be: that is, $fix(H)$ is not only the *minimal* fixed point but also the *maximal* one, and therefore the *only* one. So $\gamma_1' \equiv \gamma_2' \equiv fix(H)$.

Second Proof Method - Numerical Induction

We illustrate the next two methods with proofs of the following theorem.

9.30. Theorem. If f is strict and $f \circ h = g \circ f$, then $fix\ g = f(fix\ h)$.

Proof: Our second proof method is ordinary numerical induction.

Inductive hypothesis: assume for some $n \geq 0$, $g^n(\bot) = f(h^n(\bot))$.

$$g^{n+1}(\bot) = g(g^n(\bot)) = g(f(h^n(\bot)))$$

$$= f(h(h^n(\bot)))$$

$$= f(h^{n+1}(\bot)).$$

But, since f is strict, the hypothesis holds for $n = 0$. So, by induction, for all n, $g^n(\bot) = f(h^n(\bot))$.

Now $\{h^n(\bot) : n \geq 0\}$ is a directed set, since $\bot \sqsubseteq h(\bot)$ by definition of $\bot$, and if $h^{n-1}(\bot) \sqsubseteq h^n(\bot)$ then by monotonicity $h^n(\bot) \sqsubseteq h^{n+1}(\bot)$.

$$\text{So } fix\ g = \bigsqcup_{n=0}^{\infty} g^n(\bot)$$

$$= \bigsqcup_{n=0}^{\infty} f(h^n(\bot)) \qquad \text{(induction result)}$$

$$= f(\bigsqcup_{n=0}^{\infty}(h^n(\bot))) \qquad \text{(Continuity of } f\text{, since } \{h^n(\bot)\} \text{ is a directed set)}$$

$$= f(fix\ h).$$

Third Proof Method - Fixpoint Induction.

Our third method, called *fixpoint induction* (sometimes *computational induction*), is basically the μ-rule of De Bakker and Scott [2]. It is as powerful as numerical induction, but often simpler to apply. If we can find an assertion $q(x)$ such that

1. $q(\bot)$ holds;

2. if $q(x)$ holds then $q(H(x))$ holds too;

then we can infer

$q(fix\ H)$.

q is often some equality, or perhaps an inequality $\sqsubseteq$, and $q(fix\ H)$ is the desired theorem. (As we shall discuss below, not every assertion is admissible as q.) The method is discussed in some detail by Manna, Ness and Vuillemin [28].

Fixpoint induction is often used in a proof by the first of our three methods. As an example, we give another proof of Theorem 9.30.

Second Proof of 9.30:

1. $f(fix\ h) = f(h(fix\ h))$ (fixed point of h)
$\quad = g(f(fix\ h))$ (assumption).

So $f(fix\ h)$ is a fixed point of g; and hence $fix\ g \sqsubseteq f(fix\ h)$.

2. Using fixpoint induction, the assertion called $q(x)$ in our description of the technique is

$f(x) \sqsubseteq fix\ g$.

We assume $q(x)$ holds for some x, and prove that $q(h(x))$ also holds.

So assume $f(x) \sqsubseteq fix\ g$. Now

$f(h(x)) = g(f(x))$ (assumption)
$\sqsubseteq g(fix\ g)$ (inductive hypothesis, and monotonicity of g)
$= fix\ g$ (fixed point of g).

So $q(h(x))$ holds as required. Moreover, since f is strict, $f(\bot) = \bot \sqsubseteq fix\ g$, so $q(\bot)$ also holds. So, by fixpoint induction, $q(fix\ h)$ holds; that is, $f(fix\ h) \sqsubseteq fix\ g$.

So, from (1) and (2), $f(fix\ h) = fix\ g$ as required.

In fact we can prove 9.30 more simply still. Since the pair $\langle fix\ h, fix\ g\rangle$ is the least fixed point of the function

$$\lambda\langle x,y\rangle.\langle h(x),g(y)\rangle$$

we can use fixpoint induction on both fixed points simultaneously. That is to say, we find an assertion $q(x,y)$ such that $q(\perp,\perp)$ holds and such that assuming $q(x,y)$ we can prove $q(h(x),q(y))$; then we can infer $q(fix\ h, fix\ g)$. We illustrate this as follows:

Third Proof of 9.30: Our assertion $q(x,y)$ is

$$f(x) = y.$$

$q(\perp,\perp)$ obviously holds, since f is strict; so assume that $q(x,y)$ holds for some x and y. Then

$$\begin{aligned} f(h(x)) &= g(f(x)) && \text{(assumption)} \\ &= g(y) && \text{(hypothesis)} \end{aligned}$$

So $q(h(x),g(y))$ also holds; hence by fixpoint induction $q(fix\ h, fix\ g)$ holds: that is, $f(fix\ h) = fix\ g$ as required.

Inclusivity Note that not every kind of assertion is an admissible $q(x)$ for proofs by fixpoint induction. An example of one that is not is

$$q(x) \equiv \text{'}x \text{ is not total'},$$

that is

$$q(x) \equiv \exists y{:}y{\equiv}\mathrm{N} \wedge y \geq 0 \wedge x(y) \equiv \perp.$$

If this *were* admissible, we could easily show that the factorial function was not total. Let $H(f) = \lambda n.n{=}0 \rightarrow 1,\ n \times f(n-1)$. Then $q(\perp)$ obviously holds;

and assuming $q(x)$ holds we can prove $q(H(x))$; so fixpoint induction would give $q(\mathit{fix}\ H)$, which is false.

We can obtain a criterion for admissible assertions if we try to justify the technique of fixpoint induction using ordinary numerical induction. If $q(\bot)$ holds, and if from $q(x)$ we can prove $q(h(x))$, then a simple numerical induction shows that $q(h^n(\bot))$ holds for all $n \geq 0$. We want this to imply that $q(\bigsqcup_{n=0}^{\infty} h^n(\bot))$ holds too. Since $\{h^n(\bot)\ n \geq 0\}$ is directed, it can be seen that this implication is true provided that q is *inclusive*.

9.31. Definition. An assertion $q(x)$ is *inclusive* if for all directed subsets X of its domain,

$$\bigwedge\{q(x) \mid x \in X\} \Rightarrow q(\bigsqcup X).$$

(The notation $\bigwedge$P, where P is a set of assertions, means that every assertion in P is true.)

It is instructive to think of q as mapping its domain D, say, into T′, the two-element lattice $\{\mathit{true}, \mathit{untrue}\}$, where $\mathit{true} \sqsubseteq \mathit{untrue}$. Then q is *inclusive* if

$$\bigsqcup\{q(x) \mid x \in X\} \sqsupseteq q(\bigsqcup X) \quad \text{(for all directed } X \subseteq D)$$

Recall that q is *monotonic* if

$$\bigsqcup\{q(x) \mid x \in X\} \sqsubseteq (\bigsqcup X) \quad \text{(for all directed } X \subseteq D)$$

and q is *continuous* if

$$\bigsqcup\{q(x) \mid x \in X\} \equiv q(\bigsqcup X) \quad \text{(for all directed } X \subseteq D).$$

So fixpoint induction may be validly used only to prove *inclusive* assertions. Showing that an assertion is inclusive is sometimes tricky. Manna,

Ness and Vuillemin [28] give the following class ⟨AP⟩ of assertions which are always admissible.

⟨AP⟩ ::= ⟨AP⟩ ∧ ⟨AP⟩ | $\bar{y}$ ⟨EP⟩

⟨EP⟩ ::= ⟨EP⟩ ∨ ⟨EP⟩ | $Q(\bar{y})$ | $\alpha(x)(y) \sqsubseteq \beta(x)(y)$

where $Q(\bar{y})$ is any first order predicate and α and β are continuous functions. This shows that the usual simple kind of assertion is always admissible, namely a conjunction of equalities or inequalities between terms of the form $A(x)$ where A is continuous.

This technique of fixpoint induction is of central importance, and we shall be using it several times below.

Exercises. In these exercises, remember that all Γ and E are completely strict commands and expressions. (We say that Γ or E is strict, idempotent etc. if the corresponding γ or ω has that property.)

4. Show that ⌜while E do Γ_0; if E then Γ_1 else Γ_2⌝ ≡ ⌜while E do Γ_0;Γ_2⌝.

5. Show that ⌜(while E do Γ_0); (while E do Γ_1)⌝ ≡ ⌜while E do Γ_0⌝.

6. If Γ_1 commutes with Γ_0 and E, prove, by fixpoint induction or otherwise, that

⌜(while E do Γ_0);Γ_1⌝ ≡ ⌜Γ_1;(while E do Γ_0)⌝.

Side Effects

Up to now we have been assuming that though the value of an expression may depend on the state, evaluating an expression causes no change in the state: that is to say, expressions do not have side effects. (This, of course, does not prevent an implementation from changing the state of its own working storage when evaluating an expression; it merely insists that no change is detectable by the semantics of the language.) We now wish to remove this restriction, and doing so obliges us to change our formalism slightly.

Previously the value ω of an expression was an element of $[S \to T]$; that is, it was a function mapping a state to a result value. But now we want the evaluation of an expression in a state to produce not only a result but also a (possibly different) state. So now ω is to be an element of $[S \to [T \times S]]$. Command values are still simply state transformation functions, elements of $[S \to S]$ exactly as before; and of course the syntax of our language is unchanged.

Turning to the semantic functions, we first consider $\mathscr{E}$, the valuation function for expressions. This now has functionality

$$\mathscr{E} : [\mathrm{Exp} \to [S \to [T \times S]]]$$

and the various clauses in its definition are changed. $\mathscr{E}[\![\Pi]\!]$ is still some particular completely strict ω associated with Π, but note that ω is now an element of $[S \to [T \times S]]$, not of $[S \to T]$ as before. The equations for the truth-value constants are changed in the obvious way.

$$\mathscr{E}[\![\mathrm{true}]\!] = \mathit{strict}(\lambda\sigma.\langle \mathit{true}, \sigma\rangle) \tag{9.40}$$

$$\mathscr{E}[\![\mathrm{false}]\!] = \mathit{strict}(\lambda\sigma.\langle \mathit{false}\ \sigma\rangle) \tag{9.41}$$

Notice that evaluating these constants produces no side effects.

For the conditional expression, and the conditional command, we must arrange that the test expression is evaluated in the given state, and that the truth-value component of the result of this is used to select the appropriate arm of the conditional, which is then applied to the state resulting from the evaluation of the test. To specify this, it is convenient to define a new combinator, $\star$.

9.32. Definition. For $f \in [E \to [S \to D]]$ and $g \in [S \to [E \times S]]$, $f \star g$ is the element of $[S \to D]$ such that for any $\sigma \in S$,

$$(f \star g)\sigma = (f\omega)\sigma' \text{ where } \langle \omega, \sigma' \rangle = g\sigma.$$

That is to say, $\star$ may be thought of as taking the results of applying g to σ and supplying them one at a time to g. We shall take $\star$ to be less binding than application, so that $a(b) \star c(d)$ means $(a(b)) \star (c(d))$, and assume that it associates to the right, so that $(f \star g \star h)$ means $(f \star (g \star h))$.

To see how this works, let us look at the equation for the conditional expression

$$\mathscr{E}[\![\text{if } E_0 \text{ then } E_1 \text{ else } E_2]\!] = (\lambda\beta.\beta \to \mathscr{E}[\![E_1]\!], \mathscr{E}[\![E_2]\!]) \star \mathscr{E}[\![E_0]\!]. \tag{9.35}$$

Suppose the right hand side of this equation is applied to some $\sigma \in S$, so that we have to evaluate

$$((\lambda\beta.\beta \to \mathscr{E}[\![E_1]\!], \mathscr{E}[\![E_2]\!]) \star \mathscr{E}[\![E_0]\!])\sigma.$$

We first evaluate $\mathscr{E}[\![E_0]\!]\sigma$ to produce, say, $\langle \beta', \sigma' \rangle$. Then we must evaluate

$$((\lambda\beta.\beta \to \mathscr{E}[\![E_1]\!], \mathscr{E}[\![E_2]\!])\beta')\sigma'$$

which reduces to

$$(\beta' \to \mathscr{E}[\![E_1]\!], \mathscr{E}[\![E_2]\!])\sigma'.$$

So, provided β' is proper, it is used to select one or other of the arms, which is evaluated in the state σ'. The conditional command is defined in a precise-

Table 9.3. Simple Language of Flow Diagrams with Side Effects

Syntactic Categories

$\Gamma \in$ Cmd	(commands)
$E \in$ Exp	(expressions)
$\Phi \in$ Pri	(some primitive commands)
$\Pi \in$ Pre	(some primitive predicates)

Syntax

Γ ::= Φ | dummy | if E then Γ_0 else Γ_1 | $\Gamma_0;\Gamma_1$ |
while E do Γ | Γ repeatwhile E

E ::= Π | true | false | if E_0 then E_1 else E_2

Value Domains

$\beta \in T$	(truth values)
$\sigma \in S$	(states)
$\gamma \in [S \to S]$	(command values)
$\omega \in [S \to [T \times S]]$	(expression values)

Table 9:3 (continued)

Semantic Functions

$\mathcal{C}$: $[\mathrm{Cmd} \to [S \to S]]$

$\mathcal{C}[\![\Phi]\!] \equiv$ a given completely strict γ associated with Φ (9.33)

$\mathcal{C}[\![\mathrm{dummy}]\!] \equiv I$ (9.34)

$\mathcal{C}[\![\mathrm{if}\ E\ \mathrm{then}\ \Gamma_0\ \mathrm{else}\ \Gamma_1]\!] \equiv$
$(\lambda\beta.\beta \to \mathcal{C}[\![\Gamma_0]\!], \mathcal{C}[\![\Gamma_1]\!]) \star \mathcal{E}[\![E]\!]$ (9.35)

$\mathcal{C}[\![\Gamma_0;\Gamma_1]\!] \equiv \mathcal{C}[\![\Gamma_1]\!] \circ \mathcal{C}[\![\Gamma_0]\!]$ (9.36)

$\mathcal{C}[\![\mathrm{while}\ E\ \mathrm{do}\ \Gamma]\!] \equiv$
$\mathit{fix}(\lambda\gamma.(\lambda\beta.\beta \to \gamma \circ \mathcal{C}[\![\Gamma]\!], I) \star \mathcal{E}[\![E]\!])$ (9.37)

$\mathcal{C}[\![\Gamma\ \mathrm{repeatwhile}\ E]\!] \equiv$
$\mathit{fix}(\lambda\gamma.(\lambda\beta.\beta \to \gamma, I) \star (\mathcal{E}[\![E]\!] \circ \mathcal{C}[\![\Gamma]\!]))$ (9.38)

$\mathcal{E}$: $[\mathrm{Exp} \to [S \to [T \times S]]]$

$\mathcal{E}[\![\Pi]\!] \equiv$ a given completely strict ω associated with Π (9.39)

$\mathcal{E}[\![\mathrm{true}]\!] \equiv \mathit{strict}(\lambda\sigma.\langle \mathit{true}, \sigma\rangle)$ (9.40)

$\mathcal{E}[\![\mathrm{false}]\!] \equiv \mathit{strict}(\lambda\sigma.\langle \mathit{false}, \sigma\rangle)$ (9.41)

$\mathcal{E}[\![\mathrm{if}\ E_0\ \mathrm{then}\ E_1\ \mathrm{else}\ E_2]\!]$
$(\lambda\beta.\beta \to \mathcal{E}[\![E_1]\!], \mathcal{E}[\![E_2]\!]) \star \mathcal{E}[\![E_0]\!]$ (9.42)

ly similar way, and so are the loop commands.

The remaining parts of the language definition are exactly as before, and the complete revised definition is given in Table 9.3.

A Note on Expressions and Commands

In our programming language we are making a distinction between expressions and commands. The only "value" a command can be said to have is a state transformation function (an element of $[S\to S]$). Some languages (Algol 68 [62], for example) make no such distinction, and commands, too, are endowed with a result in a more or less arbitrary fashion (so that their values are also in some domain such as $[S\to[V\times S]]$). We believe that the purpose of a command is to change something, and the primary purpose of an expression is to produce a value; and that clarity of thought is assisted by preserving the distinction. Indeed, if we confine ourselves to considering expressions without side effects, the distinction becomes even more pronounced.

All this reflects one of our prejudices about language design. Our semantic description method can, of course, accommodate either view.

Some Revised Definitions and Properties

We now give revised versions, in our new formalism, of definitions and properties 9.12 to 9.17.

9.43. Commutativity

1. A command γ and an expression ω *commute* if for all σ

$$(\omega\circ\gamma)\sigma \equiv \langle (\omega\sigma){\downarrow}1,\ \gamma((\omega\sigma){\downarrow}2)\rangle .$$

or, more informally, that γ does not affect the result part of ω and commutes with the state transformation in the same sense as that in which two commands commute.

2. Two expressions ω_0 and ω_1 commute if

ω_0 com $(\lambda\sigma.(\omega_1\sigma){\downarrow}2$ and ω_1 com $(\lambda\sigma.(\omega_0\sigma){\downarrow}2)$

where com is defined as in (1) above.

9.44. Idempotence ω is *idempotent* if $\lambda\sigma.\omega((\omega\sigma){\downarrow}2) \equiv \omega$; that is, if evaluating ω a second time in the state arising from the first evaluation gives the same result and does not change the state further.

9.45. Without Side Effects ω is *without side effects* if $\lambda\sigma.(\omega\sigma){\downarrow}2 \equiv I$; that is, if evaluating the expression does not change the state.

Properties of Conditionals Property 9.13 still holds, of course, but there is now the following similar property. If f is completely strict,

$$f\star(b\to\omega_1, \omega_2) \equiv b\to f\star\omega_1, f\star\omega_2. \tag{9.46}$$

(Corresponding to 9.15) If γ commutes with ω then

$$(\lambda\varepsilon.\varepsilon\to p, q)\star\omega\circ\theta \equiv (\lambda\varepsilon.\varepsilon\to p\circ\theta, q\circ\theta)\ \omega\ . \tag{9.47}$$

(Corresponding to 9.15) If ω is idempotent,

$$(\lambda\varepsilon.\varepsilon\to(\lambda\varepsilon.\varepsilon\to p,q)\star\omega,(\lambda\varepsilon.\varepsilon\to r,s)\star\omega)\star\omega$$

$$\equiv (\lambda\varepsilon.\varepsilon\to p,(\lambda\varepsilon.\varepsilon\to r,s)\star\omega)\star\omega$$

$$\equiv (\lambda\varepsilon.\varepsilon\to(\lambda\varepsilon.\varepsilon\to p,q)\star\omega,s)\star\omega$$

$$\equiv (\lambda\varepsilon.\varepsilon\to r,s)\star\omega\ . \tag{9.48}$$

(Corresponding to 9.16) If ω is idempotent and commutes with γ_1 and γ_2,

$$((\lambda\varepsilon.\varepsilon\rightarrow p,q)\star\omega)\circ((\lambda\varepsilon.\varepsilon\rightarrow\gamma_1,\gamma_2)\star\omega) \equiv (\lambda\varepsilon.\varepsilon\rightarrow p\circ\gamma_1,q\circ\gamma_2)\star\omega. \quad (9.49)$$

(Corresponding to 9.17) If ω_0 and ω_1 <u>commute</u> and have proper values on σ_0,

$$(\lambda\varepsilon.\varepsilon\rightarrow(\lambda\varepsilon.\varepsilon\rightarrow p,q)\star\omega_0,(\lambda\varepsilon.\varepsilon\rightarrow r,s)\star\omega_0)\star\omega_1$$
$$\equiv (\lambda\varepsilon.\varepsilon\rightarrow(\lambda\varepsilon.\varepsilon\rightarrow p,r)\star\omega_1,(\lambda\varepsilon.\varepsilon\rightarrow q,s)\star\omega_1)\star\omega_0. \quad (9.50)$$

Note also that $(k\star\omega)\circ\gamma \equiv k\star(\omega\circ\gamma)$. (9.51)

Exercises

7. Check that the other theorems of this chapter (9.10, 9.11, 9.22 and 9.23) still hold in the new formalism.

8. Devise a suitable semantic equation for the until-command defined earlier by auxiliary equation.

9. Repeat exercises 4 to 6, stating any new conditions that must be satisfied.

10. We have said that a function f is strict if $f(\bot) \equiv \bot$, and completely strict if in addition $f(?) \equiv ?$ and $f(\top) \equiv \top$. A function f on an n-tuple is *very strict* if $f\langle x_1,x_2,\ldots,x_n\rangle \equiv \bot$ when any of $x_i \equiv \bot$ $(1\le i\le n)$. State, justifying your answers where appropriate, which of these properties are exhibited by each of the following functions:

$\lambda x\lambda y.\langle x,y\rangle$;

$\lambda x.x+1$; $\lambda x.x+2$;

$Cond \equiv \lambda\langle x,y\rangle\lambda b.b\rightarrow x,y$;

$\lambda\langle x,y\rangle.x='y$ (where $='$ is a *continuous* equality function on some flat lattice, such that $(\bot='\top) \equiv (\top='\bot) \equiv \bot$);

$\lambda\langle f,x\rangle.f(x)$;

$\lambda\langle f,g\rangle.f\circ g$;

$\lambda x.x|\mathrm{D}$.

Chapter 10

ENVIRONMENTS AND OTHER EXTENSIONS

In this chapter we shall reintroduce programmer-defined names into our language of flow diagrams, and also make several other extensions. Let us first review the extensions we might wish to introduce:

1. Programmer-defined names and environments;
2. More value types and operations;
3. Abstraction and application;
4. Recursion;
5. Use of commands within expressions and *vice versa*;
6. Jumps;
7. Assignment;
8. Type checking, coercion etc.;
9. Explicit storage allocation and control;
10. Parallel Processing.

Not all these extensions will be covered in detail here. Indeed, as we have said, (10) is beyond the scope of this course. We shall not deal with (8) and (9) either, though here, too, work has been done (by Robert Milne [33], and by Peter Mosses [36] for Algol 60).

In this chapter we make extension (1), which will cause us to reformulate once more all the semantic clauses. Then we shall introduce nos. (2), (3) and, after a fashion, (5); we defer (4). In the next chapter we deal with jumps, one of the two principal imperative features: this will cause us to re-fashion everything yet again, and we shall then re-introduce the earlier extensions, together with re-cursion. Finally, the other imperative feature, assignment, gets its own chapter.

We shall be starting off from the latest version of our semantics, which allows expressions to have side-effects. However, many of these extensions (though not, for example, (5)) are equally applicable to the earlier version without side-effects.

Environments

We here reintroduce the syntactic category Ide of identifiers, and environments $\rho \in U = [\mathrm{Ide} \to D]$. As before, the microsyntax of identifiers is irrelevant, provided it allows us to settle questions of equality of two of them.

At present the only values we shall be able to denote are the truth values, so $D = T$. We take the opportunity to introduce here the name E for the domain of results of expressions: at present also $E = T$.

The only new syntactic constructs we have are the following:

$$E ::= I \mid \mathrm{let}\ I = E_0\ \mathrm{in}\ E_1$$

$$\Gamma ::= \mathrm{let}\ I = E\ \mathrm{in}\ \Gamma$$

That is, apart from allowing identifiers as expressions, the only new constructs are expressions and commands embodying initialised definitions of new names. Once the ρ's are introduced they get everywhere, however, and we must revise all the previous definitions of the semantic functions.

The value of a command or expression now depends on the environment, too; so the functionality of $\mathscr{C}$, previously $[\mathrm{Cmd} \to [S \to S]]$, is now $\mathrm{Cmd} \to U \to S \to S$. (From now on let us drop most of the square brackets round these expressions for domains of continuous function spaces; we shall assume that the arrows associate to the right, so that Cmd→U→S→S means [Cmd→[U→[S→S]]]. This association rule allows brackets to be dropped from domain expression just when the association rule for application allows parentheses to be dropped from the corresponding element expressions: if $f \in$ A→B→C→D, for example, and $a \in$ A, etc., we can write $d = fabc$.) Similarly, $\mathcal{E}$, previously of functionality Exp→S→[E×S], is now an element of Exp→U→S→[E×S].

The previous semantic equations are revised simply by inserting the environment parameter in the appropriate place. Thus, for example, the equation for the conditional command, previously

$$\mathcal{C}[\![\text{if } E \text{ then } \Gamma_0 \text{ else } \Gamma_1]\!] \equiv (\lambda\beta.\beta\rightarrow \mathcal{C}[\![\Gamma_0]\!], \mathcal{C}[\![\Gamma_1]\!])\star\,\mathcal{E}[\![E]\!]$$

now becomes

$$\mathcal{C}[\![\text{if } E \text{ then } \Gamma_0 \text{ else } \Gamma_1]\!]\rho \equiv (\lambda\beta.\beta\rightarrow \mathcal{C}[\![\Gamma_0]\!]\rho, \mathcal{C}[\![\Gamma_1]\!]\rho)\star\,\mathcal{E}[\![E]\!]\rho$$

so the environment of the overall construct is used for evaluating the components.

There are completely new clauses for the new syntactic constructs. The clause for identifiers is as follows:

$$\mathcal{E}[\![I]\!]\rho \equiv \mathit{strict}(\lambda\sigma.\langle \rho[\![I]\!], \sigma\rangle)$$

The result part is obtained from the environment and the state is unchanged. Notice that apart from the overall requirement, enforced by *strict*, that the state be treated completely strictly (that is, that Theorem 9.11 continue to apply), the result of an expression consisting of an identifier does not

Table 10.1. Flow Diagram Language with Environments

Syntactic Categories

$I \in$ Ide	(identifiers)
$\Gamma \in$ Cmd	(commands)
$E \in$ Exp	(expressions)
$\Phi \in$ Pri	(some primitive commands)
$\Pi \in$ Pre	(some primitive expressions)

Syntax

$$\Gamma ::= \Phi \mid \texttt{dummy} \mid \texttt{if } E \texttt{ then } \Gamma_0 \texttt{ else } \Gamma_1 \mid \Gamma_0;\Gamma_1 \mid$$
$$\texttt{while } E \texttt{ do } \Gamma \mid \texttt{let } I = E \texttt{ in } \Gamma$$

$$E ::= I \mid \Pi \mid \texttt{true} \mid \texttt{false} \mid \texttt{if } E_0 \texttt{ then } E_1 \texttt{ else } E_2 \mid$$
$$\texttt{let } I = E_0 \texttt{ in } E_1$$

Value Domains

T	(truth values)
$\sigma \in S$	(machine states)
$\gamma \in C = S \to S$	(state transformations)
$\varepsilon \in E = T$	(expression results)
$\omega \in W = S \to [E \times S]$	(expression "evaluations")
$\delta \in D = T$	(denotations)

Table 10.1 (continued)

Semantic Functions

$\mathscr{C}$: Cmd→U→C

$\mathscr{C}[\![\ \Phi\ ]\!]\rho \equiv$ a given completely strict γ associated with Φ (10.1)

$\mathscr{C}[\![\text{dummy}]\!]\rho \equiv I$ (10.2)

$\mathscr{C}[\![\text{if E then }\Gamma_0\text{ else }\Gamma_1]\!]\rho \equiv$
$(\lambda\varepsilon.\varepsilon\rightarrow\mathscr{C}[\![\Gamma_0]\!]\rho,\mathscr{C}[\![\Gamma_1]\!]\rho)\star\mathscr{E}[\![E]\!]\rho$ (10.3)

$\mathscr{C}[\![\Gamma_0;\Gamma_1]\!]\rho \equiv \mathscr{C}[\![\Gamma_1]\!]\rho\circ\mathscr{C}[\![\Gamma_0]\!]\rho$ (10.4)

$\mathscr{C}[\![\text{while E do }\Gamma]\!]\rho \equiv$
$\mathit{fix}(\lambda\gamma.(\lambda\varepsilon.\varepsilon\rightarrow\gamma\circ\mathscr{C}[\![\Gamma]\!]\rho,I)\star\mathscr{E}[\![E]\!]\rho)$ (10.5)

$\mathscr{C}[\![\text{let I = E in }\Gamma]\!]\rho \equiv$
$(\lambda\delta.\mathscr{C}[\![\Gamma]\!](\rho[\delta/I]))\star\mathscr{E}[\![E]\!]\rho$ (10.6)

$\mathscr{E}$: Exp→U→W

$\mathscr{E}[\![\ I\ ]\!]\rho \equiv \mathit{strict}(\lambda\sigma.\langle\rho[\![I]\!],\sigma\rangle)$ (10.7)

$\mathscr{E}[\![\ \Pi\ ]\!]\rho \equiv$ a given completely strict ω associated with Π (10.8)

$\mathscr{E}[\![\text{true}]\!]\rho \equiv \mathit{strict}(\lambda\sigma.\langle \mathit{true},\sigma\rangle)$ (10.9)

$\mathscr{E}[\![\text{false}]\!]\rho \equiv \mathit{strict}(\lambda\sigma.\langle \mathit{false},\sigma\rangle)$ (10.10)

$\mathscr{E}[\![\text{if }E_0\text{ then }E_1\text{ else }E_2]\!]\rho \equiv$
$(\lambda\varepsilon.\varepsilon\rightarrow\mathscr{E}[\![E_1]\!]\rho,\mathscr{E}[\![E_2]\!]\rho)\star\mathscr{E}[\![E_0]\!]\rho$ (10.11)

$\mathscr{E}[\![\text{let I = }E_0\text{ in }E_1]\!]\rho \equiv$
$(\lambda\delta.\mathscr{E}[\![E_1]\!](\rho[\delta/I]))\star\mathscr{E}[\![E_0]\!]\rho$ (10.12)

depend on the state. This may be contrary to some readers' expectations: in most programming languages names denote variables whose values can be changed by assignments and certainly *do* depend on the state of the store. But this is part of the semantics of the assignment operator, which we do not cover until Chapter 12. (Even then, to anticipate slightly, we shall say that the identifer denotes a *location*, and *which* location it denotes is independent of the state; the state affects only the *contents* of the location.)

The other new clause for expressions is as follows:

$$\mathcal{E}[\![\texttt{let } I=E_0 \texttt{ in } E_1]\!]\rho \equiv (\lambda\delta.\ \mathcal{E}[\![E_1]\!](\rho[\delta/I]))\star\ \mathcal{E}[\![E_0]\!]\rho$$

To see what this says, apply the right hand side to a state σ. E_0 is evaluated in the overall environment ρ and the original state σ: $\mathcal{E}[\![E_0]\!]\rho\sigma$ gives a value $\langle\varepsilon,\sigma'\rangle$, say. The result part, ε, is associated with the identifier I in a new environment, $\rho[\varepsilon/I]$, and the body of the expression, E_1, is evaluated in this modified environment and the state arising from the first evaluation of E_0: so the final value is given by $\mathcal{E}[\![E_1]\!](\rho[\varepsilon/I])\sigma'$. The new command clause is very similar.

The complete definition of our present language is given in Table 10.1.

In the equations of Table 10.1, notice that although the ρ parameter has been supplied and explicitly manipulated, the final argument, σ, is absent. This convention (for it is no more than that) helps to highlight one or two points about implementation. For example, it roughly indicates how much of the evaluation may be performed at compile time. This includes much of the mechanics concerning the environment.

though all matters concerning the state must wait till execution time (of course, as the use of the bound variable δ in $\rho[\delta/I]$ suggests, most actual values in the environment are not known until execution time). The absence of the symbol σ from the equations also helps to emphasise that we must normally ensure that the *same* state σ is not used at two arbitrarily separated points in a formula: that is to say, we must avoid defining the semantics so that implementation involves making a copy of the state of the machine, which is not economically feasible. (This was one of the few bugs in the definition of Algol 60 [38]: the effect of the statement $\ulcorner$if E then $\Gamma\urcorner$ when the result of E was *false* was said to be equivalent to the null statement. This called for making a copy of the initial state in order to undo any side effect of E.) This principle is not a logical necessity: an experiment [41] at the University of Newcastle, to design a "highly reliable" system, involves making a copy of the state before each section of program. After the section a test is performed to determine whether the effect is satisfactory; if so, the new state is adopted, but if not the system can revert to the initial state and discard the new one. The semantics of this would involve more than the "single thread" treatment of σ that we practise in the present equations; it is, of course, expensive in memory. The environment, on the other hand, may be much more freely manipulated, and we often revert to a previous environment, when for example we leave a block in a block-structured language.

In 10.7 our use of *strict* (as in 10.9 and 10.10) ensures that we can continue to assume that all commands and expressions are completely strict (considered as functions on states). This assumption also means that the question of call by name *versus* call by value, which gave us concern in Chapter 8, does not arise in 10.6 or 10.12: since everything is completely strict on the state, call by value semantics is obtained.

D, the domain of denotations, is so far very simple; it is simply T, so it is not reflexive. In fact, so far our language requires no reflexive domains at all (this may partly be because we have given no attention to the structure of S). As we increase the complexity of our language, we shall find that D and other domains will become reflexive. Already, however, we need the lattice theory to show that the fixed point expression in 10.5 is well-defined.

In the let definitions (10.6 and 10.12) the expression in the definition itself is evaluated in the outer environment. That is to say, a definition like

$$\ulcorner \texttt{let } I = \sim I \texttt{ in } \Gamma \urcorner$$

is not recursive. This is a language design choice. In fact we do not yet have much of a choice, as we do not yet know how to do recursion; but later we shall be able, if we wish, to redefine the semantics of these definitions to make them recursive. It is up to us.

Notice that the expression

$\ulcorner$let I = E_0 in $E_1\urcorner$

is very similar in effect to

$\ulcorner(\lambda I.E_1)(E_0)\urcorner$

in the λ-calculus. Now, however, we may have side effects; so we cannot simply replace occurrences of I in E_1 by the expression E_0, because then multiple evaluations of E_0 might cause multiple side effects. In other words, owing to side effects, the syntactic β-conversion rule is now no longer a correct implementation.

Suppose that we extend our programming language by introducing an operator $\ulcorner=\urcorner$, to test equality of two expressions. Now, because of side effects, we cannot say

$\ulcorner E = E\urcorner \equiv \ulcorner$true$\urcorner$

because the two evaluations of E might give different results. However, in the initialised definition we evaluate the expression (with its side effects) *only once*, at "definition time". The resulting value is denoted by I, and stays the same throughout the scope of the definition. Moreover, we have seen from 10.7 that the evaluation of a name causes no side effects. So though E = E might be false, the value of $\ulcorner$let I = E in I = I$\urcorner$ is always *true*, just so long as E has a proper value. Thus the use of initialised definitions brings us back some of the advantages of referential transparency. Of course, this particular discussion would not arise if we were still working in the earlier formalism in which expressions did not have side effects; however, even then, since the value of an expression still depends on the state, we could not assume that identical expressions, even in the same environment, always gave the same result.

For this reason, note that the Substitution Lemma (8.12) is *not* applicable to this language. Lemma 8.11 is, however, still valid.

Exercise

1. Extend our earlier definition of the language (without side effects) so as to incorporate names and environments.

More Value Types and Operators

The next extension we consider is to increase the richness of the space E (of expression values) and D (denotations), by allowing them to contain other types of values besides the truth values T. For example, we might well include the integers N, so that

$$E = D = T + N.$$

As soon as we have done this, we should check that it does not invalidate any of the apparatus we already have. In fact, now some of the small print in our definition of the conditional (9.1) comes into play, since T is now merely one summand of E. We also need some additional operators, to operate on values of these new types, producing results in E: '+' and '>' would be among the obvious candidates.

There is no great difficulty in this extension. If we wished to include an operator for addition over the integers, we could have a clause like

$$\mathcal{E}[\![E_0 + E_1]\!]\rho = \mathit{Add} * \mathit{le}\langle\ \mathcal{E}[\![E_0]\!]\ ,\ \mathcal{E}[\![E_1]\!]\ \rangle \qquad (10.13)$$

le, a new operator which we shall meet again, is a list evaluation operator. One possible definition is

$$\mathit{le}\langle \omega_0,\omega_1\rangle\sigma \quad \langle\langle \varepsilon_0,\varepsilon_1\rangle,\sigma_2\rangle$$

where $\langle \varepsilon_0,\sigma_1\rangle = \omega_0\sigma$

and $\langle \varepsilon_1,\sigma_2\rangle = \omega_1\sigma_1$.

le evaluates the two expressions in its argument one at a time, accumulating side effects. As defined here, it evaluates from left to right. We can similarly define le_n to evaluate an n-tuple in the same way, so that our original *le* is le_2. But le_n can also be defined to specify other orders of evaluation. One possible such definition is

$$\mathit{le}_n\langle \omega_0,\omega_1,\ldots,\omega_{n-1}\rangle\sigma = \langle\langle \varepsilon_0,\varepsilon_1,\ldots,\varepsilon_{n-1}\rangle\ \sigma_n\rangle$$

$$\begin{aligned} \text{where}\quad \langle \varepsilon_0,\sigma_{\pi_0+1}\rangle &= \omega_0\sigma_{\pi_0} \\ \langle \varepsilon_1,\sigma_{\pi_1+1}\rangle &= \omega_1\sigma_{\pi_1} \\ &\cdots \\ \langle \varepsilon_{n-1},\sigma_{\pi_{n-1}+1}\rangle &= \omega_{n-1}\sigma_{\pi_{n-1}}\ , \end{aligned}$$

where $\langle \pi_0,\pi_1,\ldots,\pi_{n-1}\rangle$ is some permutation of the integers 0 to n-1. This defines a list evaluation in which the order is unspecified. The point is that all issues concerned with the order of evaluation of operand lists are confined to the definition of one function le_n. Notice that both definitions we have so far given specify sequential evaluation in some order or other. However, if we tried to cope with concurrent operations, le_n would be where that was specified, too.

Add, in the semantic equation for addition (10.13), is of functionality $[E \times E] \to S \to [E \times S]$. $Add\langle x,y\rangle$ is a completely strict function on states such that $Add\langle x,y\rangle\sigma$ is equal to $\langle (x|N)+(y|N)$ in $E,\sigma\rangle$ if $(x|N),(y|N)$ and σ are proper, and the appropriate improper value otherwise. So, in 10.13, the operands are evaluated to produce a pair of results together with a state in which all side effects are accumulated; then, if everything is proper, the results are added and the sum, injected back into E, is paired with the final state.

Functions and Routines

There are two aspects to the introduction of functions and routines into our language. One concerns the normal idea of a function, considered as a parameterised expression representing a mapping; the other concerns the possibility of manipulating the value of a command, as distinct from simply executing it. We shall deal with these aspects separately.

We shall omit recursion for the present. Our basic strategy is to build up to a crisis over the treatment of jumps, after which all the equations will have to be altered (just as they were when we added ρ); so we feel that it is preferable to leave the extra complications of recursion until after that watershed. It might be asked why are we studying these inadequate formalisms (this one, and the other without side effects) in such detail at all. The answer is that later, in sufficiently simple cases, we shall still sometimes find it convenient to come back to them.

To return to the present: the constructs we add to the syntax to deal with functions and application are

$$E ::= \mathrm{fn}I.E \mid E_0(E_1) .$$

Their intended meaning will be fairly obvious. For manipulating commands we add

$$E ::= \mathrm{rt}\ \Gamma \quad \text{and} \quad \Gamma ::= \mathrm{call}\ E .$$

The expression $\ulcorner \mathrm{rt}\ \Gamma \urcorner$ denotes the value of the command Γ. Conversely, the command $\ulcorner \mathrm{call}\ E \urcorner$ where E denotes the value of some command, has the effect of executing that command.

The semantics of these new constructs will require an augmentation of the value domains D and E. We now let

$$\varepsilon \in E = T + C + [D \to W]$$
and $\delta \in D = E$.

The C (that is, $S \to S$) component of E is the command values; the $D \to W$ component (or $D \to S \to [E \times S]$) is the functions. Notice that when these latter are applied, and given a parameter value in D, an expression valuation in $S \to [E \times S]$, is produced, to be applied as usual to the state then regnant at the point of application: that is, as we should expect, a procedure is executed whenever it is applied - and the state at definition time is irrelevant.

Note that the domain E has now become reflexive, so for the first time we have to rely on our theory to demonstrate its existence.

The new clauses in the definitions of $\mathscr{C}$ and $\mathscr{E}$ are as follows:

$$\mathcal{E}[\![\mathtt{fn}\ \mathrm{I.E}]\!]\rho \equiv \mathit{strict}(\lambda\sigma.\langle(\lambda\delta.\mathcal{E}[\![\mathrm{E}]\!](\rho[\delta/\mathrm{I}])\ \mathtt{in}\ \mathrm{E}),\sigma\rangle) \qquad (10.14)$$

Notice that the result is in the [D→W] component of E. Notice also that evaluation of this expression causes no change in the state, and that the result part is independent of the state.

$$\mathcal{E}[\![\mathrm{E}_0(\mathrm{E}_1)]\!]\rho \equiv \mathit{Apply}*\mathit{le}\langle\mathcal{E}[\![\mathrm{E}_0]\!]\rho,\mathcal{E}[\![\mathrm{E}_1]\!]\rho\rangle \qquad (10.15)$$
$$\text{where}\quad \mathit{Apply}\langle\varepsilon_0,\varepsilon_1\rangle \equiv \mathit{strict}(\varepsilon_0|[\mathrm{D}\to\mathrm{W}])(\varepsilon_1)$$

le is the list evaluation operator. $\mathit{Apply}\langle\varepsilon_0,\varepsilon_1\rangle$ is an element of W, which is finally applied to the state resulting from the list evaluation.

$$\mathcal{E}[\![\mathtt{rt}\ \Gamma]\!]\rho \equiv \mathit{strict}(\lambda\sigma.\langle(\mathcal{C}[\![\Gamma]\!]\rho\ \mathtt{in}\ \mathrm{E}),\sigma\rangle) \qquad (10.16)$$

We bind up the environment, but do not apply the command to any state. The result is in the C component of E. The converse is

$$\mathcal{C}[\![\mathtt{call}\ \mathrm{E}]\!]\rho \equiv \mathit{Run}*\mathcal{E}[\![\mathrm{E}]\!]\rho \qquad (10.17)$$
$$\text{where}\quad \mathit{Run}(\varepsilon) \equiv \mathit{strict}(\varepsilon|\mathrm{C})$$

$\mathit{Run}(\varepsilon)$ is an element of C, which is applied to the state resulting from the evaluation of E.

The "in E" which appears in 10.14, 10.16 and elsewhere quickly gets tiresome. We shall continue to try to be rigorous about it, but probably in practice it would be preferable to make a convention which would enable us to omit it almost always (though it is not always easy to do so, particularly since these semantic definitions are sometimes supplied as input to computer programs, which would therefore have to be able to observe any such convention automatically.)

The use of *strict* in the definition of *Apply* and *Run* (10.15 and 10.17) is not absolutely necessary. It does, however, simplify the task of checking that Theorems 9.10 and 9.11 are still true after this latest extension, which now ought to be our tacit duty. If *strict* were not used in these places, there would be the possibility of finding some horrible function or command value from the environment and applying it directly to the state: in fact the theorems would no longer be true for *all* environments. But it would be possible to proceed by defining a condition for environments to be "suitable", and showing that all the environments which arose in practice satisfied this condition. However, this strategy produces extra complications (due to the reflexive nature of our domains) which we do not yet wish to face - we shall return to such problems in Chapter 13. Meanwhile, we adopt the simpler approach of fixing the definitions.

Exercise

2. Make these extensions to the language in the formalism without side effects.

Having defined these new clauses, the first result we shall prove concerns *immediate function application*.

10.18. Theorem. $\ulcorner(\text{fn}I.E_0)(E_1)\urcorner \equiv \ulcorner\text{let } I{=}E_1 \text{ in } E_0\urcorner$.

Proof: Let us assume the "left-to-right" definition for *le* (a similar argument can be used for the other). Then for any ρ and proper σ,

$$\mathcal{E}[\![(\mathtt{fn}\,I.E_0)(E_1)]\!]\rho\sigma \equiv \mathit{Apply{\star}le}\langle \mathcal{E}[\![\mathtt{fn}\,I.E_0]\!]\rho, \mathcal{E}[\![E_1]\!]\rho\rangle\sigma \qquad \text{(by 10.15)}$$

$$\equiv \mathit{Apply{\star}le}\langle \mathit{strict}(\lambda\sigma.\langle(\lambda\delta.\mathcal{E}[\![E_0]\!](\rho[\delta/I])\ \mathtt{in}\ E),\sigma\rangle), \mathcal{E}[\![E_1]\!]\rho\rangle\sigma \qquad \text{(by 10.14)}$$

$$\equiv \mathit{Apply}\langle(\lambda\delta.\mathcal{E}[\![E_0]\!](\rho[\delta/I])\ \mathtt{in}\ E),\varepsilon\rangle\sigma' \quad \text{where } \langle\varepsilon,\sigma'\rangle \equiv \mathcal{E}[\![E_1]\!]\rho\sigma$$

$$\equiv \mathit{strict}((\lambda\delta.\mathcal{E}[\![E_0]\!](\rho[\delta/I])\ \mathtt{in}\ E|[D\to W])(\varepsilon))\sigma'$$

$$\equiv \mathcal{E}[\![E_0]\!](\rho[\varepsilon/I])\sigma' \qquad \text{(since all expression values are already completely strict)}$$

$$\equiv (\lambda\delta.\mathcal{E}[\![E_0]\!](\rho[\delta/I]))\star\mathcal{E}[\![E_1]\!]\rho\sigma$$

$$\equiv \mathcal{E}[\![\mathtt{let}\ I=E_1\ \mathtt{in}\ E_0]\!]\rho\sigma.$$

But, since all expressions are completely strict, the result also holds for improper σ; so the two expressions are equivalent.

Exercise

3. Prove the following similar result for the other new clauses:

$$\ulcorner\mathtt{call(rt}\ \Gamma)\urcorner \equiv \Gamma.$$

We have only provided for parameterised expressions in our language, and so we do not have any primitive productions for parameterised routines (parameterised commands). However, we may easily construct appropriate forms. A suitable form for the definition of such a routine is

$$\ulcorner\mathtt{fn}\ I.\mathtt{rt}\ \Gamma\urcorner.$$

We have therefore

$$\mathcal{E}[\![\mathtt{fn}\ I.\mathtt{rt}\ \Gamma]\!]\rho \equiv \mathit{strict}(\lambda\sigma.\langle\lambda\delta.\mathit{strict}(\lambda\sigma.\langle\mathcal{L}[\![\Gamma]\!](\rho[\delta/I])\ \mathtt{in}\ E,\sigma\rangle)\ \mathtt{in}\ E,\sigma\rangle). \qquad (10.19)$$

Routine application is written

$\ulcorner$call $E_0(E_1)\urcorner$

and so we have

$$\mathscr{C}[\![\text{call } E_0(E_1)]\!]\rho \equiv Run \star Apply \star le\langle \mathscr{E}[\![E_0]\!]\rho, \mathscr{E}[\![E_1]\!]\rho\rangle . \tag{10.20}$$

Exercise

4. Prove the following result about immediate routine application:

$\ulcorner$call(fn I.rt Γ)(E)$\urcorner$ $\equiv$ $\ulcorner$let I=E in $\Gamma\urcorner$.

val and res

We now have several constructions which use expressions inside commands. These are:

$\ulcorner$if E then Γ_0 else $\Gamma_1\urcorner$
$\ulcorner$while E do $\Gamma\urcorner$
$\ulcorner$let I=E in $\Gamma\urcorner$
$\ulcorner$call E$\urcorner$.

But the only way we can have a command inside an expression is in $\ulcorner$rt $\Gamma\urcorner$. This merely makes the *value* of a command the result of an expression: there is no way to arrange for the *execution* of a command to affect the result of the overall expression. To provide this facility we introduce:

E ::= val Γ res E .

The semantic equation for this is quite simple. The idea is that we evaluate E in the state that results from executing the command Γ. So we have:

$\mathscr{E}[\![\texttt{val}\ \Gamma\ \texttt{res}\ E]\!]\rho \equiv \mathscr{E}[\![E]\!]\rho \circ \mathscr{C}[\![\Gamma]\!]\rho.$ (10.21)

It might be imagined that this kind of expression would most often be used as the body of a function. Indeed, in some languages this is the only context in which a construct corresponding to this would be allowed. But we are treating it as a perfectly general kind of expression, quite distinct from the concept of abstraction. Notice that the evaluation of this kind of expression in general always has a side effect.

Although this is the form of val expression we shall adopt for the time being, it is not quite as convenient as we would like it to be. We would like to be able to write

$$\ulcorner\texttt{val let}\ I = E_0\ \texttt{in}\ \Gamma$$
$$\texttt{res}\ E_1\urcorner.$$

How should we parse this? We might well want to be able to use I in E_1, so we would like to write

$$\ulcorner\texttt{val let}\ I = E_0\ \texttt{in}\ (\Gamma\ \texttt{res}\ E_1)\urcorner,$$

but this is not well-formed. If, instead, we wrote

$$\ulcorner\texttt{val}\ (\texttt{let}\ I = E_0\ \texttt{in}\ \Gamma)\ \texttt{res}\ E_1\urcorner$$

then E_1 would not be in the scope of the I. One solution is to write

$$\ulcorner\texttt{let}\ I = E_0\ \texttt{in val}\ \Gamma\ \texttt{res}\ E_1\urcorner$$

which has the desired effect, but becomes cumbersome with nested blocks. For example, the expression

$$\ulcorner\mathtt{val}\ (\mathtt{let}\ I_0 = E_0\ \mathtt{in}\ \Gamma_0;\ (\mathtt{let}\ I_1 = E_1\ \mathtt{in}\ \Gamma_1\ \mathtt{res}\ E_2))\urcorner$$

has to become

$$\ulcorner\mathtt{let}\ I_0 = E_0\ \mathtt{in}\ \mathtt{val}\ \Gamma_0\ \mathtt{res}\ (\mathtt{let}\ I_1 = E_1\ \mathtt{in}\ (\mathtt{val}\ \Gamma_1\ \mathtt{res}\ E_2))\urcorner.$$

Then, calling this whole expression E, we would have

$$\mathcal{E}[\![E]\!]\rho = (\lambda\delta_0.(\lambda\delta_1.\mathcal{E}[\![E_2]\!]\rho_{\delta_0\delta_1}\circ\mathcal{C}[\![\Gamma_1]\!]\rho_{\delta_0\delta_1}) \star\mathcal{E}[\![E_1]\!]\rho_{\delta_0}\circ\mathcal{C}[\![\Gamma_0]\!]\rho_{\delta_0})\star\mathcal{E}[\![E_0]\!]\rho$$

where $\rho_{\delta_0} = \rho[\delta_0/I_0]$
and $\rho_{\delta_0\delta_1} = \rho_{\delta_0}[\delta_1/I_1]$.

Later, we shall be able to improve on this cumbrousness, but we shall tolerate it for now.

Chapter 11

JUMPS AND CONTINUATIONS

The two main imperative features of programming languages are jumps and assignments. Assignments are the commands which, above all, effect changes of state: we have already discussed how that complicates the mathematics of programming by arranging that the value of an expression depends closely on the previous history of the evaluation. Jumps complicate matters still further by destroying any connection between the chronological history of an evaluation and the structure of the written program. For this reason, and others, the jump and the goto statement have become a *bête noire* of those concerned to promote the writing of intelligible programs. We shall find, however, that when we have successfully accommodated the general form of the jump within our formalism, the same mechanisms will be used to explicate the more restricted transfers of control that are still tolerated by most of the proponents of lucidity.

Some jumps are worse than others, of course. The simplest kind of jump (sometimes called a *hop*) transfers only at one single level of command; there is no jumping into or out of blocks or any other nested construct. This kind of jump can be fairly easily dealt with in our theory so far, though the details are somewhat messy.

Hops

We add two new commands:

Γ ::= goto E | begin I_1:Γ_1;I_2:Γ_2;...;I_n:Γ_n end

The first is the jump itself. The second is a block containing labels. We assume that each such block undergoes a preliminary syntactic transformation so that it consists of some number n of chunks of which each begins with a distinct label I_i and each except the last ends with a jump to one of the I_i; no other jumps are allowed inside the chunk (except of course those within interior blocks). This is achieved by adding new labels and jumps if necessary, including the adding of jumps to balance conditional commands so that either both arms end with a jump or neither does. This is a purely formal syntactic transformation; A. van Wijngaarden [63] has given a much more detailed description of a very similar transformation for Algol 60, but it would be tedious for us to define ours with any greater formality, and so we shall shortly illustrate it with an example.

We now define the semantics of these new commands. We know, of course, that we can use jumps to write loops; so we shall not be too surprised to find the fixed point operator *fix* involved with their semantics. We have

$$\mathscr{C}[\![\text{goto } E]\!]\rho = \mathit{Jump}\star\ \mathscr{E}[\![E]\!]\rho \tag{11.1}$$

$$\text{where } \mathit{Jump}(\varepsilon) = \varepsilon|C$$

$$\mathscr{C}[\![\text{begin } I_1{:}\Gamma_1;I_2{:}\Gamma_2;\ldots;I_n{:}\Gamma_n \text{ end}]\!]$$
$$= (\mathit{fix}(\lambda\langle\gamma_1,\gamma_2,\ldots,\gamma_n\rangle.\langle\mathscr{C}[\![\Gamma_1]\!]\rho',\mathscr{C}[\![\Gamma_2]\!]\rho',\ldots\mathscr{C}[\![\Gamma_n]\!]\rho'\rangle$$
$$\text{where } \rho' = \rho[\gamma_1 \text{ in } D/I_1][\gamma_2 \text{ in } D/I_2]\ldots[\gamma_n \text{ in } D/I_n]$$
$$))\!\downarrow\!1. \tag{11.2}$$

Notice that the semantics of ⌜goto E⌝ are exactly the

the same as the semantics of ⌜rt E⌝ (this might well sow a slight doubt in our minds about the validity of the scheme). In 11.2 the general idea is to associate the value γ_i of each chunk with its label I_i in the environment; but since in general each γ_i depends on other I's (in particular by jumping to one of them) the system is mutually recursive, and so the n-tuple of values must be the solution of a fixed point expression; finally, since the block is entered at the beginning, the first element of the n-tuple, the value of the first command, is selected as the overall value. Note that as all the I's are distinct the ordering of the post-fixed modifiers of ρ is irrelevant.

We illustrate with an example. We consider the following piece of program, which is reminiscent of the way Fortran (or machine code) programmers write Algol.

⌜**begin** Γ_1;
  if E **then goto** I_3 **else dummy**;
  goto I_4;
I_3 : Γ_{13};
  goto I_5;
I_4 : Γ_{14};
I_5 : Γ_{15} **end**⌝

We shall assume that none of the I's occurs free in any of the Γ's or in E. Our preliminary syntactic transformation changes this to the following.

```
Γ ≡ ⌜begin I_1: Γ_11:
          if  E  then goto I_3 else(dummy; goto I_2);
      I_2: goto I_4;
      I_3: Γ_13;
          goto I
      I_4: Γ_14
          goto I ;
      I_4: Γ_15 end⌝
```

where the new I's are all new distinct identifiers.

Then

$\mathscr{C}[\![\Gamma]\!]\rho =$

$(fix(\lambda\langle \gamma_1, \gamma_2, \gamma_3, \gamma_4, \gamma_5\rangle.\{$

$\langle (\lambda\varepsilon.\varepsilon\rightarrow Jump{*}\ \mathscr{E}[\![I_3]\!]\rho', Jump{*}\ \mathscr{E}[\![I_2]\!]\rho'\circ I){*}\ \mathscr{E}[\![E]\!]\rho'\circ\mathscr{C}[\![\Gamma_{11}]\!]\rho',$

$Jump{*}\ \mathscr{E}[\![I_4]\!]\rho',$

$Jump{*}\ \mathscr{E}[\![I_5]\!]\rho'\circ\mathscr{C}[\![\Gamma_{13}]\!]\rho',$

$Jump{*}\ \mathscr{E}[\![I_5]\!]\rho'\circ\mathscr{C}[\![\Gamma_{14}]\!]\rho',$

$\mathscr{C}[\![\Gamma_{15}]\!]\rho'\rangle$

where $\rho' = \rho[\gamma_1 \text{ in } D/I_1][\gamma\ \text{ in } D/I_2]..[\gamma_5 \text{ in } D/I_5]\ \}))\downarrow 1.$

Now $\mathscr{E}[\![I]\!]\rho = strict(\lambda\sigma.\langle\rho[\![I]\!],\sigma\rangle)$, and if $\rho[\![I]\!] = \gamma$ in D then, for proper σ,

$Jump{*}strict(\lambda\sigma.\langle\rho[\![I]\!]\ \sigma\rangle)\sigma$

$\quad = Jump(\rho[\![I]\!])\sigma$

$\quad = Jump(\gamma \text{ in } D)\sigma$

$\quad = (\gamma \text{ in } D|C)\sigma = \gamma\sigma.$

And, because γ is completely strict, this result also holds for improper σ. So

$Jump\star\ \mathcal{E}[\![I_i]\!]\rho' = \gamma_i.$ $(i=1,2,3,4,5)$

Also, since the E's are not free in the Γ's, by Lemma 8.11,

$\mathcal{C}[\![\Gamma_i]\!]\rho' = \mathcal{C}[\![\Gamma_i]\!]\rho$

and $\mathcal{E}[\![E]\!]\rho' = \mathcal{E}[\![E]\!]\rho.$

Now let $\mathcal{C}[\![\Gamma_i]\!]\rho = \gamma_i$ $(i=1,13,14,15)$

$\mathcal{E}[\![E]\!]\rho = \omega$

and $\mathcal{C}[\![\Gamma]\!]\rho = \gamma.$

Then

$$\begin{aligned}\gamma = (fix(\lambda\langle\gamma_1,\gamma_2,\ldots,\gamma_5\rangle.\{\\
&\langle(\lambda\varepsilon.\varepsilon\to\gamma_3,\gamma_1\circ I)\star\omega\circ\gamma_{11},\\
&\gamma_4,\\
&\gamma_5\circ\gamma_{13},\\
&\gamma_5\circ\gamma_{14},\\
&\gamma_{15}\quad\rangle\}))\downarrow 1.\end{aligned}$$

Now if we let

$\langle\gamma_0',\gamma_1',\ldots,\gamma_5'\rangle = fix(\lambda\langle\gamma_1,\gamma_2,\ldots,\gamma_5\rangle.\{\ldots\})$ then by the fixed point property,

$$\begin{aligned}\langle\gamma_1'\ \gamma_2'\ \ldots\ \gamma_5'\rangle = \langle&(\lambda\varepsilon.\varepsilon\to\gamma_3',\gamma_1')\star\omega\circ\gamma_{11},\\
&\gamma_4',\\
&\gamma_5'\circ\gamma_{13},\\
&\gamma_5'\circ\gamma_{14},\\
&\gamma_{15}\quad\rangle.\end{aligned}$$

Matching each component of these quintuples gives a set of simultaneous equations which involves no circularity, and can therefore be solved directly.

Thus

$\gamma_5' = \gamma_{15}$

$\gamma_4' = \gamma_{15}\circ\gamma_{14}$

$\gamma_3' = \gamma_{15}\circ\gamma_{12}$

$\gamma_2' = \gamma_{15}\circ\gamma_{14}$

$\gamma_1' = (\lambda\varepsilon.\varepsilon\rightarrow\gamma_{15}\circ\gamma_{13},\gamma_{15}\circ\gamma_{14})*\omega\circ\gamma_{11}.$

Now $\gamma = (\mathit{fix}(\ldots))\downarrow 1$

$= \langle\gamma_1',\gamma_2',\ldots,\gamma_5'\rangle\downarrow 1 = \gamma_1'.$

So $\gamma = (\lambda\varepsilon.\varepsilon\rightarrow\gamma_{15}\circ\gamma_{13},\gamma_{15}\circ\gamma_{14})*\omega\circ\gamma_{11}$

$= \gamma_{15}\circ(\lambda\varepsilon.\varepsilon\rightarrow\gamma_{13},\gamma_{14})*\omega\circ\gamma_{11}.$

Note that $\gamma = \mathscr{C}[\![\Gamma_{11}$;(if E then Γ_{13} else Γ_{14});$\Gamma_{15}]\!]\rho$ which is the more stylish way of writing the same program, and involves no assumptions about free occurrences of I's in the Γ's.

This use of *fix* which leads to no circularity is an example of what are called *pseudo fixed points*. They arise from the analysis of loop-free programs.

Exercise.

1. If I does not occur free in E or Γ, show that

⌜begin I:if E then(Γ;goto I)else dummy end⌝

≡ ⌜while E do Γ⌝.

This approach, however, fails in more complicated situations. For example, it cannot deal properly with jumps out of detached commands. We consider the following example, in which again we assume the I's are not free in the Γ's.

$$\gamma \equiv \ulcorner\texttt{begin } I_1\texttt{:let } I_2 = \texttt{rt}(\Gamma_{11}\texttt{;goto } I_4)$$
$$\texttt{in}(\Gamma_{12}\texttt{;call } I_2\texttt{;}\Gamma_{13})\texttt{;goto } I_4\texttt{;}$$
$$I_4\texttt{: } \Gamma_{14}$$
$$\texttt{end}\urcorner$$

where the second $\ulcorner\texttt{goto } I_4\urcorner$ may well have been introduced by one of our syntactic transformations. Notice though, that the transformations as we have defined them cannot deal satisfactorily with the first $\ulcorner\texttt{goto } I_4\urcorner$, as it is not at the top level. We expect that the command $\ulcorner\Gamma_{12}\texttt{;call } I_2\texttt{;}\Gamma_{13}\urcorner$ will be first to be executed; but the routine associated with I_2 contains a jump to I_4, so that we never reach Γ_{13}; the whole program should therefore be equivalent to $\ulcorner\Gamma_{12}\texttt{;}\Gamma_{11}\texttt{;}\Gamma_{14}\urcorner$. However, using the same sort of argument and notation as before, we get

$$\gamma = (\mathit{fix}(\lambda\langle\gamma_1,\gamma_4\rangle.\langle\gamma_4\circ\mathscr{C}\llbracket\texttt{let } I_2\texttt{=rt}(\Gamma_{11}\texttt{;goto } I_4)\texttt{in}(\Gamma_{12}\texttt{;}$$
$$\texttt{call } I_2\texttt{;}\Gamma_{13})\rrbracket\rho',\mathscr{C}\llbracket\Gamma_{14}\rrbracket\rho'\rangle$$
$$\text{where } \rho' = \rho[\gamma_1 \text{ in } D/I_1][\gamma_4 \text{ in } D/I_4] \qquad))\downarrow 1.$$

Now $\mathscr{C}\llbracket\Gamma_{14}\rrbracket\rho' = \mathscr{C}\llbracket\Gamma_{14}\rrbracket\rho = \gamma_{14}$, say. So again we have a pseudo fixed point, which gives

$$\gamma = \gamma_{14}\circ\mathscr{C}\llbracket\texttt{let } I_2 \texttt{ rt}(\Gamma_{11}\texttt{;goto } I_4)\texttt{in}(\Gamma_{12}\texttt{;call } I_2\texttt{;}\Gamma_{13})\rrbracket$$
$$(\rho[\gamma_{14} \text{ in } D/I_4])$$
$$= \gamma_{14}\circ(\lambda\delta.\gamma_{13}\circ\mathscr{C}\llbracket\texttt{call } I_2\rrbracket(\rho_1[\delta/I_2])\circ\gamma_{12})*$$
$$\mathit{strict}(\lambda\sigma.\langle\mathscr{C}\llbracket\Gamma_{11}\texttt{;goto } I_4\rrbracket\rho_1 \text{ in } E,\sigma\rangle)$$
$$\text{where } \rho_1 = \rho[\gamma_{14} \text{ in } D/I_4]$$
$$= \gamma_{14}\circ(\lambda\delta.\gamma_{13}\circ(\delta|C)\circ\gamma_{12})((\gamma_{14}\circ\gamma_{11})\text{in } E)$$
$$\gamma_{14}\circ\gamma_{13}\circ\gamma_{14}\circ\gamma_{11}\circ\gamma_{12}.$$

What we wanted, of course, was $\gamma_{14} \circ \gamma_{11} \circ \gamma_{12}$. However, our method was unable to specify that the conclusion of the program originally expected, after the completion of the $\ulcorner$call $I_2 \urcorner$, should be abandoned when the $\ulcorner$goto $I_4 \urcorner$ was obeyed; so that final conclusion, $\gamma_{14} \circ \gamma_{13}$, got tacked on to the correct solution.

Continuations

The heart of our problem is really the equation

$$\mathscr{C}[\![\Gamma_1;\Gamma_2]\!]\rho \;=\; \mathscr{C}[\![\Gamma_2]\!]\rho \circ \mathscr{C}[\![\Gamma_1]\!]\rho.$$

The sequencing in our language has been expressed by using functional composition. This is too strong. There is no way that Γ_1 can decide that Γ_2 should not be obeyed (except for the special cases of non-termination or error stop, when we rely on the complete strictness of everything to allow these effects to percolate through). The only way we can introduce jumps into this scheme of things is by syntactically transforming the programs into chunks, inside which there are no jumps (so normal sequencing can apply), and between which all the sequencing is managed explicitly. This fails when the sequencing is not syntactically obvious: from $\ulcorner$call $I \urcorner$, for example, one cannot tell whether a jump is involved or not.

In the reference we have already cited [63], van Wijngaarden gets over this problem by making yet more wholesale syntactic transformations in order to *make* the sequencing syntactically obvious: for example, the "return links" of all procedure calls are supplied as extra parameters. But to indulge in too much mechanical rewriting of a program before we begin to consider what it means is against the spirit of our approach, which tries to express the semantics of a program in terms of the meanings of its component parts as actually written. We therefore do it differently: in effect, we do in the semantics what van Wijngaarden does by syntax.

For $\ulcorner \Gamma_1;\Gamma_2 \urcorner$, then, we have to allow Γ_1 the option of deciding whether or not to go on to Γ_1. We do this by making the value of a command a function taking one more parameter, called the *continuation*. We now write

$$\mathscr{C}[\![\Gamma]\!]\rho\theta.$$

The new parameter, θ, is the *dynamic* effect of the remainder of the program; so, at any rate initially, we think of it as a state transformation, and hence

$$\theta \in \mathrm{C} = [\mathrm{S}\to\mathrm{S}].$$

So now $\mathscr{C}$ is of type $\mathrm{Cmd}\to\mathrm{U}\to\mathrm{C}\to\mathrm{C}$ or, in full, $\mathrm{Cmd}\to[\mathrm{Ide}\to\mathrm{D}]\to[\mathrm{S}\to\mathrm{S}]\to\mathrm{S}\to\mathrm{S}$.

The clause for $\ulcorner \Gamma_1;\Gamma_2 \urcorner$ is now as follows:

$$\mathscr{C}[\![\Gamma_1;\Gamma_2]\!]\rho\theta \quad = \quad \mathscr{C}[\![\Gamma_1]\!]\rho\{\mathscr{C}[\![\Gamma_2]\!]\rho\theta\}$$

That is to say, executing $\ulcorner \Gamma_1;\Gamma_2 \urcorner$ with continuation θ involves executing Γ_1 with the continuation consisting of executing Γ_2 with the original continuation, θ. By convention, as an aid to the eye, continuations are enclosed in braces {}. Commands are supplied with continuations basically so that they have the option of ignoring them. Thus, as we shall see, the value of $\mathscr{C}[\![\mathbf{goto}\ \mathrm{E}]\!]\rho\theta$ will not depend on θ at all.

The use of continuations was developed independently by Christopher Wadsworth and Lockwood Morris; it is inspired by the "tail functions" of Mazurkiewicz [29].

Mike Fischer [12] has also used essentially the same technique, but for a rather different purpose. The paper by Strachey and Wadsworth [59] gives a good exposition.

Our formalism has now become more curried than ever. Instead of $\mathscr{C}[\![\Gamma]\!]\rho\theta\sigma$ we could have chosen to write

$$C\langle\Gamma,\rho,\theta,\sigma\rangle.$$

We could regard this quadruple as the state of some interpreter which goes through state transitions, and write

$$C\langle\Gamma,\rho,\theta,\sigma\rangle \quad = \quad C\langle\Gamma',\rho',\theta',\sigma'\rangle$$

and so on. This would make it resemble the *sharing* machine of Peter Landin [24] (where Γ is the Control part, ρ the Environment, σ the sharing relation, and θ a mixture of the Stack and the Dump with much housekeeping detail omitted). But we prefer the curried approach, partly for conciseness, but also because each successive stage of the currying has its own abstract meaning. Thus for a command:

$\mathscr{C}[\![\Gamma]\!]$ is the meaning of Γ in vacuo.

$\mathscr{C}[\![\Gamma]\!]\rho$ has the environment bound in, rather like a function closure, and is meaningful independently of any θ or σ. The values of functions and routines will be of this kind.

$\mathscr{C}[\![\Gamma]\!]\rho\theta$ represents a computation "all fired up and ready to go", complete with its own continuation. The values of labels are objects like this. (Cf. also Peter Landin's "program closures".)

$\mathscr{C}[\![\Gamma]\!]\rho\theta\sigma$ is a particular execution.

So far we have mentioned only the continuations of commands; we must now deal with expressions. The continuation of a command inherits only a state from its preceding activity; but the continuation of an expression inherits a result as well as a state. A command continuation was of type $[S\to S] = C$; an expression continuation could therefore be of type $[[E\times S]\to S]$, but we prefer to curry it:

$$\kappa \in K \quad = \quad [E\to[S\to S]] \quad = \quad [E\to C].$$

It is important to note that a command's continuation is the dynamic effect of the rest of the program, or what would happen afterwards if the command terminated normally with the usual sequencing. It is *not* the translation of the command's lexical successors in the program text. So, for example, in analysing the program fragment $\ulcorner I{:}\Gamma_1;\Gamma_2;\text{goto } I;\Gamma_3;\Gamma_4\urcorner$ the continuation relevant for the command Γ_2 would involve Γ_1 and Γ_2 itself, but not Γ_3 or Γ_4 (except possibly by jumps from the other commands).

We have been fairly vague throughout about what we mean by "the rest of the program", or indeed by "program" itself. We now say that a program is a command Γ which runs in an initial environment ρ_0 and an initial continuation θ_0. The simplest model is obtained by saying that ρ_0 is the so-called *arid* environment, the environment in which nothing is declared, so that any attempt to look something up in it is an error: so $\rho_0 = \lambda I.?$. Similarly, θ_0 is the identity transformation $\lambda\sigma.\sigma$, since after the whole program is finished there is nothing else to do. However, this is a little too simple. More realistically, ρ_0 will have been formed by the addition of any "standard functions" in the language (such as *sqrt* or *sin* in Algol 60) to a yet more primitive environment which itself provides access to the particular installation's subroutine library etc. The continuation θ_0 will also specify something involving a return to the operating system.

Previously, each command was taken to be a state transformation, and could be thought of as handing on its final state to the next command (or expression) in the execution sequence. Now, however, we are considering each command together with its continuation as specifying the transformation between some "current" state and the *final* state of the program. But there is really no need for this final outcome to be the final state if it is not required as the starting state for further processing. So we prefer to introduce a new domain, A ("answers"), of final outcomes; so that now $C = S \to A$ and $K = E \to C = E \to S \to A$. In this book we shall leave the exact nature of A unspecified, but in any actual application we could choose A so as to arrange that our analysis gave us what we wanted. Sometimes, indeed, we might still wish to consider the final state, so that then A would be S as before. At other times we might want to reflect the fact that much of a program's state is promptly cleared up by the system as soon as the program ends and is not particularly relevant to the overall effects of the program; then elements of A might merely contain information about what had been output on the peripherals. Or again, to take a very simple example, we might be concerned solely about program termination: then we could take A to be the two-element lattice $\{\bot, \mathit{finished}\}$ with $\bot \sqsubseteq \mathit{finished}$, and consider the outcome of programs with the initial continuation $\lambda\sigma.\mathit{finished}$. (But note that we should not expect miracles from this technique - the Halting Problem remains undecidable.)

We now give (in Table 11.1) the semantics of a simplified version of our language (which we shall subsequently extend). Since we are initially allowing only truth values and labels, we have $E = D = T+C$. Notice that $\mathscr{C}[\![\text{dummy}]\!]\rho = I$, apparently just as before; now, however, I is in the domain $[C \to C]$, whereas before I was in $[S \to S]$. Again, now $\mathscr{C}[\![\Gamma_1;\Gamma_2]\!]\rho = \mathscr{C}[\![\Gamma_1]\!]\rho \circ \mathscr{C}[\![\Gamma_2]\!]\rho$, whereas before $\mathscr{C}[\![\Gamma_1;\Gamma_2]\!]\rho = \mathscr{C}[\![\Gamma_2]\!]\rho \circ \mathscr{C}[\![\Gamma_1]\!]\rho$; again, the change in functionality is the key to the difference.

In 11.17 we introduce one error continuation, *Wrong*, to be used in various failure situations. It is used in 11.11 for when a required identifier is not declared in the environment, in 11.9 for when the destination of a jump is not of the right type, and in the conditional operator, *Cond* (11.18), for when the test turns out not to be a truth value. It would of course be possible to have separate continuations in all these cases, so that different action could be taken, but we do not bother to be so discriminating.

Notice that the value of $\mathscr{C}[\![\text{goto } E]\!]\rho\theta$ is independent of θ; and that for the block with labels (11.10) each chunk has for its continuation the value of the succeeding chunk, except for the final one which has the overall continuation - this technique in the semantics replaces the need to make any syntactic transformations to ensure that each chunk ends with an explicit jump.

The reader is urged to go through the clauses in the semantic functions very carefully, and to make sure that they are completely understood.

Comment on the while-*loop*. When we first concocted a clause for the while-loop (in Chapter 9), we were guided by the requirement that

$$\ulcorner \texttt{while } E \texttt{ do } \Gamma \urcorner \equiv \ulcorner \texttt{if } E \texttt{ then}(\Gamma;\texttt{while } E \texttt{ do } \Gamma)\texttt{else dummy} \urcorner.$$

We do the same to get clause 11.7 here, but there are two possible ways to go. The one we actually used was:

$$\begin{aligned}\theta' &= \mathscr{C}[\![\texttt{while } E \texttt{ do } \Gamma]\!]\rho\theta \\ &= \mathscr{C}[\![\texttt{if } E \texttt{ then}(\Gamma;\texttt{while } E \texttt{ do } \Gamma)\texttt{else dummy}]\!]\rho\theta \\ &= \mathscr{E}[\![E]\!]\rho\{\mathit{Cond}(\mathscr{C}[\![\Gamma]\!]\rho\theta',\mathit{I}\theta)\} \\ &= \mathit{fix}\ \lambda\theta'.(\mathscr{E}[\![E]\!]\rho\{\mathit{Cond}(\mathscr{C}[\![\Gamma]\!]\rho\theta',\theta)\}).\end{aligned}$$

But instead we could have said:

$$\begin{aligned}\gamma &= \mathscr{C}[\![\texttt{while } E \texttt{ do } \Gamma]\!]\rho \\ &= \mathscr{C}[\![\texttt{if } E \texttt{ then}(\Gamma;\texttt{while } E \texttt{ do } \Gamma)\texttt{else dummy}]\!]\rho \\ &= \lambda\theta.\ \mathscr{E}[\![E]\!]\rho\{\mathit{Cond}(\mathscr{C}[\![\Gamma;\texttt{while } E \texttt{ do } \Gamma]\!]\rho\theta,\mathit{I}\theta)\} \\ &= \lambda\theta.\ \mathscr{E}[\![E]\!]\rho\{\mathit{Cond}((\mathscr{C}[\![\Gamma]\!]\rho\circ\gamma)\theta,\theta)\} \\ &= \mathit{fix}(\lambda\gamma.\lambda\theta.\ \mathscr{E}[\![E]\!]\rho\{\mathit{Cond}((\mathscr{C}[\![\Gamma]\!]\rho\circ\gamma)\theta,\theta)\}).\end{aligned}$$

So $\mathscr{C}[\![\texttt{while } E \texttt{ do } \Gamma]\!]\rho\theta =$

$$(\mathit{fix}(\lambda\gamma.\lambda\theta.\ \mathscr{E}[\![E]\!]\rho\{\mathit{Cond}((\mathscr{C}[\![\Gamma]\!]\rho\circ\gamma)\theta,\theta)\}))\theta.$$

Table 11.1. Flow Diagram Language with Jumps

Syntactic Categories

$I \in$ Ide	(identifiers)
$\Gamma \in$ Cmd	(commands)
$E \in$ Exp	(expressions)
$\Phi \in$ Pri	(some primitive commands)
$\Pi \in$ Pre	(some primitive predicates)

Syntax

Γ ::= Φ | dummy |
    if E then Γ_1 else Γ_2 | $\Gamma_1;\Gamma_2$ | while E do Γ |
    let I = E in Γ | goto E|
    begin $I_1:\Gamma_1$; $I_2:\Gamma_2$; ...; $I_n:\Gamma_n$ end

(in the final production, all the I_i ($1 \leq i \leq n$) are assumed distinct).

E ::= I | Π | true | false |
    if E_0 then E_1 else E_2 | let I = E_0 in E_1

Value Domains

T	(truth values)
$\sigma \in$ S	(machine states)
A	("answers": final outcomes)
$\theta \in C = [S \to A]$	(command continuations)
$\varepsilon \in E = [T + C]$	(expression values)
$\delta \in D = E$	(denotations)
$\kappa \in K = [E \to C]$	(expression continuations)
$\omega \in W = [K \to C]$	(expression "closures")
$\gamma \in G = [C \to C]$	(command "closures")
$\rho \in U = [Ide \to D]$	(environments)

Table 11.1 (continued): *Semantic Functions*

$\mathscr{C}$: Cmd→U→G

$\mathscr{C}[\![\Phi]\!]\rho$ = a given γ associated with Φ (11.3)

$\mathscr{C}[\![\text{dummy}]\!]\rho = I$ (11.4)

$\mathscr{C}[\![\text{if E then } \Gamma_1 \text{ else } \Gamma_2]\!]\rho\theta =$
$\quad \mathcal{E}[\![E]\!]\rho\{Cond\ \mathscr{C}[\![\Gamma_1]\!]\rho\theta, \mathscr{C}[\![\Gamma_2]\!]\rho\theta$ (11.5)

$\mathscr{C}[\![\Gamma_1;\Gamma_2]\!]\rho = \mathscr{C}[\![\Gamma_1]\!]\rho \circ \mathscr{C}[\![\Gamma_2]\!]\rho$ (11.6)
$\quad$(So $\mathscr{C}[\![\Gamma_1;\Gamma_2]\!]\rho\theta = \mathscr{C}[\![\Gamma_1]\!]\rho\{\mathscr{C}[\![\Gamma_2]\!]\rho\theta\}$.)

$\mathscr{C}[\![\text{while E do } \Gamma]\!]\rho\theta =$
$\quad fix(\lambda\theta'.\ \mathcal{E}[\![E]\!]\rho\{Cond(\mathscr{C}[\![\Gamma]\!]\rho\theta',\theta)\})$ (11.7)

$\mathscr{C}[\![\text{let I=E in } \Gamma]\!]\rho\theta =$
$\quad \mathcal{E}[\![E]\!]\rho\{\lambda\delta.\mathscr{C}[\![\Gamma]\!](\rho[\delta/I])\theta\}$ (11.8)

$\mathscr{C}[\![\text{goto E}]\!]\rho\theta = \mathcal{E}[\![E]\!]\rho\{Jump\}$ (11.9)
$\quad$where $Jump(\varepsilon) = \varepsilon \mathsf{E} C \to (\varepsilon|C), Wrong$

$\mathscr{C}[\![\text{begin } I_1:\Gamma_1;I_2:\Gamma_2;\ldots;I_{n-1}:\Gamma_{n-1};I_n:\Gamma_n \text{ end}]\!]\rho =$
$\quad (fix(\lambda\langle\theta_1,\theta_2,\ldots,\theta_{n-1},\theta_n\rangle.$
$\quad \langle\mathscr{C}[\![\Gamma_1]\!]\rho'\theta_2, \mathscr{C}[\![\Gamma_2]\!]\rho'\theta_3,\ldots,\mathscr{C}[\![\Gamma_{n-1}]\!]\rho'\theta_n, \mathscr{C}[\![\Gamma_n]\!]\rho'\theta\rangle$
where $\rho'\ \rho[\theta_1 \text{ in } D/I_1][\theta_2 \text{ in } D/I_2]\ldots[\theta_n \text{ in } D/I_n]\quad))\downarrow 1$ (11.10)

$\mathcal{E}$: Exp→U→W

$\mathcal{E}[\![I]\!]\rho\kappa = (\rho[\![I]\!]) = ? \to Wrong, \kappa(\rho[\![I]\!])$ (11.11)

$\mathcal{E}[\![\Pi]\!]\rho$ = a given ω associated with Π (11.12)

$\mathcal{E}[\![\text{true}]\!]\rho\kappa = \kappa(true \text{ in E})$ (11.13)

$\mathcal{E}[\![\text{false}]\!]\rho\kappa = \kappa(false \text{ in E})$ (11.14)

$\mathcal{E}[\![\text{if } E_0 \text{ then } E_1 \text{ else } E_2]\!]\rho\kappa =$
$\quad \mathcal{E}[\![E_0]\!]\rho\{Cond(\mathcal{E}[\![E_1]\!]\rho\kappa, \mathcal{E}[\![E_2]\!]\rho\kappa)\}$ (11.15)

$\mathcal{E}[\![\text{let I=}E_0 \text{ in } E_1]\!]\rho\kappa =$
$\quad \mathcal{E}[\![E_0]\!]\rho\{\lambda\delta.\ \mathcal{E}[\![E_1]\!](\rho[\delta/I])\kappa\}$ (11.16)

Auxiliary Definitions

Wrong: an element of C; the error continuation, not further defined (11.17)

Cond: [C×C]→K
$\quad Cond(\theta_1,\theta_2) = \lambda\varepsilon.\varepsilon \mathsf{E} T \to (\varepsilon|T) \to \theta_1, \theta_2$ (11.18)
$\quad Wrong$

Exercise.

2. Prove these two expressions for $\mathscr{C}[\![\text{while E do } \Gamma]\!]\rho\theta$ equal; that is, putting $\omega = \mathscr{E}[\![E]\!]\rho$ and $\gamma = \mathscr{C}[\![\Gamma]\!]\rho$, show that $fix(\lambda\theta'.\omega\{Cond(\gamma\theta',\theta)\}) = (fix(\lambda\gamma'.\lambda\theta'.\omega\{Cond((\gamma\circ\gamma')\theta',\theta')\}))\theta$.

3. Investigate also the possibility of dropping the ρ as well as the θ from the initial circular equation for the while-loop.

Rederivation of some Earlier Results

We can now re-establish some of the results we proved in the earlier formalism:

1. $\ulcorner$if ~E then E_1 else $E_2\urcorner \equiv \ulcorner$if E then E_2 else $E_1\urcorner$

We recall that the operator '~' was defined by means of the auxiliary equation
$\ulcorner$~E$\urcorner \equiv \ulcorner$if E then false else true$\urcorner$. So

$\mathscr{E}[\![\text{if} \sim E \text{ then } E_1 \text{ else } E_2]\!]\rho\kappa =$

$\quad \mathscr{E}[\![\text{if(if E then false else true)then } E_1 \text{ else } E_2]\!]\rho\kappa$

$= \quad \mathscr{E}[\![\text{if E then false else true}]\!]\rho\{Cond(\mathscr{E}[\![E_1]\!]\rho\kappa, \mathscr{E}[\![E_2]\!]\rho\kappa)\}$

$= \quad (\lambda\kappa'.\ \mathscr{E}[\![E]\!]\{Cond\ \kappa'(false),\kappa'(true))\})\{Cond(\mathscr{E}[\![E_1]\!]\rho\kappa,$
$\mathscr{E}[\![E_2]\!]\rho\kappa)\}$

$= \quad \mathscr{E}[\![E]\!]\rho\{Cond(\mathscr{E}[\![E_2]\!]\rho\kappa, \mathscr{E}[\![E_1]\!]\rho\kappa)\}$

(since $(Cond(\mathscr{E}[\![E_1]\!]\rho\kappa, \mathscr{E}[\![E_2]\!]\rho\kappa))false = \mathscr{E}[\![E_2]\!]\rho\kappa$ etc.)

$= \quad \mathscr{E}[\![\text{if E then } E_2 \text{ else } E_1]\!]\rho\kappa.$

So, since this holds for all ρ and κ
$\ulcorner$if ~E then E_1 else $E_2\urcorner \equiv \ulcorner$if E then E_2 else $E_1\urcorner$.

Notice that we now no longer have to deal separately

with the case where σ is improper, and we are no longer taking precautions to ensure that all commands and expressions are doubly strict. The point is now that if a command fails to terminate or ends in error, its continuation is simply not applied, so the properties of the continuation are all irrelevant: we no longer have to rely on strictness to ensure that non-termination or error correctly percolates.

2. repeatwhile. The definition of the repeatwhile command is now:

$$\mathscr{C}[\![\Gamma \text{ repeatwhile } E]\!]\rho\theta = fix(\lambda\theta'.\mathscr{C}[\![\Gamma]\!]\rho\{\mathscr{E}[\![E]\!]\rho\{Cond(\theta',\theta)\}\})$$

We now check our earlier theorems:

$$\ulcorner\Gamma \text{ repeatwhile } E\urcorner \equiv \ulcorner\Gamma;\text{while } E \text{ do } \Gamma\urcorner \qquad (9.22)$$

$$\ulcorner\text{while } E \text{ do } \Gamma\urcorner \equiv \ulcorner\text{if } E \text{ then}(\Gamma \text{ repeatwhile } E)\text{else dummy}\urcorner \qquad (9.23)$$

Letting $\omega = \mathscr{E}[\![E]\!]\rho$ and $\gamma = \mathscr{C}[\![\Gamma]\!]\rho$, we define $H_0(\theta) = \omega\{Cond(\gamma\theta\ \theta_c)\}$ and $\theta'_0\ \ fix(H_0)$, so that $\theta'_0 = \mathscr{C}[\![\text{while } E \text{ do } \Gamma]\!]\rho\theta_c$. We also define $H_1(\theta) = \gamma\{\omega\{Cond(\theta,\theta_c)\}\}$ and $\theta'_1 = fix(H_1)$ and thus $\theta'_1 = \mathscr{C}[\![\Gamma \text{ repeatwhile } E]\!]\rho\theta_c$. If we also let $\theta_2 = \omega\{Cond(\theta'_1, \theta_c)\}$, our theorems now become

$$\theta'_1 = \gamma\theta'_0, \qquad \text{(from 9.22)}$$

$$\theta'_0 = \theta_2\ . \qquad \text{(from 9.23)}$$

The proofs now follow exactly the same steps as our earlier proof:

1. $\theta_1' = H_1(\theta_1')$ (fixed point of H_1)

$= \gamma\{\omega\{Cond(\theta_1',\theta_c)\}\}$ (definition of H_1)

$= \gamma\theta_2$. (definition of θ_2)

2. $H_0(\theta_2) = \omega\{Cond(\gamma\theta_2,\theta_c\ \}$ (definition of H_0)

$= \omega\{Cond(\theta_1,\theta_c)\}$ (result (1))

$= \theta_2$. (definition of θ_2)

So θ_2 is a fixed point of H_0; so $\theta_0' \sqsubseteq \theta_2$; and so on.

Exercise

4. Complete this proof.

3. Hops. We next re-prove our earlier result that, provided the I's do not occur free in the Γ's or in E then:

```
⌜begin I₁:Γ₁₁;
          if E then goto I₃ else dummy;
           goto I₄;
       I₃:Γ₁₃;
           goto I₅;
       I₄:Γ₁₄;
       I₅:Γ₁₅ end⌝
          ≡ ⌜Γ₁₁;(if E then Γ₁₃ else Γ₁₄);Γ₁₅⌝.
```

Now we no longer have to enforce the syntactic rules about chunks between labels containing no jumps save one at the end. We shall call the chunk between I_1 and I_3 Γ_3, and that between I_3 and I_4 Γ_3. So

$$\mathscr{C}[\![\Gamma_1]\!]\rho\theta = (\mathscr{C}[\![\Gamma_{11}]\!]\rho \circ \mathscr{C}[\![\texttt{if E then goto } I_3 \texttt{ else dummy}]\!]\rho$$
$$\circ\, \mathscr{C}[\![\texttt{goto } I_4]\!]\rho)\theta$$
$$= \mathscr{C}[\![\Gamma_{11}]\!]\rho\{\mathscr{C}[\![\texttt{if E then goto } I_3 \texttt{ else dummy}]\!]\rho$$
$$\{\mathscr{C}[\![\texttt{goto } I_4]\!]\rho\theta\}\}$$
$$= \mathscr{C}[\![\Gamma_{11}]\!]\rho\{\mathscr{C}[\![\texttt{if E then goto } I_3 \texttt{ else dummy}]\!]\rho$$
$$\{Jump\ (\rho[\![I_4]\!]\}$$

(since $(\rho[\![I]\!] = ? \rightarrow Wrong, Jump(\rho[\![I]\!])) \equiv Jump(\rho[\![I]\!])$,
as $? \notin C$)

$$= \mathscr{C}[\![\Gamma_{11}]\!]\rho\{\mathscr{E}[\![E]\!]\rho\{Cond(Jump(\rho[\![I_3]\!]),$$
$$Jump(\rho[\![I_4]\!]))\}\}$$

and $\mathscr{C}[\![\Gamma_3]\!]\rho\theta = \mathscr{C}[\![\Gamma_{13}]\!]\rho\{Jump(\rho[\![I_5]\!])\}$.

Now, calling the left hand side of the desired result Γ, and writing γ for $\mathscr{C}[\![\Gamma]\!]\rho$, we have

$$\gamma\theta = (fix(\lambda\langle\theta_1,\theta_3,\theta_4,\theta_5\rangle .$$
$$\langle\mathscr{C}[\![\Gamma_1]\!]\rho'\theta_3 . \mathscr{C}[\![\Gamma_3]\!]\rho'\ \theta_4 . \mathscr{C}[\![\Gamma_{14}]\!]\rho'\theta_5 . \mathscr{C}[\![\Gamma_{15}]\!]\rho'\theta\rangle$$

where $\rho' = \rho[\theta_1 \text{ in } D/I_1][\theta_3 \text{ in } D/I_3][\theta_4 \text{ in } D/I_4]$
$[\theta_5 \text{ in } D/I_5]$ $))\downarrow 1$.

Now as the I's are not free in the Γ_i (i=11, 13, 14, 15) or in E we can say

$$\mathscr{C}[\![\Gamma_i]\!]\rho' = \mathscr{C}[\![\Gamma_i]\!]\rho = \gamma_i \quad (i=11,13,14,15)$$

and $\mathscr{E}[\![E]\!]\rho' = \mathscr{E}[\![E]\!]\rho = \omega$.

Also $Jump(\rho'[\![I_j]\!]) = (\theta_j \text{ in } D|C) = \theta_j$

(for j=3,4,5), as θ_j belongs to the C subdomain of D. So if the fixed point in the above equation is

$\langle\theta_1',\theta_3',\theta_4',\theta_5'\rangle$

then we have, substituting in,

$\theta_1' = \gamma_{11}\{\omega\{Cond(\theta_3',\theta_4')\}\}$

$\theta_3' = \gamma_{13}\{\theta_5'\}$

$\theta_4' = \gamma_{14}\{\theta_5'\}$

$\theta_5' = \gamma_{15}\{\theta\}$.

This is an example of a pseudo fixed point, which can be solved directly. Hence

$$\gamma\theta = \theta_1' = \gamma_{11}\{\omega\{Cond(\gamma_{13}\{\gamma_{15}\theta\},\gamma_{14}\{\gamma_{15}\theta\})\}\}.$$

So $\gamma = \gamma_{11}\circ(\lambda\theta'.\omega\{Cond(\gamma_{13}\theta',\gamma_{14}\theta')\})\circ\gamma_{15}$

$= \mathscr{C}[\![\Gamma_{11};(\text{if } E \text{ then } \Gamma_{13} \text{ else } \Gamma_{14});\Gamma_{15}]\!]\rho$,

as required.

It remains for us to show that the example which did not work out correctly earlier now does. Before doing so, however, we must make the earlier extensions to the language.

Extensions

More Types and Operators. Just as before, new data types may be added to E (and D):

E = T + C + N + ...

D = E

and we can also add new functions acting on values of these new types. Let us do it a little more generally than last time. We add a new

Syntactic Category

$\Omega \in$ Ops

Syntax

$\Omega ::= + \mid - \mid \times \mid / \mid = \mid > \mid < \mid \quad \ldots$

$E ::= E_1 \;\Omega\; E_2$

We also need a new

Semantic Function

$\mathcal{O}: \text{Ops} \to [E \times E] \to W$

$\mathcal{O}[\![+]\!]\langle \varepsilon_1, \varepsilon_2 \rangle \kappa = \nu \in N \to \kappa(\nu \text{ in } E), \textit{Wrong}$

where $\nu = (\varepsilon_1 | N) + (\varepsilon_2 | N)$
and + is a completely strict version
of the usual addition function on
the integers;

and so on.

We also add the new clause to the definition of $\mathcal{E}$. First we give a left to right version.

$$\mathcal{E}[\![E_1 \Omega E_2]\!]\rho\kappa = \mathcal{E}[\![E_1]\!]\rho\{\lambda\varepsilon_1 .\ \mathcal{E}[\![E_2]\!]\rho\{\lambda\varepsilon_2 . \mathcal{O}[\![+]\!]\langle \varepsilon_1\ \varepsilon_2 \rangle \kappa\}\} \tag{11.19}$$

For an unspecified order of evaluation we must re-introduce *le*, the list evaluation operator, which we define as follows:

$$le\langle \omega_1, \omega_2 \rangle \kappa = \omega_{\pi_1}\{\lambda\varepsilon_{\pi_1} . \omega_{\pi_2}\{\lambda\varepsilon_{\pi_2} . \kappa\langle \varepsilon_1, \varepsilon_2 \rangle\}\} \tag{11.20}$$

where $\langle \pi_1, \pi_2 \rangle$ is either $\langle 1,2 \rangle$ or $\langle 2,1 \rangle$. (Language purists are invited to analyse the liberties we are taking here with our mathematical notation, which of course far exceed what we would tolerate in a programming language, in making the very names of our bound variables dependent on a run-time decision.) Then

$$\mathscr{E}[\![E_1 \Omega E_2]\!]\rho\kappa =$$

$$le\langle \mathscr{E}[\![E_1]\!]\rho,\ \mathscr{E}[\![E_2]\!]\rho\rangle \{\lambda\langle\varepsilon_1,\varepsilon_2\rangle . \mathscr{O}[\![\Omega]\!]\langle\varepsilon_1,\varepsilon_2\rangle\kappa\} \qquad (11.21)$$

We could call the pair $\langle E_1,E_2\rangle$ *regular* if the result is independent of the particular permutation $\langle\pi_1,\pi_2\rangle$ used for the evaluation. Note that this does *not* imply that the expressions are without side effects, but merely that they commute. Nor does it imply that the expressions could be evaluated simultaneously, merely in any order.

Functions and Routines. As before, we extend the syntax:

$$E ::= \mathtt{fn}I.E \mid E_0(E_1) \mid \mathtt{rt}\ \Gamma$$

$$\Gamma ::= \mathtt{call}\ E$$

and augment the value domains:

$$E = T + C + N + \ldots + [E \to W] + G.$$

Notice that now the subdomain for labels, C, is not the same as the subdomain for abstracted commands, G. Elements of the former come with their own continuation, while in the latter a continuation has to be provided (called the return link in implementation terminology). This is of course the essential difference between a jump and a subroutine call.

The new semantic equations are as follows:

$$\mathscr{E}[\![\mathtt{fn}I.E]\!]\rho\kappa = \kappa((\lambda\delta.\ \mathscr{E}[\![E]\!](\rho[\delta/I]))\mathtt{in}\ E) \qquad (11.22)$$

Note that $(\lambda\delta.\ \mathscr{E}[\![E]\!](\rho[\delta/I]))$ in an element of $E \to W$; when supplied with its argument value it still requires a continuation (in K) and a state. Note, too, that the state plays no active role in 11.22 itself:

the abstraction value and the unchanged state are simply passed to κ.

$$\mathscr{E}[\![E_0(E_1)]\!]\rho\kappa =$$
$$= \mathit{le}\langle \mathscr{E}[\![E_0]\!]\rho, \mathscr{E}[\![E_1]\!]\rho\rangle\{\lambda\langle\varepsilon_0,\varepsilon_1\rangle.\mathit{Apply}\varepsilon_0\varepsilon_1\kappa\} \qquad (11.23)$$

where $\mathit{Apply}\ \varepsilon_0\varepsilon_1\kappa = \varepsilon_0\mathbf{E}[E\to W] \to (\varepsilon_0|E\to W)\varepsilon_1\kappa, \mathit{Wrong}$

The two subexpressions are evaluated and then, provided the type is right, the argument, the continuation and the state are supplied to the abstraction. The clauses for routines are similar:

$$\mathscr{E}[\![\mathrm{rt}\Gamma]\!]\rho\kappa \quad \kappa(\mathscr{C}[\![\Gamma]\!]\rho \text{ in } E) \qquad (11.24)$$

$$\mathscr{C}[\![\mathrm{call}\ E]\!]\rho\theta = \mathscr{E}[\![E]\!]\rho\{\lambda\varepsilon.\mathit{Run}\varepsilon\theta\} \qquad (11.25)$$

where $\mathit{Run}\varepsilon\theta = \varepsilon\mathbf{E}G \to (\varepsilon|G)\theta, \mathit{Wrong}$.

Notice, in both these pairs of equations, how if the equation specifies an expression value immediately, without further evaluation then that value is supplied to the continuation (11.22 and 11.24); but if, after evaluating the subcomponents, further evaluation is required, then the continuation is supplied to the function which specifies the further evaluation (11.23 and 11.25). Some readers may be finding it difficult at present to appreciate how the state is handled by these equations - it is never mentioned explicitly in the current formalism. If so, they might prefer to return to this chapter after reading some of the following one, in which for the first time we examine commands (assignments) in which the state actually gets changed.

We can now reconsider the example which went wrong before, namely:

$$\Gamma \equiv \ulcorner \text{begin } I_1\text{: let } I_2 = \text{rt}(\Gamma_{11}\text{;goto } I_4) \text{ in}(\Gamma_{12}\text{;call } I_2;\Gamma_{13}); \quad I_4\text{: } \Gamma_{14} \text{ end}\urcorner$$

where the I's do not occur free in any Γ_i $(11 \le i \le 14)$.
We want to prove that

$$\Gamma \equiv \ulcorner \Gamma_{12};\ \Gamma_{11};\ \Gamma_{14}\urcorner.$$

We have

$$\mathscr{C}[\![\Gamma]\!]\rho\theta = (\mathit{fix}(\lambda\langle\theta_1,\theta_4\rangle.$$
$$\langle\mathscr{C}[\![\text{let } I_2 = \text{rt}(\Gamma_{11}\text{;goto } I_4)\text{in}(\Gamma_{12}\text{;call } \Gamma_3;\Gamma_{13})]\!]\rho'\theta_4,\ \mathscr{C}[\![\Gamma_{14}]\!]\rho'\theta\rangle$$

where $\rho' = \rho[\theta_1 \text{ in } D/\ _1][\theta_4 \text{ in } D/I_4]$ $))\downarrow 1.$

As the I's do not occur free in the Γ's, we can say

$$\mathscr{C}[\![I_i]\!]\rho' = \mathscr{C}[\![I_i]\!]\rho = \gamma_i \quad (i=11,12,13,14).$$

This is yet another example of a pseudo fixed point equation, and so if the fixed point is $\langle\theta_1',\theta_4'\rangle$, we have

$$\theta_4' = \gamma_{14}$$

and $\theta_1' = \mathscr{C}[\![\text{let } I_2\text{=rt}(\Gamma_{11}\text{;goto } I_4)\text{in}(\Gamma_{12}\text{;call } I_3;\Gamma_{13})]\!]$
$(\rho[\theta_4 \text{ in } D/I_4])\theta_4'$

(since I_1 does not occur free).

So $\mathscr{C}[\![\Gamma]\!]\rho\theta = \theta_1'$

$$= \mathscr{E}[\![\text{rt}(\Gamma_{11}\text{;goto } I_4)]\!]\rho_2\{\lambda\delta_1.\mathscr{C}[\![\Gamma_{12}\text{;call } I_2;\Gamma_{13}]\!](\rho_2[\delta_2/I_2])\theta_4'\}$$

where $\rho_2 = \rho[\theta_4 \text{ in } D/I_4]$

$= \{\lambda\delta_2.(\gamma_{12}\circ\mathscr{C}[\![\texttt{call } I_2]\!](\rho_2[\delta_2/I_2])\circ\gamma_{13})\theta_4'\}$

$(\mathscr{C}[\![\Gamma_{11};\texttt{goto } I_4]\!]\rho_2 \text{ in } E)$

Now $\mathscr{C}[\![\texttt{call } I_2]\!](\rho_2[\delta_2/I_2]) =$

$= \lambda\theta.(\ \mathscr{E}[\![I_1]\!](\rho[\delta_2/I_2])\{\lambda\varepsilon.\mathit{Run}\ \varepsilon\theta\})$

and if δ_2 is an element of G this reduces to $(\delta_2|G)$.
Also,

$\mathscr{C}[\![\Gamma_{11};\texttt{goto } I_4]\!]\rho_2 = \gamma_{11}\circ(\lambda\theta.\ \mathscr{E}[\![I_4]\!]\rho_2\{\mathit{Jump}\})$

$= \gamma_{10}\circ(\lambda\theta.\mathit{Jump}(\theta_4' \text{ in } D))$

$= \gamma_{11}\circ(\lambda\theta.\theta_4').$

So $\mathscr{C}[\![\Gamma]\!]\rho\theta = \theta_1'$

$= \{\lambda\delta_2.(\gamma_{12}\circ(\delta_2|G)\circ\gamma_{13})\theta_4'\}(\gamma_{11}\circ(\lambda\theta.\theta_4') \text{ in } E)$

$= (\gamma_{12}\circ(\gamma_{11}\circ(\lambda\theta.\theta_4')\text{in } E|G)\circ\gamma_{13})\theta_4'$

$= (\gamma_{12}\circ\gamma_{11}\circ(\lambda\theta.\theta_4')\circ\gamma_{13})\theta_4'$

$= \gamma_{12}\circ\gamma_{11}\circ((\lambda\theta.\theta_4')\{\gamma_{13}\{\theta_4'\}\})$

$= \gamma_{12}\circ\gamma_{11}\circ\theta_4'$

$= (\gamma_{12}\circ\gamma_{11}\circ\gamma_{14})\theta$

$= \mathscr{C}[\![\Gamma_{12};\Gamma_{11};\Gamma_{14}]\!]\rho\theta$ as required.

So we have now cured the error in our earlier formalism.

Exercise

5. Repeat the proof of exercise 1 in the new scheme.

valof and resultis

We could now reintroduce the val and res construction we had earlier, but this time, because of the greater flexibility of the approach with continuations, we can define something rather more general (much closer, in fact, to the language BCPL [44]). We introduce the new syntactic forms:

E ::= valof Γ

Γ ::= resultis E

The idea is that when an expression E_0 of the form ⌜valof Γ⌝ is encountered, the command Γ is executed until a command is reached of the form ⌜resultis E_1⌝. Then E_1 is evaluated, whereupon the evaluation of E_0 ceases and the value resulting from the evaluation of E_1 is taken to be the value of the original E_0. Failure occurs if Γ terminates without reaching a resultis command.

We see that when executing Γ the continuation of E_0 must be kept at hand ready to be used when ⌜resultis E_1⌝ is reached, and we must decide where to keep it. Now valof blocks can be nested, and the matching between resultis commands and valof expressions is done lexically, in the same way as occurrences of variables are matched with the appropriate variable definition. So it would seem that the environment (rather than the state, or anything else) is the appropriate vehicle. We therefore make our environments into pairs:

$\rho \in U = [Ide \to D] \times K$

where the first component is the identifier mapping as before, and the second is an expression continuation for use by resultis commands. However, we shall make a slight abuse of notation and continue to write $\rho[\![I]\!]$ and $\rho[\delta/I]$ as before, even though we shall be referring only to the first component of ρ; moreover, we shall write $\rho[\![\mathtt{res}]\!]$ and $\rho[\kappa/\mathtt{res}]$ to refer to the second component and modifications of the second component.

This notational shorthand suggests an alternative method, namely adding res to Ide as a new special identifier, not accessible to the programmer, and adding K to the domain D; U would then still be simply Ide→D. But this would be clumsy, as it would imply not only that expression continuations could be denoted by ordinary identifiers, which (for this language) is not the case, but also that res could denote values such as integers. So we prefer to keep D as the domain of denotable values, and change instead the structure of U.

Now we can give the new semantic equations.

$$\mathcal{E}[\![\mathtt{valof}\ \Gamma]\!]\rho\kappa = \mathcal{C}[\![\Gamma]\!](\rho[\kappa/\mathtt{res}])\{\mathit{Wrong}\} \qquad (11.26)$$

The continuation *Wrong* is used if Γ terminates without encountering a resultis. The other equation is just as might be expected:

$$\mathcal{C}[\![\mathtt{resultis}\ \mathrm{E}]\!]\rho\theta = \mathcal{E}[\![\mathrm{E}]\!]\rho\{\rho[\![\mathtt{res}]\!]\} \qquad (11.27)$$

Exercise.

6. Show that we can now deal correctly with jumps out of definitions, by showing that

```
⌜begin I1: let I2 = valof(Γ11;
                          goto I5;
                          Γ12;
                          resultis E)
                    in Γ13;
             Γ14;
          I5: Γ15
  end⌝                  ≡ ⌜Γ11;Γ15⌝
```

if the I's do not occur free in the Γ's or I.

break and return

We can use the technique we employed for resultis (for taking us out of a valof block) to provide other kinds of exit commands too. Let us introduce the following two commands:

Γ ::= break|return

to make exits from the smallest enclosing while-loop and routine respectively. Again we must augment the structure of the environment, this time to include the two requisite command continuations. So

$\rho \in U = [\mathrm{Ide} \to D] \times K \times C \times C.$

We use similar notational devices as previously, now with brk and ret in addition to res. We must alter the clauses for ⌜while E do Γ⌝ and ⌜rt Γ⌝ to make the appropriate changes to the environment. So now we have

$$\mathscr{C}[\![\mathrm{while}\ E\ \mathrm{do}\ \Gamma]\!]\rho\theta = \mathit{fix}(\lambda\theta'.\ \mathscr{E}[\![E]\!]\rho'\{\mathit{Cond}(\mathscr{C}[\![\Gamma]\!]\rho'\theta',\theta)\})$$

$$\text{where } \rho' = \rho[\theta/\mathrm{brk}]. \qquad (11.28 \text{ replacing } 11.7)$$

$$\mathscr{C}[\![\mathrm{break}]\!]\rho\theta = \rho[\![\mathrm{brk}]\!] \qquad (11.29)$$

$$\mathscr{E}[\![\mathrm{rt}\ \Gamma]\!]\rho\kappa = \kappa(\lambda\theta.\mathscr{C}[\![\Gamma]\!](\rho[\theta/\mathrm{ret}])\theta\ \mathrm{in}\ E) \qquad (11.30)$$

$$\mathscr{C}[\![\mathrm{return}]\!]\rho\theta = \rho[\![\mathrm{ret}]\!] \qquad (11.31)$$

Notice that this alteration means that it is no longer true that ⌜call(rt Γ)⌝≡ Γ. This result now holds only if (under the obvious interpretation) return does not occur free in Γ.

Exercises

7. Prove this result.

Prove the following equivalences, giving any restrictions on their validity.

8. $\ulcorner$let I = rt Γ in call I$\urcorner$ ≡ $\ulcorner$call rt Γ$\urcorner$.

9. $\ulcorner$call((fn I.rt Γ)(E))$\urcorner$ ≡ $\ulcorner$let I = E in Γ$\urcorner$.

Jump-Free Commands

A class of commands with particularly regular properties may be described as *jump-free*. Such commands have the property that their continuations are eventually used, unless indeed the commands themselves fail to terminate or end in error. If such a command does end successfully, then its continuation is applied to some state, which may or may not be the original state; and it is useful to consider explicitly the state transformation corresponding to the command. Similar considerations apply to expressions; and in fact if we suitably confine our attention to the jump-free situation we can salvage some of our earlier techniques, of pre-continuation semantics.

It might be thought that a command which ends in error should not be called jump-free, since such a catastrophe usually results in a jump into the operating system. But it is preferable to define jump-freeness in a way which allows a purely *syntactic* check to tell that a command is jump-free: this would obviously be impracticable if an error stop were to be treated as a jump. Moreover, if parallel processing was involved (see, for example, [21]) then things would be still more complicated, as the failing process might have spawned various offspring processes which would need abortion. So it is perhaps appropriate not to regard a catastrophic error as a jump, but to rely on some *deus ex machina* to bring the proceedings to a suitable conclusion.

In our semantics a command which ends in error applies *Wrong* to some state. For the sake of simplicity in this section, we shall assume that *Wrong* is merely $\lambda\sigma.?_A$. This makes for a less complicated formulation of jump-freeness - if a more general form of *Wrong* is allowed, the equality between the two sides of 11.32 would have to be replaced by a more elaborate relation; but results such as Theorem 11.34 would not be affected by the change.

We may thus define the property we have in mind as follows.

11.32. Definition. A command Γ in some environment ρ, or γ, is *jump-free* if there exists a completely strict $\psi \in S \rightarrow S$ such that for all θ:

$$\mathscr{C}[\![\Gamma]\!]\rho\theta = \gamma\theta = (strict\ \theta)\circ\psi.$$

So ψ is the state transformation corresponding to γ. (In particular, if the domain A happens to be S, so that C is S→S, then by putting $\theta = I_C$ we would get $\gamma I = (strict\ I)\circ\psi$; so we could reformulate the condition that γ is jump-free as $\gamma\theta = (strict\ \theta)\circ(\gamma I)$.) Note that the function *strict* is used here to avoid the possibility of some non-strict θ "recovering" after a non-terminating or erroneous computation.

An *expression* is jump-free if it yields a value to

its continuation, with or without a side-effect. So E in ρ, or ω, is jump-free if there exist completely strict χ in $S \to E$ and ψ in $S \to S$ such that

$$\mathcal{E}[\![E]\!]\rho\kappa\sigma = \omega\rho\kappa\sigma = (\mathit{strict}\ \kappa\ (\chi\sigma))(\psi\sigma) \text{ for all } \kappa,\sigma.$$

11.33. Definition. An expression is *without side-effects* if, in addition to the above, $\psi = I$, so that for all κ and σ:

$$\omega\kappa\sigma = (\mathit{strict}\ \kappa)(\chi\sigma)\sigma.$$

Notice that we are saying here that an expression which fails to terminate or has an error *ipso facto* has a side-effect, because changing a state to $\perp$ or applying *Wrong* would not be the identity transformation.

Let us introduce the infix combinator $\circledast$, with the definition

$$(f \circledast g)\sigma = f(g\sigma)\sigma.$$

Using this, we can restate the condition for ω to be without side-effects as that there exists a completely strict χ such that $\omega\kappa = (\mathit{strict}\ \kappa) \circledast \chi$ for all κ.

Jump-free Loops With these definitions we now prove the following theorem.

11.34. Theorem. If E_0 is without side-effects and Γ_0 is jump-free then ⌜while E_0 do Γ_0⌝ is jump-free.

Proof: We shall assume that the command break does not occur free (in the obvious sense) in Γ_0 (note that if it did and could ever be obeyed then Γ_0 would not be jump-free, so that this assumption is not too drastic.) Let $\omega_0 = \mathscr{E}[\![E_0]\!]\rho$, $\gamma_0 = \mathscr{C}[\![\Gamma_0]\!]\rho$ and $\gamma_1 = \mathscr{C}[\![\texttt{while } E_0 \texttt{ do } \Gamma_0]\!]\rho$. We are assuming that there exist a completely strict χ_0 such that $\omega_0\kappa = (\mathit{strict}\ \kappa)\circledast\chi_0$ for all κ, and a completely strict ψ_0 such that $\gamma_0\theta = (\mathit{strict}\ \theta)\circ\psi_0$ for all θ; and we have to prove that there is also a completely strict ψ_1 such that $\gamma_1\theta = (\mathit{strict}\ \theta)\circ\psi_1$ for all θ. Using either 11.7 or the newer form 11.28, together with the obvious extension of Lemma 8.11, we have $\psi_1\theta = \mathit{fix}(H_\theta)$ where $H_\theta(\theta') = \omega_0\{\mathit{Cond}(\gamma_0\theta',\theta)\}$. Using our assumptions, remembering that *Cond* is already completely strict, we obtain

$$H_\theta(\theta') = \mathit{Cond}((\mathit{strict}\ \theta')\circ\psi_0,\theta)\circledast\chi_0.$$

We shall now show that our required ψ_1 is $\mathit{fix}(H)$, where $H : [S\to S]\to[S\to S]$ is defined by

$$H(\psi') = \mathit{Cond}((\mathit{strict}\ \psi')\circ\psi_0,I)\circledast\chi_0.$$

We immediately note, since $\mathit{fix}(H) = H(\mathit{fix}(H))$, that $\mathit{fix}(H)$ is completely strict. For the main result, namely that for all θ, $\mathit{fix}(H_\theta) = (\mathit{strict}\ \theta)\circ(\mathit{fix}(H))$, we shall use fixpoint induction. Since $\mathit{strict}(\theta)$ is strict we have immediately that $\bot = (\mathit{strict}\ \theta)\circ\bot$; so now we assume that $\theta_1 = (\mathit{strict}\ \theta)\circ\psi_1$ and must prove that $H_\theta(\theta_1) = (\mathit{strict}\ \theta)\circ(H(\psi_1))$. We have

$$\begin{aligned} H_\theta(\theta_1) &= \mathit{Cond}((\mathit{strict}((\mathit{strict}\ \theta)\circ\psi_1))\circ\psi_0,\theta)\circledast\chi_0 \\ &= \mathit{Cond}((\mathit{strict}\ \theta)\circ(\mathit{strict}\ \psi_1)\circ\psi_0,\theta)\circledast\chi_0 \\ &= \mathit{Cond}((\mathit{strict}\ \theta)\circ(\mathit{strict}\ \psi_1)\circ\psi_0,\mathit{strict}\ \theta)\circledast\chi_0 \end{aligned}$$

(since, as χ_0 is completely strict, the arms of *Cond* are never used on improper states)

$$= (\mathit{strict}\ \theta)\circ \mathit{Cond}((\mathit{strict}\ \psi_1)\circ\psi_0, I)\circledast\chi_0$$
(by 9.13 and 11.18)
$$= (\mathit{strict}\ \theta)\circ(H(\psi_1)).$$

Thus the result holds as required, for all θ; so the condition that γ_1 is jump-free is satisfied. That is to say, as we would expect, if the test of a loop is well-behaved (we have assumed, for simplicity's sake, that the test is without side-effects, but a jump-free test is sufficient) and if the body of the loop is jump-free, then so is the whole loop.

Exercises

10. Generalise this proof so that it applies to loops in which the test expression is merely jump-free.

11. Formulate and prove correct a set of syntactic constraints which are sufficient for a command, or an expression, to be jump-free in all environments. [Unfortunately you will have to be draconian and ban application completely; otherwise you would have to confine yourself to suitable environments (in which, for example, all denoted abstractions were jump-free) and trying to formulate this criterion would lead you into difficulties of circularity like those which await our attention in Chapter 13.]

Continuation Removal For any command Γ satisfying the constraints demanded by the previous exercise and for each environment ρ there exists a ψ satisfying the equation given in Definition 11.32. Let us introduce an alternative function, $\P\mathscr{C}$, to produce this ψ, so that $\P\mathscr{C}$: Cmd→U→S→S, and for all jump-free commands we have

$$\mathscr{C}[\![\Gamma]\!]\rho\theta = (\mathit{strict}\ \theta)\circ(\P\mathscr{C}[\![\Gamma]\!]\rho).$$

Similarly for jump-free expressions, for which there exist χ and ψ such that

$$\mathscr{E}[\![E]\!]\rho\kappa\sigma = \mathit{strict}\ \kappa\ (\chi\sigma)\ (\psi\sigma)$$

we let

$$\P\mathscr{E}[\![E]\!]\rho = \lambda\sigma.\langle\chi\sigma,\psi\sigma\rangle$$

so that $\P\mathscr{E}$: Exp→U→S→[E×S].

We can derive some of the properties of these alternative functions from our existing semantic equations. For example, if Γ_0 and Γ_1 are jump-free, we have

$$\begin{aligned}\mathscr{C}[\![\Gamma_0;\Gamma_1]\!]\rho\theta &= \mathscr{C}[\![\Gamma_0]\!]\rho\{\mathscr{C}[\![\Gamma_1]\!]\rho\theta\}\\ &= \mathit{strict}(\mathscr{C}[\![\Gamma_1]\!]\rho\theta)\circ(\P\mathscr{C}[\![\Gamma_0]\!]\rho)\\ &= (\mathit{strict}\ \theta)\circ(\P\mathscr{C}[\![\Gamma_1]\!]\rho)\circ(\P\mathscr{C}[\![\Gamma_0]\!]\rho).\end{aligned}$$

So $\P\mathscr{C}[\![\Gamma_0;\Gamma_1]\!]\rho = (\P\mathscr{C}[\![\Gamma_1]\!]\rho)\circ(\P\mathscr{C}[\![\Gamma_0]\!]\rho)$.

It will be noticed that this equation closely resembles equation 10.4 in our earlier scheme, before we introduced continuations. In fact for jump-free constructs it is possible to revert entirely to such a formulation. The advantage of that is that it is possible to consider the individual state transformations engendered by the component constructs, and thus more easily to discuss the intermediate states reached during the execution. We shall therefore meet jump-free commands again, when we discuss the Axiomatic Approach, in Chapter 14, since that is much concerned with making assertions about such states.

Milne and Strachey [34] discuss continuation removal allowing for more general forms of *Wrong* than the simple one we have adopted for this section. They also mention the problems of dealing with functional application, when the functionalities of abstraction values are not the same in the two formulations. When we have amassed enough apparatus we shall return to this particular point, in the final exercise of Chapter 13.

Recursion

Finally in this chapter we make good our earlier omission and introduce some clauses for recursive definitions. In the λ-calculus, a recursive definition is normally of a form like $\ulcorner Y(\lambda f. \ldots)\urcorner$. In our language we shall alter this slightly, to $\ulcorner$rec f. ...$\urcorner$. So we could add to the syntax

E ::= rec I.E

but in fact we are here really interested in $\ulcorner$rec I.E$\urcorner$ only when E is an abstraction (a function or a routine). We therefore simplify matters by confining ourselves to this case. The advantage of this is that the value of E does not depend on the state, nor does evaluating E affect the state. (Relaxing this restriction causes much complication, possibly involving the incorporation in the value of E of part, at least, of the state, for subsequent reference: Milne and Strachey [34] deal with this more general form in considerable detail.)

So we add *two* new productions to the syntax.

$E ::= \texttt{rec}\ I_0\ \texttt{fn}\ I_1.E \mid \texttt{rec}\ I\ \texttt{rt}\ \Gamma$

These two constructs introduce a name whose scope is to be the body of the expression, and which is to denote the value of the whole expression. They therefore obviously lead to fixed point formulae. The semantic equations are as follows.

$$\mathcal{E}[\![\texttt{rec}\ I_0\ \texttt{fn}\ I_1.E]\!]\rho\kappa = \kappa(\mathit{fix}(\lambda\phi.\lambda\delta.\mathcal{E}[\![E]\!](\rho[\delta/I_1][\phi\ \texttt{in}\ \mathrm{D}/I_0]))\texttt{in}\ \mathrm{E}) \quad (11.35)$$

$$\mathcal{E}[\![\texttt{rec}\ I\ \texttt{rt}\ \Gamma]\!]\rho\kappa = \kappa(\mathit{fix}(\lambda\gamma.\mathcal{G}[\![\Gamma]\!](\rho[\gamma\ \texttt{in}\ \mathrm{D}/I]))\texttt{in}\ \mathrm{E}) \quad (11.36)$$

The bound variable ϕ in the first of these is assumed to denote a value in the function domain $\mathrm{D}\to\mathrm{W}$; as usual, the γ in the second is in G, which is $\mathrm{C}\to\mathrm{C}$.

Exercise

12. The variables used recursively above, and also the parameters of functions, have been only single names. Extend the syntax and semantics of our language to allow lists of names in both these positions, thus providing for mutual recursion and for functions of more than one argument.

You have already seen (Exercises 1 and 5) how a while-loop can be written instead using labels and jumps. Let us now show that it can also be done using a recursive routine.

11.37. Theorem. Provided neither I, return nor break occurs free in E or Γ:

$$\ulcorner \mathtt{call(rec\ I\ rt\ if\ E\ then(\Gamma;call\ I)else\ dummy)} \urcorner \equiv \ulcorner \mathtt{while\ E\ do\ \Gamma} \urcorner .$$

Proof: For any θ let $\theta_0 =$ $\mathscr{C}[\![\mathtt{call(rec\ I\ rt\ if\ E\ then(\Gamma;call\ I)else\ dummy}]\!]\rho\theta$. Then

$$\theta_0 = \mathscr{E}[\![\mathtt{rec\ I\ rt\ if\ E\ then(\Gamma;call\ I)else\ dummy}]\!]\rho\{\lambda\varepsilon.\mathit{Run}\ \varepsilon\ \theta\}$$

$$= (\lambda\varepsilon.\mathit{Run}\ \varepsilon\ \theta)(\mathit{fix}(\lambda\gamma'.\mathscr{C}[\![\mathtt{if\ E\ then(\Gamma;call\ I)else\ dummy}]\!](\rho[\gamma'\ \mathtt{in}\ \mathtt{D/I}]))\mathtt{in\ E})$$

(using Lemma 8.11, since return does not occur free in E or Γ)

$$= (\lambda\varepsilon.\mathit{Run}\ \varepsilon\ \theta)(\mathit{fix}(\lambda\gamma'.\lambda\theta'.\mathscr{E}[\![\mathrm{E}]\!]\rho_{\gamma'}\{\mathit{Cond}(\mathscr{C}[\![\Gamma;\mathtt{call\ I}]\!]\rho_{\gamma'},\theta',I\theta')\})\ \mathtt{in\ E})$$

where $\rho_{\gamma'} = \rho[\gamma'\ \mathtt{in\ D/I}]$.

Now since neither I nor break occurs free in E or Γ, we can write (for any θ):

$$\mathscr{C}[\![\Gamma]\!]\rho_{\gamma'} = \mathscr{C}[\![\Gamma]\!]\rho = \mathscr{C}[\![\Gamma]\!](\rho[\theta/\mathtt{brk}]) = \gamma,$$
$$\mathscr{E}[\![\mathrm{E}]\!]\rho_{\gamma'} = \mathscr{E}[\![\mathrm{E}]\!]\rho = \mathscr{E}[\![\mathrm{E}]\!](\rho[\theta/\mathtt{brk}]) = \omega.$$

And also

$$\mathscr{C}[\![\mathtt{call\ I}]\!]\rho_{\gamma'},\theta' = \mathscr{E}[\![\mathrm{I}]\!]\rho_{\gamma'},\{\lambda\varepsilon'.\mathit{Run}\ \varepsilon'\theta'\} = (\gamma'\ \mathtt{in\ D|G})\theta' = \gamma'\theta'.$$

So

$$\theta_0 = (\lambda\varepsilon.\mathit{Run}\varepsilon\theta)(\mathit{fix}(\lambda\gamma'\lambda\theta'.\omega\{\mathit{Cond}((\gamma\circ\gamma')\theta',\theta')\})\mathtt{in\ E})$$
$$= \mathit{fix}(\lambda\gamma'\lambda\theta'.\omega\{\mathit{Cond}((\gamma\circ\gamma')\theta',\theta')\})\theta$$
$$= \mathit{fix}(\lambda\theta'.\omega\{\mathit{Cond}(\gamma\theta',\theta)\}) \qquad \text{(Exercise 2)}$$
$$= \mathscr{C}[\![\mathtt{while\ E\ do\ \Gamma}]\!]\rho\theta$$

as required.

Chapter 12

ASSIGNMENT AND THE STORE

The State

So far we have not come across any commands which actually change the state of the machine: we have been relying in a vague kind of way on the primitives, Pri and possibly Pre, to alter σ, for nothing else will. So it is high time that we discussed the assignment command.

Let us first look at some examples.

$$x := y$$
$$y := (\text{if } a{>}b \text{ then } a \text{ else } b)$$
$$(\text{if } a{>}b \text{ then } a \text{ else } b) := y$$
$$n := n{+}1$$

Obviously the constructs on each side of the assignment operator are expressions, and thus the syntax of the assignment command is

$$\Gamma ::= E_0 := E_1 \quad .$$

Equally obviously (consider in particular the fourth example) the two expressions are to be treated somewhat differently. Let us use the term *L-value* for the result of evaluating an expression on the left hand side of an assignment, and *R-value* for the result of evaluating one on the right. Clearly an L-value will be something like an address in memory, and an R-value will be something which could be its contents. The assignment command causes the contents associated with the particular L-value to be changed.

To formalise all this we introduce a new flat lattice, L, of *locations*, which may be finite or countably infinite in number. (Notice that at this level of abstraction we are not assuming that the locations are numbered off in any particular way.) L will be a component of D.

D = T + C + ... + L.

An L-value, α, will be an element of L. R-values, on the other hand, are elements of a domain of "storable values", which we shall call V. We make V different from D, as it is not necessarily true that everything that can be denoted can also be stored (or *vice versa*). For example, in Algol 60 procedures and strings would be in D but not in V, while integers and reals would be in V but not D. The domain E of expression results is often D+V, but again there is no logical necessity for this. Actually in our own example language we shall be fairly liberal, and let all sorts of things be stored which many languages would forbid.

The state σ includes, among other things, a mapping from L to V. So after obeying a command like

x := 3

the situation is as shown in Fig. 12.1.

Fig. 12.1. The environment and the store.

The association between the name $\ulcorner x \urcorner$ and the location is part of the environment; the association between the location and its content is part of the state. Some workers (e.g. Austin Henderson [16]) prefer to think of each location or cell as having its own private contents function, rather than one single global state σ: but this seems to be mainly a matter of notational taste.

The two-stage mapping between the name $\ulcorner x \urcorner$ and the R-value 3 is undoubtedly tiresome. It is, however, necessary if we are to be able to deal properly with such things as side effects and sharing. At a particular procedure call, for example, there may be several locations called x around: the procedure definition may be in the scope of one of them and the call in another. If the procedure body contains an assignment to x, the question then is important: "which x gets changed?". And this cannot even be asked without the locations and the resulting two-stage map in the language model. Again, if parameter passing by reference is allowed, a formal parameter of some procedure call may be denoting the same location as one of the free variable names: then there would be two different names, both accessible, and both denoting the same location, so that an assignment to one would affect the R-value denoted by the other. An explanation of this also requires explicit locations. Definitions by reference (as allowed, for example, in Algol 68), also cause this problem.

Separating environment from state allows us to prescribe different behaviours for them in the semantics, to avoid difficulties of implementation. On the one hand we may make state changes irreversible, because it is not normally possible to copy and reinstate the contents of the entire computer store; on the other hand, environments, which can be dealt with largely at compile time, do not normally have very many names in play, and so preservation and restoration of the environment is usually quite practicable.

If, however, in some particularly simple language none of these problems could arise, then it might be preferable to describe it in terms of a single mapping, directly from names to R-values, without mentioning locations at all (the complexity of the left hand expression in an assignment command would have to be severely restricted). We would then lose the property of our language according to which each occurrence of a name denotes the same value throughout the scope of its definition, where the scope may be determined merely by a superficial glance at the program: for the environment would now be dynamically varying. This property was a facet of referential transparency, and we have discussed its advantages at some length. But its benefit is doubtful if the only thing about a name that remains constant is the location, for except when specifically analysing matters such as side effects we are really more interested in the R-values, whose dynamic behaviour requires different techniques.

As most languages are *not* as simple as this, however, we shall continue to study the two-map model.

So far, we know that the state contains a contents mapping, in $[L \to V]$. This is not quite enough information, however: we also need to know which of the locations are in use. So we will have another function, from locations to truth values, which gives *true* if a particular location is in use. We call these two functions the *Map* and the *Area* of a state σ, so that

$Map(\sigma) \in [L \to V]$

$Area(\sigma) \in [L \to T]$.

We shall say that $\sigma \sqsubseteq \sigma'$ if $Map(\sigma) \sqsubseteq Map(\sigma')$ and $Area(\sigma) \sqsubseteq Area(\sigma')$. So, ignoring input/output completely for now, a possible model for states would be

$S = [L \to V] \times [L \to T]$

with $Map(\sigma) = \sigma{\downarrow}1$ and $Area(\sigma) = \sigma{\downarrow}2$. Other models are equally possible (for example $S = [L \to [T \times V]]$), but this is the one we shall adopt.

Primitive store functions

We next define some functions acting on the store.

1. *Conts*: $[L \to [S \to V]]$

$Conts(\alpha)(\sigma) = Area(\sigma)(\alpha) \to Map(\sigma)(\alpha), ?.$ (12.1)

Notice that the contents of location α in state σ is an error result if α is not in the area of σ.

2. *Update*: $[[L \times V] \to [S \to S]]$

Update is the first function to specify a state transformation. $Update(\alpha,\beta)\sigma$ produces a new state σ′ such that the contents of α in σ′ is β and everything else is as it was. We may define the effect by axioms.

If α and β are proper:

$$Map(Update(\alpha,\beta)\sigma) \;=\; \lambda\alpha'.(\alpha=\alpha')\rightarrow\beta, Map(\sigma)\alpha' \qquad (12.2)$$

$$Area(Update(\alpha,\beta)\sigma) \;=\; Area(\sigma). \qquad (12.3)$$

We shall also assume that *Update* is very and completely strict, so that the result is improper if either α or β is improper. This appears somewhat arbitrary and ought really to be justified. But we shall not do so, as it would lead us into some complications: for a fuller account see Robert Milne's thesis [33]. We shall assume, too, that *Update*(α,β) is completely strict. We could therefore give the definition of *Update* by the following equation:

$$Update(\alpha,\beta) \;=\; strict(\lambda\sigma.\; strict(\lambda\alpha.strict(\lambda\beta.\; \langle(\lambda\alpha'.\alpha'=\alpha\rightarrow\beta, Map\sigma\alpha'), Area\;\sigma\rangle\;)\beta\;)\alpha\;) \qquad (12.4)$$

but the axiomatic definition may be more useful at this stage.

We shall need to find new and unused locations as a program proceeds, so our third function is:

3. *New*: [S→L]
New(σ) for proper σ is a location not in the area of σ, so

$$Area(\sigma)(New(\sigma)) = false. \qquad (12.5)$$

For proper σ, *New*(σ) is proper provided there is an α such that *Area*(σ)α = *false*. Notice that we do not want to imply that *New*(σ) depends only on *Area*(σ) and is independent of *Map*(σ), as this ought to be an implementation decision. That is, although we do of course insist that if $\sigma_1 = \sigma_2$ then $New(\sigma_1) = New(\sigma_2)$, we do not wish to insist that if merely $Area(\sigma_1) = Area(\sigma_2)$ then $New(\sigma_1) = New(\sigma_2)$. (However, notice that if $Area(\sigma_1) = Area(\sigma_2)$ then also $Area(\sigma_1) = Area(\sigma_1 \sqcup \sigma_2)$; moreover, by monotonicity $New(\sigma_1 \sqcup \sigma_2) \sqsupseteq New(\sigma_1)$, so that since L is a flat lattice, $New(\sigma_1) = New(\sigma_1 \sqcup \sigma_2) = New(\sigma_2)$. Thus the unwelcome restriction seems to have crept in anyway. But note that $\sigma_1 \sqcup \sigma_2$ is not necessarily proper even if σ_1 and σ_2 are, so that all this is another of the complications about the properties of improper stores which we have agreed to ignore, and which are expounded by Milne [33].)

Having found a new location we need to adjoin it to the area in use, and to remove it again at the end of its extent. So the remaining two functions, *Extend* and *Lose*, are for this purpose.

4. *Extend*: $L \to S \to S$

$Map \circ Extend(\alpha) = Map$ (12.6)

$Area(Extend(\alpha)\sigma)(\alpha') = (\alpha = \alpha') \to true, Area(\sigma)\alpha'$
(assuming all values are proper). (12.7)

5. *Lose*: $L \to S \to S$

$Map \circ Lose(\alpha) = Map$

$Area(Lose(\alpha)\sigma)(\alpha') = (\alpha = \alpha') \to false, Area(\sigma)\alpha'$ (12.8)
(again assuming all values are proper). (12.9)

(Instead of the two functions *Extend* and *Lose* we could have defined a single function more analogous to *Update*:

AlterArea: $[L \times T] \to [S \to S]$

$Map \circ AlterArea(\alpha, \tau) = Map$

$Area(AlterArea(\alpha, \tau)\sigma)\alpha' = (\alpha = \alpha' \to \tau, Area(\sigma)\alpha')$.

In this case our *Extend*(α) would be *AlterArea*(α,*true*) and *Lose*(α) would be *AlterArea*(α,*false*).)

Store Functions with Continuations

We have now defined the set of primitive functions acting on the store. But it is convenient immediately to give another set, this time involving continuations. A particular advantage of this, besides making our style generally more uniform, is that we shall be able to arrange that the error continuation *Wrong* gets used automatically in appropriate situations without having to test for error explicitly in the semantic equations themselves.

The new functions are *Contents*, *Assign*, *Newstore* and *Release*, corresponding respectively to *Conts*, *Update*, *New* and *Lose*. They are defined as follows.

$$Contents\,\alpha\kappa\sigma = Area\,\sigma\alpha \rightarrow \kappa(Map\,\sigma\alpha)\sigma,\ Wrong\,\sigma \qquad (12.10)$$

$$Assign\,\alpha\beta\sigma = \alpha\in L \wedge \beta\in V \rightarrow \theta\circ Update(\alpha,\beta),\ Wrong \qquad (12.11)$$

$$Newstore\,\kappa\sigma = New\,\sigma = ? \rightarrow Wrong\,\sigma,\ \kappa(New\,\sigma)(Extend(New\,\sigma)\sigma) \qquad (12.12)$$

$$Release\,\alpha\theta\sigma = Area\,\sigma\alpha \rightarrow \theta(Lose\,\alpha\sigma),\ Wrong\,\sigma. \qquad (12.13)$$

We now have sufficient apparatus to approach the semantics of the assignment statement itself.

The Assignment Command

Syntax

$\Gamma ::= E_1 := E_2$

Value Domains We adjoin L to D, and introduce a new domain V of storable values. So we have

$\delta \in D = T + N + C + [D \to W] + G + L.$

We shall use α for values in L. We also let

$\beta \in V = T + N + C + [D \to W] + G$

thus allowing functions, routines and labels to be first-class citizens. Since all of V is in D we put $\varepsilon \in E = D$. By a slight licence of notation, we shall treat V as a subcomponent of E, and allow $(\varepsilon | V)$, say, thus collapsing a small hierarchy.

Semantic Functions We have seen already that we need to evaluate an expression in either of two ways: in *L-mode* to produce an L-value, or in *R-mode* to produce an R-value. For most expressions, one or other of these is more natural. For example, if I denotes a location α, then L-mode would be the natural way to evaluate I: for R-mode, in fact, one would first evaluate the L-value and then take the contents. ⌜I + 3⌝, on the other hand, has no associated location, so R-mode would be the natural way to evaluate it. The normal mode of evaluation we shall call *E-mode*, and continue to use $\mathcal{E}$ for the corresponding semantic function. We also introduce new functions, $\mathcal{L}$ and $\mathcal{R}$, for L-mode and R-mode evaluation. Thus for our previous example, where I denotes $\alpha \in L$, so that $\rho[\![I]\!] = \alpha$ in D, we have:

$\mathcal{L}[\![I]\!]\rho\kappa = \kappa\alpha$, and $\mathcal{E}[\![I]\!]\rho\kappa = \kappa(\alpha \text{ in } E)$

$\mathcal{R}[\![I]\!]\rho\kappa = \mathit{Contents}\,\alpha\kappa.$

On the other hand, if I′ denotes an integer $\nu \in N$, then

$\mathcal{R}[\![I']\!]\rho\kappa = \kappa\nu$, and $\mathcal{E}[\![I']\!] = \kappa(\nu \text{ in } E)$.

What should be done about $\mathcal{L}[\![I']\!]\rho\kappa$? This is a choice of language design, and we give two alternative possibilities.

1. An attempt to find the L-value of such an I' is an error; so we have simply

$\mathcal{L}[\![I']\!]\rho\kappa = \mathit{Wrong}$.

2. We find a new location, initialise its contents to (ν in V), and use that location. To specify this we use the store functions *Newstore* and *Assign*. So

$\mathcal{L}[\![I']\!]\rho\kappa = \mathcal{E}[\![I']\!]\rho\{\lambda\varepsilon.\mathit{Newstore}\{\lambda\alpha.\mathit{Assign}\alpha(\varepsilon|V)\{\kappa\alpha\}\}\}$.

The reader is recommended to study this equation carefully, so that the way the continuation mechanism is working is clearly understood.

We must now generalise all this, so that we can cope with arbitrary expressions, taking into account, too, any possible side effects in their evaluation and forcing the answer into the required mode. The easiest way is to introduce new functions *lv* and *rv*, which are intended to operate on expression continuations. They convert a continuation expecting a particular kind of value into one which accepts a general expression value and converts it if necessary. So *lv* and *rv* are of the following functionalities:

lv: $[L \rightarrow C] \rightarrow [E \rightarrow C]$
rv: $[V \rightarrow C] \rightarrow [E \rightarrow C]$

where, as usual, C is S→A. (We shall, perhaps loosely, use κ for elements of L→C and V→C as well as the usual E→C.) For all E, ρ and suitable κ we define:

$$\mathcal{L}[\![E]\!]\rho\kappa = \mathcal{E}[\![E]\!]\rho\{lv\kappa\} \tag{12.14}$$

$$\mathcal{R}[\![E]\!]\rho\kappa = \mathcal{E}[\![E]\!]\rho\{rv\kappa\}. \tag{12.15}$$

lv and *rv* may be defined as follows.

$$lv = \lambda\kappa\lambda\varepsilon.\ \varepsilon\mathsf{E}\mathsf{L} \rightarrow \kappa(\varepsilon|\mathsf{L}),\quad \varepsilon\mathsf{E}\mathsf{V} \rightarrow \mathit{Newstore}\{\lambda\alpha.\mathit{Assign}\alpha(\varepsilon|\mathsf{V})\{\kappa\alpha\}\},\quad \mathit{Wrong}. \tag{12.16}$$

$$rv = \lambda\kappa\lambda\varepsilon.\ \varepsilon\mathsf{E}\mathsf{L} \rightarrow \mathit{Contents}(\varepsilon|\mathsf{L})\kappa,\quad \varepsilon\mathsf{E}\mathsf{V} \rightarrow \kappa(\varepsilon|\mathsf{V}),\quad \mathit{Wrong}. \tag{12.17}$$

Now at last we can give the semantics of the assignment command. Firstly, assuming left-to-right evaluation, we have:

$$\mathscr{C}[\![E_1 := E_2]\!]\rho\theta = \mathcal{L}[\![E_1]\!]\rho\{\lambda\alpha.\ \mathcal{R}[\![E_2]\!]\rho\{\lambda\beta.\mathit{Assign}\alpha\beta\theta\}\} \tag{12.18}$$

and, secondly, using the list evaluator *le*:

$$\mathscr{C}[\![E_1 := E_2]\!]\rho\theta = le\ \langle\mathcal{L}[\![E_1]\!]\rho, \mathcal{R}[\![E_2]\!]\rho\rangle\{\lambda\langle\alpha,\beta\rangle.\mathit{Assign}\alpha\beta\theta\}. \tag{12.19}$$

Notice that the definition of *Assign* (12.11) actually specifies the application of the continuation θ. This, together with the equations above, tells us that if E_1 and E_2 are jump-free then so is $\ulcorner E_1 := E_2 \urcorner$.

Initialised Definition

So far the only definitions we have are of the form

$\ulcorner$let I = E in Γ$\urcorner$

for commands, and similarly for expressions. In the bodies of these, I denotes simply the result of evaluating E in E-mode: we call this *definition by denotation*. Let us now introduce one more form, which we shall write as follows.

Γ ::= let I := E in Γ

We call this an *initialised definition*. The general idea is that a new location is allocated and its contents initialised to the result of E; in the body I will denote this new location.

We have a choice about the extent of this new location (not about the *scope* of I, which is as usual). The store is extended at definition time; but we can choose whether to lose the new location after execution of the body, or to retain it indefinitely. In the old days before jumps each would be equally simple. The first would be specified by something such as

$$\mathit{Lose}(\alpha)\circ\mathscr{C}[\![\Gamma]\!]\rho'\circ\mathit{Extend}(\alpha)$$

and for the second we would merely omit the $\mathit{Lose}(\alpha)$. But now limited extents bring the following kinds of extra complication:

1. Jumps out of the scope of a definition would have to reset the area correctly. So the value of a label would have to include the area, as well as the usual θ value in C. It therefore has to be computed at run time when the area is set, on block entry. This considerably complicates the clause for the semantics of labels.

2. Having labels as storable values makes matters even worse; for then, by assigning a label to a variable of larger scope, we can have the possibility of jumping back into a block again. The trouble here is that a location might be released and then re-

allocated by *Newstore* for some quite different purpose when it was still accessible in its former role via a label closure.

3. First-class procedures also bring the same kind of problem (the so-called upward funarg problem).

We therefore sidestep all these problems by assuming indefinite extents. Peter Mosses's account of the semantics of Algol 60 [36] is an example of the other decision. Note that we are not saying that the extents of variables are *really* everlasting: the implementation can provide a suitable garbage collector algorithm for retrieving for reuse those locations which have become inaccessible. Robert Milne also discusses this formally in his thesis [33].

Our new semantic clause may therefore be written as follows:

$$\mathscr{C}[\![\text{let I := E in }\Gamma]\!]\rho\theta = \mathcal{R}[\![E]\!]\rho\{\lambda\beta.\mathit{Newstore}\{\lambda\alpha.\mathit{Assign}\,\alpha\beta\{\mathscr{C}[\![\Gamma]\!](\rho[\alpha\text{ in D/I}])\theta\}\}\}. \quad (12.20)$$

Alternatively, (for many languages) we may make use of the function *lv* defined above (12.16), and write somewhat more concisely:

$$\mathscr{C}[\![\text{let I := E in }\Gamma\,\rho\theta = \mathcal{R}[\![E]\!]\rho\{\lambda\beta.\mathit{lv}(\lambda\alpha.\mathscr{C}[\![\Gamma]\!](\rho[\alpha\text{ in D/I}])\theta)(\beta\text{ in E})\}. \quad (12.21)$$

Yet another way is to use an auxiliary equation. We could say

$$\ulcorner\text{let I := E in }\Gamma\urcorner \equiv \ulcorner\text{let I = copy(E) in }\Gamma\urcorner. \quad (12.22)$$

Here, the copy operator is supposed to give a new

location initialised to the R-value of E; so

$$\mathcal{E}[\![\text{copy}(E)]\!]\rho\kappa = \mathcal{R}[\![E]\!]\rho\{\lambda\beta.\,lv\,\kappa(\beta \text{ in } E)\}. \qquad (12.23)$$

Exercise

1. For what sort of language could we *not* use 12.21 as an alternative to 12.20, even if *lv* were defined as in 12.46?

Parameter Passing

Besides definitions, the other principal way in which we introduce new names into programs is as formal parameters in function or routine definitions; and just as there are several possible forms of definition, so there are similarly various different ways of passing parameters. The only version we have so far encountered (11.22 and 11.23) corresponds to our first form of definition: the new formal parameter name is associated with the E-value of the actual parameter in the function call. This version, though simple to describe, is not commonly available in any actually existing programming language. The version corresponding to initialised definition is much more widespread — it is, for example, Algol 60's call by value — so we now give its definition too.

The way a parameter is to be passed is usually specified as part of the function definition (though it would be equally possible to do so instead at each application of the function). We shall therefore retain, for the present, just one equation for application — that given above (11.23), in which the parameter is evaluated in E-mode, — and specify any further coercion required as part of the equation for abstraction. Thus, for call by value, we first require a new location initialised to that R-value. So, instead of the simple form of abstraction

$$\mathcal{E}[\![\mathrm{fn}\,I.E]\!]\rho\kappa = \kappa((\lambda\varepsilon.\ \mathcal{E}[\![E]\!](\rho[\varepsilon\ \mathrm{in}\ D/I]))\mathrm{in}\ E)$$

we have, employing the same trick as in 12.21 of using *lv*:

$$\mathcal{E}[\![\mathrm{fn\ val}\ I.E]\!]\rho\kappa = \kappa((\lambda\varepsilon.\lambda\kappa'.rv(\lambda\beta.lv(\lambda\alpha.\ \mathcal{E}[\![E]\!](\rho[\alpha\ \mathrm{in}\ D/I])\kappa')(\beta\ \mathrm{in}\ E))\varepsilon)\mathrm{in}\ E). \quad (12.24)$$

Notice carefully why κ' now has to make an explicit appearance.

If desired, the alternative ways of doing the equation for initialised definition can also be employed for call by value.

Exercises

2. Give an equation for abstraction with call by value which uses *Newstore* explicitly instead of using *lv*.

3. Give equations for abstractions with parameters called by R-value and by L-value (the latter is generally known as "call by reference"). Do you know any languages which use these methods of passing parameters?

Call by Name We now consider a more complicated form of parameter passing, available in Algol 60 as "call by name". We do this principally to provide a further example of the flexibility of our definition techniques: we are not implying that call by name should be a part of every programming language.

In call by name, the actual parameter of a function

application is not evaluated immediately; instead, it is evaluated afresh whenever the formal parameter is used during execution of the function body. To specify this, we must not only change the equation for abstraction, but we must also alter the definition of application so as to arrange that the parameter is not necessarily evaluated at once, and of identifiers themselves so that if a name denotes an unevaluated expression the evaluation may be done when required.

The value of a parameter passed by name will be of the form $\mathcal{E}[\![E]\!]\rho$; the actual parameter expression will always be evaluated using the environment of the function call, but a continuation and store will be supplied each time the parameter is evaluated during the function's execution. The parameter's functionality is therefore $W = K \to C$, and the functionality of the function value itself is therefore $W \to W$. The abstraction equation might therefore be

$$\mathcal{E}[\![\textbf{fn name } I.E]\!]\rho\kappa = \kappa(\lambda\omega.\ \mathcal{E}[\![E]\!](\rho[\omega \textbf{ in } D/I])\textbf{in } E). \tag{12.25}$$

Note that this implies that E will have $[W{\to}W]$ as a subcomponent, in which the value supplied to κ in this equation will belong. D has to have W as a subcomponent, for the parameters of these abstractions.

If we decide that a language should also include other abstractions besides those with parameters called by name, then E will also have a subcomponent $F = D \to W$ for them. So our equation for application can use a test on type to find out what kind of function is being used:

$$\mathcal{E}[\![E_0(E_1)]\!]\rho\kappa = \mathcal{R}[\![E_0]\!]\rho\{\lambda\varepsilon_0.\varepsilon_0\in[W\to W]\to(\varepsilon_0|W\to W)(\mathcal{E}[\![E_1]\!]\rho)\kappa,\ \varepsilon_0\in F\to\mathcal{E}[\![E_1]\!]\rho\{\lambda\varepsilon_1.(\varepsilon_0|F)\varepsilon_1\kappa\},\ \mathit{Wrong}\}. \quad (12.26)$$

Similarly, the equation for identifiers uses a type test to determine whether the denoted value needs further evaluation.

$$\mathcal{E}[\![I]\!]\rho\kappa = (\lambda\varepsilon.\varepsilon=?\to\mathit{Wrong},\ \varepsilon\in W\to(\varepsilon|W)\kappa,\ \kappa\varepsilon\ )(\rho[\![I]\!]).$$

Exercises

4. Why should call by name not be a part of every programming language?

5. In this definition of call by name, as in Algol 60, the actual parameter is evaluated, whenever required, in the environment of the function call. Revise the definition so as to use instead the environment in force where the formal parameter is used.

Our Complete Example Language

We are now ready to present the complete definition we have been building up. This will differ in two ways from the pieces we have presented along the way. First, we shall now change $\mathcal{E}$ to $\mathcal{L}$ or $\mathcal{R}$ where appropriate. Second, we repair the lack of any form of numerical constant. We bring back the syntactic category:

$N \in \mathrm{Nml}$ (numerals)

and extend the expression syntax:

$E ::= N\ .$

We introduce a new semantic function $\mathcal{N}$: Nml $\rightarrow$ N, which would be defined as in Chapter 3 (though probably for decimal numerals rather than binary); and the new clause:

$\mathcal{E}[\![N]\!]\rho\kappa = \kappa(\mathcal{N}[\![N]\!]$ in E).

The complete definition is given in Table 12.1. Some of the clauses are given in two forms: a simpler form assuming left to right evaluation, and one involving *le*.

Table 12.1. The Example Language

Syntactic Categories

I ∈ Ide	(identifiers)
Γ ∈ Com	(commands)
E ∈ Exp	(expressions)
Φ ∈ Pri	(some primitive commands)
Π ∈ Pre	(some primitive predicates)
Ω ∈ Ops	(some binary operators)
N ∈ Nml	(numerals)

Syntax

Γ ::= Φ | dummy |
if E then Γ_1 else Γ_2 | Γ_1;Γ_2 | while E do Γ |
let I = E in Γ | let I := E in Γ |
goto E | begin I_1:Γ_1;I_2:Γ_2;...;I_n:Γ_n end |
(all I_i distinct, $1 \le i \le n$)
call E | resultis E | break | return | Γ repeatwhile E |
E_1 := E_2

Table 12.1 (continued)

$$E ::= I \mid \Pi \mid \texttt{true} \mid \texttt{false} \mid N \mid E_1 \Omega E_2 \mid \texttt{if } E_0 \texttt{ then } E_1 \texttt{ else } E_2 \mid$$
$$\texttt{let } I = E_1 \texttt{ in } E_2 \mid \texttt{let } I := E_1 \texttt{ in } E_2 \mid E_1(E_2) \mid$$
$$\texttt{fn } I.E \mid \texttt{rt } \Gamma \mid \texttt{valof } \Gamma \mid \texttt{rec } I_0 \texttt{ fn } I_1.E \mid \texttt{rec } I \texttt{ rt } \Gamma$$

$$\Omega ::= + \mid - \mid \times \mid / \mid = \mid > \mid < \mid \ \ldots$$

Value Domains

T	(truth values)
N	(integers)
$\alpha \in L$	(locations)
$\sigma \in S$	(machine states) e.g. $S = [L \to V] \times [L \to T]$
A	(answers: final outcomes)
$\theta \in C = [S \to A]$	(command continuations)
$\delta \in D = T+N+C+[D \to W]+G+L$	(denotations)
$\beta \in V = T+N+C+[D \to W]+G$	(storable values)
$\varepsilon \in E = D$	(expression values)
$\kappa \in K = E \to C$	(expression continuations)
$\omega \in W = K \to C$	(expression closures)
$\gamma \in G = C \to C$	(command closures)
$\rho \in U = [Ide \to D] \times K \times C \times C$	(environments)

Semantic Functions

$\mathcal{O}$: $Ops \to [E \times E] \to W$

$$\mathcal{O}[\![+]\!]\langle \varepsilon_1, \varepsilon_2 \rangle \kappa = \nu \equiv N \to \kappa(\nu \text{ in } E),\ \textit{Wrong} \qquad (12.28)$$

where $\nu = (\varepsilon_1 | N) + (\varepsilon_2 | N)$
and + is a completely strict version of the usual addition function on the integers;

etc.

Table 12.1 (continued)

$\mathscr{C}$: Cmd→U→G

$\mathscr{C}[\![\Phi]\!]\rho$ = a given γ associated with Φ (12.29)

$\mathscr{C}[\![\text{dummy}]\!]\rho = I_G$ (the identity function on C) (12.30)

$\mathscr{C}[\![\text{if } E \text{ then } \Gamma_1 \text{ else } \Gamma_2]\!]\rho\theta =$
$\mathscr{R}[\![E]\!]\rho\{\mathit{Cond}(\mathscr{C}[\![\Gamma_1]\!]\rho\theta, \mathscr{C}[\![\Gamma_2]\!]\rho\theta)\}$ (12.31)

$\mathscr{C}[\![\Gamma_1;\Gamma_2]\!]\rho = \mathscr{C}[\![\Gamma_1]\!]\rho \circ \mathscr{C}[\![\Gamma_2]\!]\rho$ (12.32)

$\mathscr{C}[\![\text{while } E \text{ do } \Gamma]\!]\rho\theta =$
$\mathit{fix}(\lambda\theta'.\ \mathscr{R}[\![E]\!]\rho'\{\mathit{Cond}(\mathscr{C}[\![\Gamma]\!]\rho'\theta', \theta)\})$ (12.33)
where $\rho' = \rho[\theta/\text{brk}]$

$\mathscr{C}[\![\text{let } I\text{=}E \text{ in } \Gamma]\!]\rho\theta =$
$\mathscr{E}[\![E]\!]\rho\{\lambda\delta.\mathscr{C}[\![\Gamma]\!](\rho[\delta/I])\theta\}$ (12.34)

$\mathscr{C}[\![\text{let } I\text{:=}E \text{ in } \Gamma]\!]\rho\theta = \mathscr{R}[\![E]\!]\rho$
$\{\lambda\beta.\mathit{lv}(\lambda\alpha.\mathscr{C}[\![\Gamma]\!](\rho[\alpha \text{ in } D/I])\theta)(\beta \text{ in } E)\}$ (12.35)

$\mathscr{C}[\![\text{goto } E]\!]\rho\theta = \mathscr{R}[\![E]\!]\rho\{\mathit{Jump}\}$ (12.36)
where $\mathit{Jump}(\varepsilon) = \varepsilon E C \rightarrow (\varepsilon|C), \mathit{Wrong}$

$\mathscr{C}[\![\text{begin } I_1:\Gamma_1;I_2:\Gamma_2;\ldots;I_n:\Gamma_n \text{ end}]\!]\rho\theta$
$= (\mathit{fix}(\lambda\langle\theta_1,\theta_2,\ldots,\theta_n\rangle.$
$\langle\mathscr{C}[\![\Gamma_1]\!]\rho'\theta_2, \mathscr{C}[\![\Gamma_2]\!]\rho'\theta_3, \ldots, \mathscr{C}[\![\Gamma_{n-1}]\!]\rho'\theta_n, \mathscr{C}[\![\Gamma_n]\!]\rho'\theta\rangle$
where $\rho' = \rho[\theta_1 \text{ in } D/I_1][\theta_2 \text{ in } D/I_2]\ldots[\theta_n \text{ in } D/I_n]$
$))\downarrow 1$ (12.37)

$\mathscr{C}[\![\text{call } E]\!]\rho\theta = \mathscr{R}[\![E]\!]\rho\{\lambda\varepsilon.\mathit{Run}\varepsilon\theta\}$ (12.38)
where $\mathit{Run}\varepsilon\theta$ $\varepsilon E G \rightarrow (\varepsilon|G)\theta, \mathit{Wrong}$

$\mathscr{C}[\![\text{resultis } E]\!]\rho\theta = \mathscr{R}[\![E]\!]\rho\{\lambda\beta.(\rho[\![\text{res}]\!])(\beta \text{ in } E)\}$ (12.39)

$\mathscr{C}[\![\text{break}]\!]\rho\theta = \rho[\![\text{brk}]\!]$ (12.40)

$\mathscr{C}[\![\text{return}]\!]\rho\theta = \rho[\![\text{ret}]\!]$ (12.41)

$\mathscr{C}[\![\Gamma \text{ repeatwhile } E]\!]\rho\theta =$
$\mathit{fix}(\lambda\theta'.\mathscr{C}[\![\Gamma]\!]\rho'\{\mathscr{R}[\![E]\!]\rho'\{\mathit{Cond}(\theta',\theta)\}\})$ (12.42)
where $\rho' = \rho[\theta/\text{brk}]$

$\mathscr{C}[\![E_1\text{:=}E_2]\!]\rho\theta = \mathscr{L}[\![E_1]\!]\rho\{\lambda\alpha.\ \mathscr{R}[\![E_2]\!]\rho\{\lambda\beta.\mathit{Assign}\alpha\beta\theta\}\}$
or $\mathit{le}\langle\mathscr{L}[\![E_1]\!]\rho, \mathscr{R}[\![E_2]\!]\rho\rangle\{\lambda\langle\alpha,\beta\rangle.\mathit{Assign}\alpha\beta\theta\}$ (12.43)

Table 12.1 (continued)

$\mathcal{L}$: Exp→U→[L→C]→C $\qquad\qquad$ $\mathcal{R}$: Exp→U→[V→C]→C

$$\mathcal{L}[\![E]\!]\rho\kappa = \mathcal{E}[\![E]\!]\rho\{lv\ \kappa\} \qquad (12.44)$$

$$\mathcal{R}[\![E]\!]\rho\kappa = \mathcal{E}[\![E]\!]\rho\{rv\ \kappa\} \qquad (12.45)$$

$\mathcal{E}$: Exp→U→W

$$\mathcal{E}[\![I]\!]\rho\kappa = \rho[\![I]\!] = ? \rightarrow Wrong, \kappa(\rho[\![I]\!]) \qquad (12.46)$$

$$\mathcal{E}[\![\Pi]\!]\rho = \text{a given } \omega \text{ associated with } \Pi. \qquad (12.47)$$

$$\mathcal{E}[\![\mathtt{true}]\!]\rho\kappa = \kappa(true \text{ in E}) \qquad (12.48)$$

$$\mathcal{E}[\![\mathtt{false}]\!]\rho\kappa = \kappa(false \text{ in E}) \qquad (12.49)$$

$$\mathcal{E}[\![N]\!]\rho\kappa = \kappa(\mathcal{N}[\![N]\!] \text{ in E}) \qquad (12.50)$$

$$\mathcal{E}[\![E_1 \Omega E_2]\!]\rho\kappa =$$
$$\mathcal{R}[\![E_1]\!]\rho\{\lambda\beta_1.\ \mathcal{R}[\![E_2]\!]\rho\{\lambda\beta_2.\mathcal{O}[\![\Omega]\!]\langle\beta_1,\beta_2\rangle\kappa\}\} \qquad (12.51)$$
$$\text{or } le\langle \mathcal{R}[\![E_1]\!]\rho, \mathcal{R}[\![E_2]\!]\rho\rangle\{\lambda\langle\beta_1,\beta_2\rangle.\mathcal{O}[\![\Omega]\!]\langle\beta_1,\beta_2\rangle\kappa\}$$

$$\mathcal{E}[\![\mathtt{if}\ E_0\ \mathtt{then}\ E_1\ \mathtt{else}\ E_2]\!] =$$
$$\mathcal{R}[\![E_0]\!]\rho\{Cond(\ \mathcal{E}[\![E_1]\!]\rho\kappa,\ \mathcal{E}[\![E_2]\!]\rho\kappa)\} \qquad (12.52)$$

$$\mathcal{E}[\![\mathtt{let}\ I{=}E_1\ \mathtt{in}\ E_2]\!]\rho\kappa =$$
$$\mathcal{E}[\![E_1]\!]\rho\{\lambda\delta.\ \mathcal{E}[\![E_2]\!](\rho[\delta/I])\kappa\} \qquad (12.53)$$

$$\mathcal{E}[\![\mathtt{let}\ I{:=}E_1\ \mathtt{in}\ E_2]\!]\rho\kappa = \mathcal{R}[\![E_1]\!]\rho$$
$$\{\lambda\beta.lv(\lambda\alpha.\mathcal{E}[\![E_2]\!](\rho[\alpha \text{ in D}/I])\kappa)(\beta \text{ in E})\} \qquad (12.54)$$

$$\mathcal{E}[\![E_1(E_2)]\!]\rho\kappa =$$
$$\mathcal{R}[\![E_1]\!]\rho\{\lambda\beta.\ \mathcal{E}[\![E_2]\!]\rho\{\lambda\varepsilon.Apply\,\beta\varepsilon\kappa\} \qquad (12.55)$$
$$\text{or } le\langle \mathcal{R}[\![E_1]\!]\rho, \mathcal{E}[\![E_2]\!]\rho\rangle\{\lambda\langle\beta,\varepsilon\rangle.Apply\,\beta\varepsilon\kappa\}$$
$$\text{where } Apply\ \varepsilon_1\varepsilon_2\kappa = \varepsilon_1 \mathrm{E}[E{\rightarrow}W] \rightarrow (\varepsilon_1|E{\rightarrow}W)\varepsilon_2\kappa, Wrong$$

$$\mathcal{E}[\![\mathtt{fn}\ I.E]\!]\rho\kappa = \kappa((\lambda\delta.\ \mathcal{E}[\![E]\!](\rho[\delta/I]))\text{in E}) \qquad (12.56)$$

$$\mathcal{E}[\![\mathtt{rt}\ \Gamma]\!]\rho\kappa = \kappa(\lambda\theta.\mathcal{C}[\![\Gamma]\!](\rho[\theta/\mathtt{ret}]) \text{ in E}) \qquad (12.57)$$

$$\mathcal{E}[\![\mathtt{valof}\ \Gamma]\!]\rho\kappa = \mathcal{C}[\![\Gamma]\!](\rho[\kappa/\mathtt{res}])\{Wrong\} \qquad (12.58)$$

$$\mathcal{E}[\![\mathtt{rec}\ I_0\ \mathtt{fn}\ I_1.E]\!]\rho\kappa =$$
$$\kappa(fix(\lambda\phi\lambda\delta.\ \mathcal{E}[\![E]\!](\rho[\delta/I_1][\phi \text{ in D}/I_0]))\text{in E}) \qquad (12.59)$$

$$\mathcal{E}[\![\mathtt{rec}\ I\ \mathtt{rt}\ \Gamma]\!]\rho\kappa =$$
$$\kappa(fix(\lambda\gamma.\mathcal{C}[\![\Gamma]\!](\rho[\gamma \text{ in D}/I]))\text{in E}) \qquad (12.60)$$

Table 12.1 (continued)

Auxiliary Definitions.

Cond	see 11.18
fix	see 6.63
le	see 11.20
lv	see 12.16
rv	see 12.17
Wrong	see 11.17.

A Specimen Evaluation

We shall now evaluate a little program in detail. This is very rarely done manually - it is, after all, what we have computers for - but the hope is that it will consolidate our understanding of what is go ng on. For simplicity we use the left to right version. of the clauses. (In the course of this evaluation we shall introduce abbreviations by means of horizontal braces, without further comment.)

We choose the program

$\ulcorner x$:= y; goto $L\urcorner$

and evaluate it in an environment ρ in which the following bindings occur:

x to (α_x in D)
y to (α_y in D)
L to (θ_L in D).

Here, α_x and α_y are locations for which $Area\sigma\alpha_x$ and $Area\sigma\alpha_y$ are *true*, $Map\sigma\alpha_x=\beta_x$ and $Map\sigma\alpha_y=\beta_y$. θ_L is in the C component of D.

We have:

$\mathscr{C}[\![x{:=}y\,;\mathrm{goto}\ L]\!]\rho\theta\sigma$

$= \mathscr{C}[\![x{:=}y]\!]\rho\{\underbrace{\mathscr{C}[\![\mathrm{goto}\ L]\!]\rho\theta}_{\theta_1}\}\sigma$ (by 12.32)

$= \mathscr{L}[\![x]\!]\rho\{\underbrace{\lambda\alpha.\ \mathscr{R}[\![y]\!]\rho\{\underbrace{\lambda\beta.Assign\alpha\beta\theta_1}_{\kappa_\alpha}\}}_{\kappa}\}\sigma$ (by 12.43)

$= \mathscr{E}[\![x]\!]\rho\{lv\ \kappa\}\sigma$ (by 12.44)

$= (\rho[\![x]\!] = \,?\, \rightarrow Wrong,(lv\ \kappa)(\rho[\![x]\!]))\sigma$ (by 12.46)

$= (lv\ \kappa)(\alpha_x \text{ in } D)\sigma$

$= (\lambda\kappa\lambda\varepsilon.\varepsilon{\in}L \rightarrow \kappa(\varepsilon|L),$

$\qquad \varepsilon{\in}V \rightarrow Newstore\{\lambda\alpha.Assign\alpha(\varepsilon|V)\{\kappa\alpha\}\},$

$\qquad Wrong$

$\quad)\kappa(\alpha_x \text{ in } D)\sigma$ (by 12.16)

$= [(\alpha_x \text{ in } D){\in}L \rightarrow \kappa\alpha_x, \ldots]\sigma$

$= \kappa\alpha_x\sigma$

$= \mathscr{R}[\![y]\!]\rho\kappa_{\alpha_x}\sigma\sigma$ (definition of κ)

(here κ_{α_x} means $[\alpha_x/\alpha]\kappa_\alpha$) (by 12.45)

$= (rv\ \kappa_{\alpha_x})(\alpha_y \text{ in } D)\sigma$

$= (\lambda\kappa\lambda\varepsilon.\varepsilon{\in}L \rightarrow Contents(\varepsilon|L)\kappa,$

$\qquad \varepsilon{\in}V \rightarrow \kappa(\varepsilon|V),$

$\qquad Wrong$

$\quad)\kappa_{\alpha_x}(\alpha_y \text{ in } D)\sigma$ (by 12.17)

$= [(\alpha_y \text{ in } D){\in}L \rightarrow Contents\alpha_y\kappa_{\alpha_x}, \ldots]\sigma$

$= Contents\alpha_y\kappa_{\alpha_x}\sigma$

$= Area\sigma\alpha_y \rightarrow \kappa_{\alpha_x}(Map\sigma\alpha_y)\sigma, Wrong\sigma$ (by 12.10)

$= \kappa_{\alpha_x}\beta_y\sigma$

$= Assign\alpha_x\beta_y\theta_1\sigma$ (definition of κ_{α_x})

$= [\alpha_x{\in}L \wedge \beta_y{\in}V \rightarrow \theta_1 \circ Update(\alpha_x,\beta_y), Wrong]\sigma$ (by 12.11)

$= [\theta_1 \circ Update(\alpha_x,\beta_y)]\sigma$

$$= \theta_1(\underbrace{Update(\alpha_x, \beta_y)\sigma}_{\sigma_1})$$

(Note that we have just transformed σ)

$= \mathscr{C}[\![\text{goto } L]\!]\rho\theta\sigma_1$ (definition of θ)

$= \mathscr{R}[\![L]\!]\rho\{Jump\}\sigma_1$ (by 12.36)

$= rv(Jump)(\theta_L \text{ in } D)\sigma_1$ (as for $\mathscr{R}[\![y]\!]$ above)

$$= (\lambda\kappa\lambda\varepsilon.\, \varepsilon\in L \to Contents(\varepsilon|L)\kappa,$$
$$\varepsilon\in V \to \kappa(\varepsilon|V),$$
$$Wrong$$
$$)(Jump)\theta_L\sigma_1$$

$= [(\theta_L \text{in } D)\in L\to\ldots,(\theta_L\text{in } D)\in V\to Jump(\theta_L\text{in } D|V),\ldots]\sigma$ (by 12.17)

$= Jump(\theta_L\text{in } V)\sigma_1$

$= [\theta_L \text{ in } V\in C \to (\theta_L\text{in } V|C), Wrong]\sigma]$ (by 12.36)

$= (\theta_L \text{ in } V|C)\sigma_1$

$= \theta_L\sigma_1.$

Exercise

6. Evaluate ⌜x := let y := 3 in y⌝ similarly.

Some Store Theorems

For these theorems we shall assume throughout that all location values (α,α′ etc.) are proper.

1. (Commutativity) If $\alpha \neq \alpha'$:

$$Update(\alpha,\beta)\circ Update(\alpha',\beta') = Update(\alpha',\beta')\circ Update(\alpha,\beta) \quad (12.61)$$

Proof: To prove any two states σ and σ′ equal we must show that $Map(\sigma) = Map(\sigma')$ and $Area(\sigma)=Area(\sigma')$. For arbitrary σ let $[Update(\alpha,\beta)\circ Update(\alpha,\beta')]\sigma = \sigma_L$.

and $[Update(\alpha',\beta')\circ Update(\alpha,\beta)]\sigma = \sigma_R$; then we must show that $\sigma_L = \sigma_R$. Now by 12.3,

$Area(\sigma_L) = Area(\sigma) = Area(\sigma_R)$; and

$$\begin{aligned} Map(\sigma_L)\alpha'' &= (\alpha''=\alpha)\rightarrow\beta,((\alpha''=\alpha')\rightarrow\beta',Map(\sigma)\alpha'') \\ &= (\alpha''=\alpha')\rightarrow\beta',((\alpha''=\alpha)\rightarrow\beta,Map(\sigma)\alpha'') \\ &\qquad \text{(proof by cases, provided } \alpha,\alpha' \text{ and } \alpha'' \text{ are proper)} \\ &= Map(\sigma_R)\alpha'' \quad \text{for all } \alpha''. \end{aligned}$$

So $Map(\sigma_L) = Map(\sigma_R)$, and the result is proved. The proofs are similar for the following results:

2. $Update(\alpha,\beta)\circ Update(\alpha,\beta') = Update(\alpha,\beta)$ (if β' is proper). (12.62)

3. $Update(\alpha,\beta)\circ Extend(\alpha') = Extend(\alpha')\circ Update(\alpha,\beta)$
and $Update(\alpha,\beta)\circ Lose(\alpha') = Lose(\alpha')\circ Update(\alpha,\beta)$. (12.63)

4. (Idempotence) $Update(\alpha, Map(\sigma)\alpha) = \sigma$. (12.64)

The following results may be of use when it is desired to prove the final states of two programs equivalent. It is sometimes easier to prove a related result instead.

5. If there exist proper α and β such that
(i) $Map\sigma\alpha = Map\sigma'\alpha$
(ii) $Update(\alpha,\beta)\sigma = Update(\alpha,\beta)\sigma'$
then $\sigma = \sigma'$. (12.65)

6. If there exists some proper α such that
(i) $Area(\sigma)\alpha = Area(\sigma')\alpha$
(ii) $Extend(\alpha)\sigma = Extend(\alpha)\sigma'$
or $Lose(\alpha)\sigma = Lose(\alpha)\sigma'$
then $\sigma = \sigma'$. (12.66)

Exercise

7. State a set of similar results using the alternative (continuation) version of the store primitives (12.10 to 12.13).

Generalised store transformations

When we began this chapter we were already regretting how the machinations of the store complicate the analysis of our programs. We now look at one way of factoring out the effects of the store, so as to separate its mathematics from the mathematics of the algorithm we are computing.

It is convenient to introduce a curried form of *Update*. We define U:[L→ [V→C]] such that

$U\alpha\beta$ = *Update*(α,β).

Remember that we are assuming that U, $U\alpha$ and $U\alpha\beta$ are all completely strict.

We can now usefully extend U to update more than one location at a time. We define U^* :[L*→[V*→C]], where members of L* and V* are n-tuples of elements of L and V respectively. $U^*\alpha^*\beta^*$ has a proper value only if

i. α^* and β^* are equal in length,
ii. all the elements of α^* are proper and distinct,
iii. all the elements of β^* are proper.

If these conditions are satisfied, $U^*\alpha^*\beta^*\sigma$ is the state obtained by updating each location α_k with β_k (by 12.61 above, the order of these updatings is irrelevant). We similarly define C^*, N^* and E^*, extended versions of *Conts*, *New* and *Extend*.

We now consider whether a whole program may be regarded as one of these extended updatings. This would be especially convenient if the β^* values depended only on the initial contents of the α^* locations. As we are neglecting input/output, and if we keep the area constant, this would always be so if we took α^* to be the whole store; but often a smaller area is sufficient.

These initial contents are $C^*(\alpha^*)\sigma$ (note that $C^* : [L^* \to [S \to V^*]]$). So if β^* depends only on these, then there is a function f such that

$$\beta^* = f(C^*(\alpha^*)\sigma).$$

Here $f{:}[V^* \to V^*]$; i.e. f is a function from values to values, having nothing to do with locations or assignment. So the final state σ' is given by

$$\begin{aligned}\sigma' &= U^*(\alpha^*)(\beta^*)\sigma \\ &= U^*(\alpha^*)(f(C^*(\alpha^*)\sigma))\sigma \\ &= ((U^*(\alpha^*))\circledast(f \circ C^*(\alpha^*)))\sigma\end{aligned}$$

where, as earlier, $(p \circledast q)\sigma = p(q\sigma)\sigma$.

Let us introduce $\Theta : [L^* \to [[V^* \to V^*] \to [S \to S]]]$ such that

$$\Theta(\alpha^*)f = (U^*(\alpha^*))\circledast(f \circ C^*(\alpha^*)).$$

Then $\sigma' = \Theta(\alpha^*)(f)\sigma$.

If, as previously, we put $Wrong = \lambda\sigma.?$, then any jump-free program may be treated in this fashion: we can thus separate the storage manipulation part, $\Theta\alpha^*$, from f, the abstract function we are computing.

Various combination rules exist:

1. $(\Theta\alpha^* f_1)\circ(\Theta\alpha^* f_0) = \Theta\alpha^*(f_1 \circ f_0)$. (12.67)
2. If ω_0 is without side effects and for all κ $\omega_0\kappa = \kappa\circledast(P \circ C^*\alpha^*)$, where P is some predicate in $[V^* \to E]$.

(i.e. if $\omega_0\kappa\sigma = \kappa(\chi\sigma)\sigma$ where $\chi\sigma = P(C^*\alpha^*\sigma)$), then

$\omega_0\{Cond(\Theta\alpha^* f_0, \Theta\alpha^* f_1)\} = \Theta\alpha^*(\lambda\varepsilon.((\varepsilon|\mathrm{T}) \to f_0, f_1) \circledast P)$. (12.68)

3. $\Theta\alpha^* I = I$. (12.69)

4. $\Theta\alpha^* \bot_{[\mathsf{V}^* \to \mathsf{V}^*]} = \bot_{\mathsf{S} \to \mathsf{S}}$. (12.70)

These may all be proved fairly simply. (1),(2) and (3) deal, respectively, with sequences, conditionals and dummy. The most interesting case is the while-loop, to which we now turn.

5. (12.71) *Theorem (Strachey).* Let $\Gamma \equi ⌜$while E_0 do Γ_0⌝, and suppose E_0 is without side effects, and Γ_0 (and hence also Γ) is jump free. Let $\gamma = \mathscr{C}[\![\Gamma]\!]\rho$, $\gamma_0 = \mathscr{C}[\![\Gamma_0]\!]\rho$ and $\omega_0 = \mathscr{R}[\![E_0]\!]\rho$, and suppose that we can find α^*, p and f, where $\alpha^* \in \mathsf{L}^n$, $p \in [\mathsf{V}^n \to \mathsf{E}]$ and $f \in [\mathsf{V}^n \to \mathsf{V}^n]$ for some n, such that

$$\omega_0\kappa = (strict\ \kappa) \circledast (p \circ C^*\alpha^*) \quad \text{for all } \kappa$$
$$\gamma_0\theta = (strict\ \theta) \circ (\Theta\alpha^* f) \quad \text{for all } \theta.$$

Then $\mathscr{C}[\![\Gamma]\!]\rho\theta = (strict\ \theta) \circ \Theta\alpha^*(fix\ H_1)$, where $H_1(g) = (\lambda\varepsilon.(\varepsilon|\mathrm{T}) \to g \circ f, I) \circledast p$.

Proof: Since Γ is jump-free, $\mathscr{C}[\![\Gamma]\!]\rho\theta = (strict\ \theta) \circ \psi$ for some ψ. From the semantic equations (and the proof of 11.34), using all our assumptions about jump-freeness etc., this ψ is given by

$$\psi = fix(\lambda\psi'.Cond((strict\ \psi') \circ \psi_0, I) \circledast (p \circ C^*\alpha^*).$$

In this equation, ψ_0 is such that, for all θ, $\gamma_0\theta = (strict\ \theta) \circ \psi_0$; thus by our assumption ψ_0 must be $\Theta\alpha^* f$. So let us define

$$H_0(\psi) = Cond((strict\ \psi) \circ \Theta\alpha^* f, I) \circ (p \circ C^*\alpha^*)$$

and we then have to prove

$$fix\ H_0 = \Theta\alpha^*(fix\ H_1),$$

which we do by fixpoint induction. The basis step is simply 12.70, and so we proceed by assuming that $g_0 = (\Theta\alpha^*)g_1$. Then

$$\begin{aligned}
H_0(g_0) &= H_0(\Theta\alpha^* g_1) \\
&= Cond((strict(\Theta\alpha^* g_1))\circ\Theta\alpha^* f, I)\circ(p\circ C^*\alpha^*) \\
&= Cond(\Theta\alpha^*(g_1\circ f), \Theta\alpha^* I)\circ(p\circ C^*\alpha^*) \\
&\qquad\qquad\qquad\text{(by 12.67 and 12.69)} \\
&= \Theta\alpha^*(Cond(g_1\circ f, I)\circledast p) \\
&= \Theta\alpha^*(H_1 g_1).
\end{aligned}$$

Hence fixpoint induction gives the required result.

Example We shall use this result to analyse the following expression.

```
E ≡ ⌜let x := N in
     let y := 1 in
       valof (while x ≠ 0 do
                (y := y×x;
                 x := x-1
                );
                resultis y
             )           ⌝
```

Here N is a numeral, and we assume that $\mathscr{N}[\![N]\!] = \nu$. We wish to show that the value yielded by E is ν!

Let us make the following abbreviations:

$\Gamma \;\equiv \ulcorner y\ :=\ y{\times}x;\ x\ :=\ x- \urcorner$

$E \;\equiv \ulcorner x{\neq}0 \urcorner$

$\Gamma \;\equiv \ulcorner \texttt{while}\ E_0\ \texttt{do}\ \Gamma_0 \urcorner$

$E_1 \equiv \ulcorner \texttt{valof}(\Gamma_1;\texttt{resultis}\ y) \urcorner$

$E_2 \equiv \ulcorner \texttt{let}\ y\ :=\ 1\ \texttt{in}\ E_1 \urcorner.$

So $E \equiv \ulcorner \texttt{let}\ x\ :=\ N\ \texttt{in}\ E_2 \urcorner$, and we are trying to show that for any ρ,κ, and suitable σ_0,

$$\mathcal{E}[\![E]\!]\rho\kappa = (\mathit{strict}\ \kappa)\beta\overline{\sigma}$$

for some $\overline{\sigma}$, where $\beta=\nu!$. Here σ_0 is 'suitable' if it is proper and $N_2\sigma_0$ produces a valid answer (N_2, E_2, C_2 and U_2 are the 2-tuple versions of *New*, *Extend*, *Conts* and curried *Update*).

Proof: For simplicity's sake we shall assume that V=N, so that only integers can be stored. Then a step by step evaluation, using the semantic equations and the definitions of the store primitives, gives

$$\mathcal{E}[\![E]\!]\rho\kappa\sigma_0 = \mathcal{E}[\![E_1]\!]\rho_1\kappa\sigma_1$$

where

$$\rho_1 = \rho[\alpha_x \text{ in } D/x][\alpha_y \text{ in } D/y]$$
$$\sigma_1 = U_2\langle\alpha_x,\alpha_y\rangle\langle\nu,1\rangle(E_2\langle\alpha_x,\alpha_y\rangle\sigma_0)$$

where $\langle\alpha_x,\alpha_y\rangle = N_2\sigma_0$. Continuing this step by step evaluation leads to

$$\mathcal{C}[\![\Gamma_1]\!]\rho_2\{\mathcal{R}[\![y]\!]\rho_2\kappa\}\sigma_1$$

where $\rho_2 = \rho_1[\kappa/\texttt{res}]$. Now $\mathcal{R}[\![y]\!]\rho_2\kappa$ can be written $\kappa \circledast \mathit{Conts}\,\alpha_y$, and if we call this θ_1, our original evaluation now becomes $\mathcal{C}[\![\Gamma_1]\!]\rho_1\theta_1\sigma_1$ (note that we can use ρ_1 here, as resultis does not occur free in Γ_1).

Let $\gamma_1 = \mathscr{C}[\![\Gamma_1]\!]\rho_1$. We can obtain an expression for $\gamma_1\theta_1$ using Theorem 12.71, for we can show that the conditions for the theorem are satisfied by the following choices for α^*, p and f:

$$\alpha^* = \langle \alpha_x, \alpha_y \rangle$$

$$p = \lambda\langle s,t\rangle.(s \neq 0)$$

$$f = \lambda\langle s,t\rangle.\langle s-1, t \times s\rangle.$$

Thus $\gamma_1\theta_1 = (\mathit{strict}\ \theta_1)\circ\Theta\alpha^*(\mathit{fix}(\lambda g.\mathit{Cond}(g\circ f, I)\circledast p))$; so

$$\begin{aligned}
\mathscr{E}[\![E]\!]\rho\kappa\sigma_0 &= \gamma_1\theta_1\sigma_1 \\
&= ((\mathit{strict}\ \theta_1)\circ\Theta\alpha^2 F)\sigma_1 \\
&\qquad \text{where } F = \mathit{fix}(\lambda g.\mathit{Cond}(g\circ f, I)\circledast p) \\
&= \mathit{strict}\ \theta_1\sigma_2 \\
&\qquad \text{where } \sigma_2 = \Theta\alpha^* F\sigma_1 \\
&= \mathit{strict}(\kappa(\mathit{Conts}\,\alpha_y\sigma_2))\sigma_2.
\end{aligned}$$

We must therefore show that $\mathit{Conts}\,\alpha_y\sigma_2 = \nu!$. Since $\sigma_2 = \Theta\alpha^* F\sigma_1$ and $\mathit{Conts}\,\alpha_y\sigma_1 = 1$, we have only to show that $F\langle s,t\rangle = \langle 0, s!\times t\rangle$, which is a simple induction. Notice particularly that this is a completely standard induction on the integers: everything to do with the various mechanisms of programming languages has been dealt with, and we are left with the mathematical core of our problem.

Notice too, though, that the fact that this central induction is carried out simply over the integers is a consequence of our initial assumption that only integers may be stored. Having the possibility of other types of value around would considerably complicate matters. However, if our language had compile-time type checking, we could rely on the compiler to remove the possibility of such complication. This, in rather formal guise, is the principal advantage of such languages.

We should perhaps have shown above that the conditions of Theorem 12.71 were satisfied by the α^*, p and f we chose; for example, we should have demonstrated that for all θ

$$\mathscr{C}[\![y{:=}y\ x;x{:=}x\text{-}1]\!]\rho_1\theta = (\mathit{strict}\ \theta)\circ(\theta\alpha^* f).$$

These are simply again a matter of tedious step by step evaluation, making occasional use of 12.67 to 12.69.

Comment on this technique We have now discussed one technique for relating an actual program to the mathematics of the underlying problem, by factoring out the details of the ancillary mechanism. However, it was necessary to discuss this ancillary mechanism, albeit separately, in considerable detail. This detailed consideration may be necessary for some cases, such as when the program exploits tricks of the programming language. But in more regular cases it is greatly preferable to make far more wholesale arrangements for avoiding the details of storage allocation: these are provided, for example, by the "axiomatic approach" [19], which we shall relate to our approach in Chapter 14.

Equivalence of while-loops

Sometimes, instead of showing that a particular program computes a particular function, we want to show that two different programs compute the same function. So our final topic in this chapter is one such equivalence result.

12.72 *Theorem (Strachey).* A sufficient set of conditions for

$$\ulcorner(\text{while } E_0 \text{ do } \Gamma_0);\Gamma_0'\urcorner \equiv \ulcorner(\text{while } E_1 \text{ do } \Gamma_1);\Gamma_1'\urcorner$$

is

1. $\ulcorner\text{if } E_0 \text{ then}(\Gamma \text{ ;if } E_1 \text{ then } \Gamma_1;\Gamma \text{ else } \Gamma' \text{ else } \Gamma'\urcorner$

   $\equiv \ulcorner\text{if } E_1 \text{ then}(\Gamma_1;\text{if } E_0 \text{ then } \Gamma_0;\Gamma \text{ else } \Gamma_0')\text{else } \Gamma_1'\urcorner$

   (for all Γ).

2. $\ulcorner\text{if } E \text{ then } \Gamma_0;\Gamma_\perp \text{ else } \Gamma_0'\urcorner \equiv$

   $\ulcorner\text{if } E_1 \text{ then } \Gamma_1;\Gamma_\perp \text{ else } \Gamma_1'\urcorner$

   where $\Gamma_\perp$ is a bottom command, such as $\ulcorner\text{while true do dummy}\urcorner$.

These conditions and the result are shown in flow diagram form in Fig.12.2. We may think of a while-loop as being derived from an if-command (by iteration): the first condition says that the if-commands corresponding to the two while-loops are, in a sense, commutative. The second condition says that the two if-commands are equivalent in all situations (including error exit etc.) which would *not* lead to another cycle round the corresponding while-loops - the non-terminating command $\Gamma_\perp$ is used to force the two sides of condition 2 to be trivially equivalent in this case too.

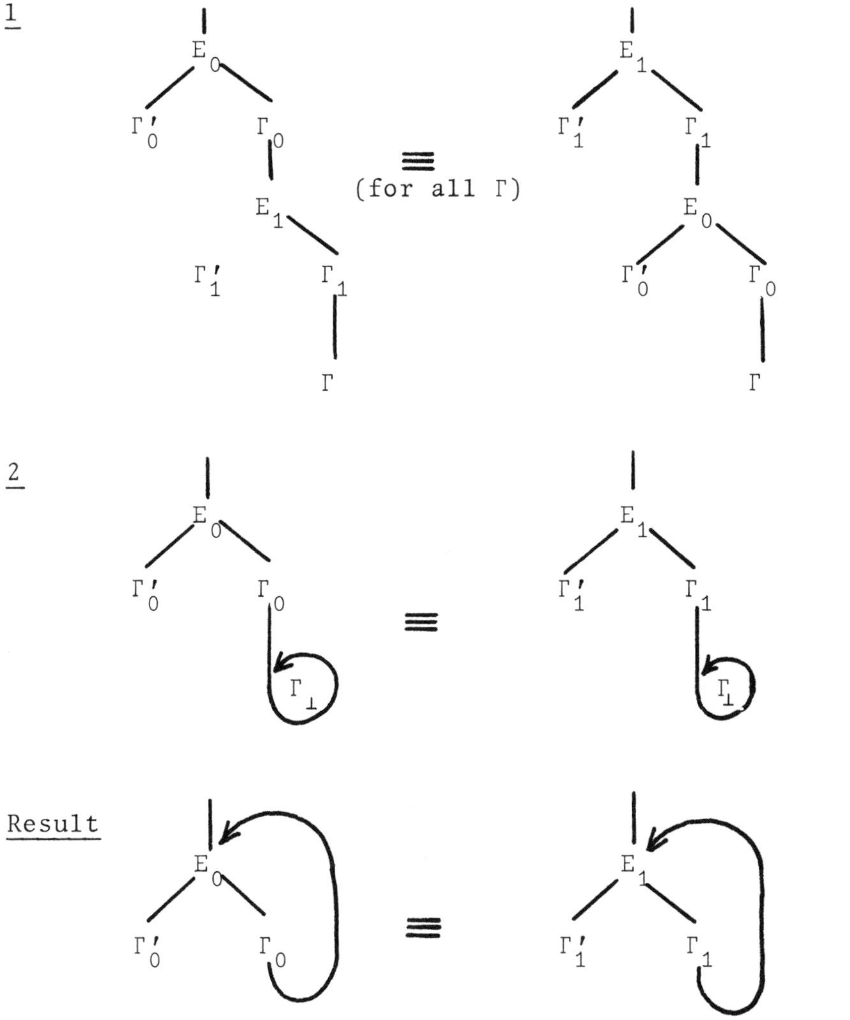

Fig 12.2. Conditions and Conclusion of Theorem 12.72

12.73. *Lemma.* If $f \circ g = g \circ f$ and $f\bot = g\bot$ then $fix(f) = fix(g)$.

Exercise

8. Prove Lemma 12.73.

Proof of 12.72. For some ρ let $\omega_0 = \mathcal{R}[\![E_0]\!]\rho$, $\gamma_0 = \mathcal{C}[\![\Gamma_0]\!]\rho$, $\gamma_0' = \mathcal{C}[\![\Gamma_0']\!]\rho$ etc. and let

$H_0\theta'\theta = \omega_0\{Cond(\gamma_0\theta, \gamma_0'\theta')$

$H_1\theta'\theta = \omega_1\{Cond(\gamma_1\theta, \gamma_1'\theta'\}$.

We have to prove that for all θ_0 (the overall continuation for each side):

$fix(H_0\theta_0) = fix(H_1\theta_0)$.

Condition 1 becomes

$H_0\theta(H_1\theta(\gamma\theta)) = H_1\theta(H_0\theta(\gamma\theta))$ (for all γ,θ)

which may be written as

$(H_0\theta \circ H_1\theta)(\gamma\theta) = (H_1\theta \circ H_0\theta)(\gamma\theta)$ (for all γ,β).

Now for any θ' we care to choose, $\lambda\theta.\theta'$ is a possible choice for γ; thus $\gamma\theta$ can range over the entire value space C, and so by extensionality

$(H_0\theta \circ H_1\theta) = (H_1\theta \circ H_0\theta)$ (for all θ).

Condition 2 becomes

$H_0\theta\bot = H_1\theta\bot$

and the result follows, by Lemma 12.73.

Example We illustrate the use of Theorem 12.72 by showing the equivalence of the following pair of programs, in which (as for the previous example) we assume that only integers can be stored.

```
⌜while a≤b do                 ⌜while a≤b do
   (f := a×f;                    (f := f×b;
    a := a+1                      b := b-1
   );                            );
 a := 0; b := 0⌝               a := 0; b := 0⌝
```

We assume that all the variables denote locations. If the initial values for f, a and b are 1,1 and n then we expect each program to set f to $n!$. However, the intended initial conditions and the intended effect are irrelevant to the present question, which is merely that the two programs are equivalent.

We must check that the two conditions are satisfied. We shall do this fairly informally, using the flowchart representation: readers who are more formally minded may verify our efforts by a step by step evaluation using the semantic equations.

The equivalences to be checked are shown diagramatically in Fig.12.3. For condition 1, if $a_0 > b_0$ both programs reach exit A in the same state. The left-hand program reaches exit B if $a_0 \leq b_0 < a_0+1$, and the right-hand program does so if $b_0-1 < a_0 \leq b_0$. But since a_0 and b_0 are integers, these conditions hold only if $a_0 = b_0$; so in this case both programs reach exit B and, since multiplication is commutative, the states are the same. Otherwise, both programs enter the command Γ with identical states (since multiplication is associative). Condition 2 is even simpler to verify: either both programs reach exit C identically, or both fail to terminate.

Thus, according to Theorem 12.72, these programs are equivalent. Notice that this is so even though none of the intermediate states reached by the two

1.

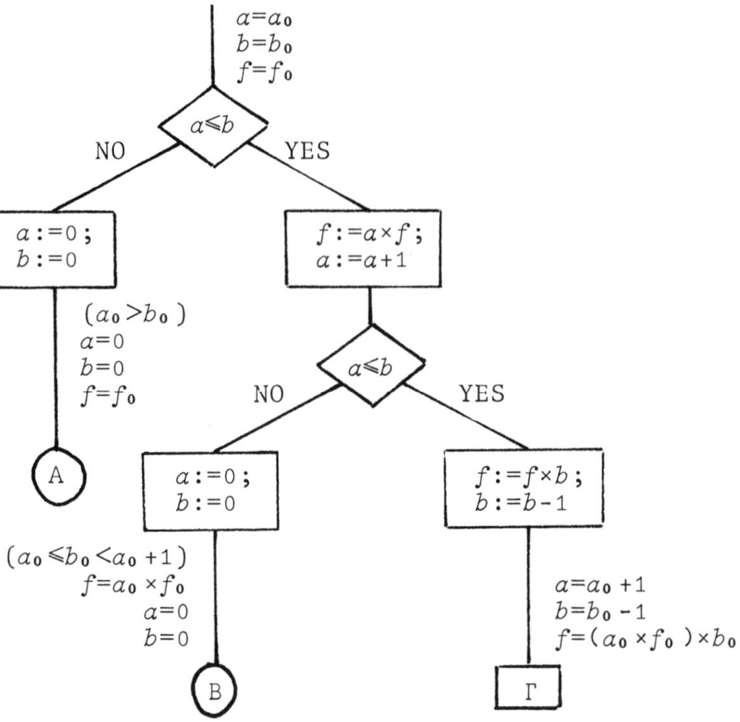

2.

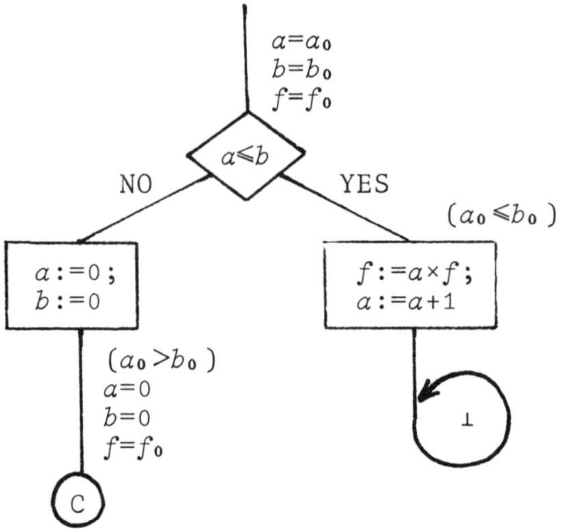

Fig. 12.3. Example Requirements: Left-hand Sides.

1.

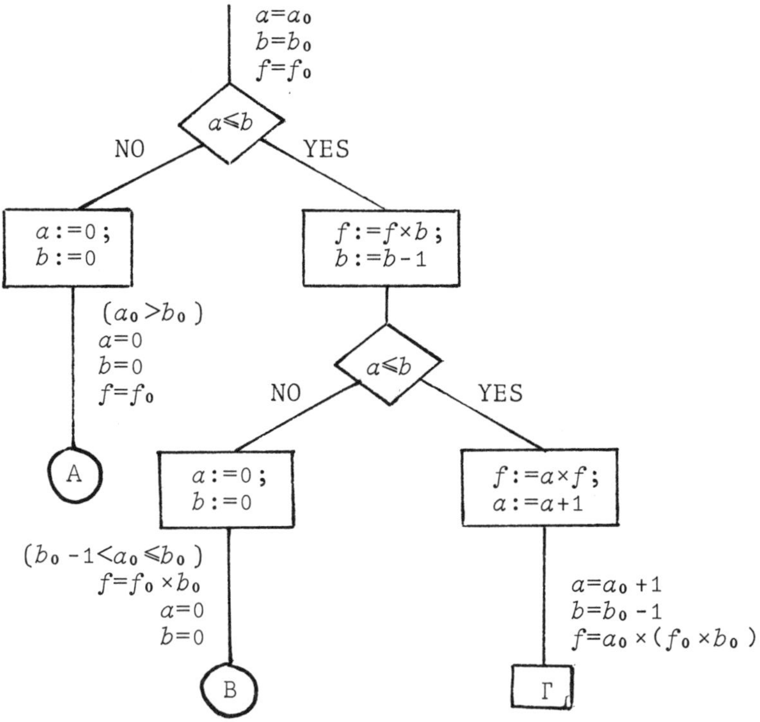

2.

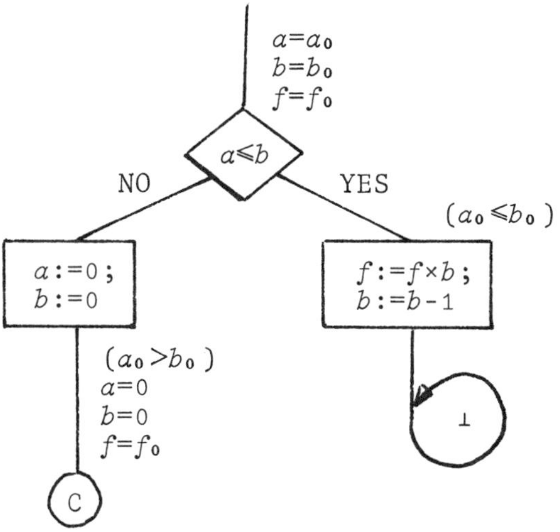

Fig. 12.3. Example Requirements: Right-hand Sides.

programs are the same - one is counting up and the other down.

Comment on this Example Unfortunately, we have not played completely fair with this example. Its proof relied on the fact that all the values were integers. As in the previous example, we could appeal to compile-time type checking to ensure that this was the case. However, this second example uses the properties of the integers rather more specifically (in particular, to prove that $a_0 \leqslant b_0 < a_0+1$ and $b_0-1 < a_0 \leqslant b_0$ are both equivalent to $a_0=b_0$. It would be simple to concoct similar examples which worked only if the variables were positive, or even, or prime - constraints, in fact, beyond the power of compile-time type checking to verify. So although compile-time type checking would be satisfactory for this *particular* example, it cannot provide a general solution.

The technique has therefore to be extended to handle explicitly the constraints which must be satisfied for the various equivalences to hold. This, of course, makes for more notational complexity. As usual, the reader is referred to Milne and Strachey [34] for a detailed analysis of the extra complications.

Chapter 13

NON-STANDARD SEMANTICS

We have by now described in some detail a technique for defining the semantics of programming languages, and we have justified it by an appeal to its mathematical foundations. So our language definitions are mathematically respectable. The question we now face is whether they are any help in producing a correct implementation of the language.

There is, of course, an enormous gap between our denotational definitions, with their abstract values in domains of complicated functionality and rich structure, and the operations performed on bit patterns by the machine instructions of a computer. Indeed, we have rather prided ourselves on keeping our language definitions free from implementation details: in this way we could avoid prejudicing an implementer towards any particular technique. Now we wish to bridge this gap, in order to show that a particular implementation is faithful to the original language definition.

This is too big a task to be done in one step. It is necessary to proceed in several stages: at each stage we give an alternative semantic definition of the language, and each definition embodies successively more and more implementation details. In fact the final stage or two will involve semantic definitions which are *operational* in nature: these specify the behaviour of an abstract machine and, perhaps, may also give the details of a compiler from the original language to the new machine code. The first definition in the sequence, the original, canonical, definition, is called the *standard semantics* of the programming language; all the others, whether denotational or operational, are *non-standard*. At each stage we formulate and prove *congruence conditions* between successive definitions in the sequence. The exact details of such conditions depend on the details of the definitions being compared, but the general idea is that two definitions are congruent if it can reasonably be claimed that they are defining the same language. Thus by a sequence of congruences we can relate the standard semantics of a language to a particular compiler and machine which implement it.

In this chapter we shall first illustrate this approach by detailed consideration of an extremely simple language (suggested for the purpose by Christopher Strachey). Then we shall briefly consider the various stages in the sequence of definitions appropriate to a more realistic programming language. Finally, by considering another very small language (due to Robert Milne), we shall illustrate some of the theoretical background to the congruence proofs which may arise in practice.

A Simple Example Language

Our first example language is comprised merely of numerals and the plus sign. Its syntax is given as follows.

Syntactic Domains

$N \in$ Nml (Numerals)

$E \in Exp$ (Expressions)

Syntax

$E ::= N \mid E_1 + E_2$

Standard Semantics We first give the standard semantics of our language which, as might be expected, is also very simple.

Semantic Domain

$\nu \in N$ (Non-negative integers)

Semantic Functions

$\mathscr{N} : Nml \rightarrow N$

This function maps numerals to the corresponding numbers. We do not bother with its details here.

$\mathscr{E}_0 : Exp \rightarrow N$

$$\mathscr{E}_0[\![N]\!] = \mathscr{N}[\![N]\!] \tag{13.1}$$

$$\mathscr{E}_0[\![E_1 + E_2]\!] = \mathscr{E}_0[\![E_1]\!] + \mathscr{E}_0[\![E_2]\!] \tag{13.2}$$

The standard semantics gives a meaning to each expression in the language; but it gives little hint about how to evaluate it.

One common approach to the implementation of this kind of language is to use a stack. We shall next give two forms of "stack semantics" for the language; but before doing so we need to give some notation for dealing with finite sequences of integers, which is, for the present, how we shall regard stacks.

Notation Let N^* be the domain of finite sequences of non-negative integers, and let $\zeta \in N^*$ be $\langle \nu_1, \nu_2, \ldots, \nu_n \rangle$. Then:

1. $\zeta{\downarrow}i = \nu_i$ if $1 \leqslant i \leqslant n$ (13.3)
$\qquad\qquad ?$ otherwise.

($\zeta{\downarrow}i$ selects the ith element in the sequence.)

2. $\zeta{\dagger}i = \langle \nu_{i+1}, \ldots, \nu_n \rangle$ if $0 \leqslant i \leqslant n$ (13.4)
$\qquad\qquad ?$ otherwise.

($\zeta{\dagger}i$ chops the first i elements off the sequence.) Note that $\zeta{\dagger}n$ is the empty sequence, $\langle\rangle$.

3. $\#\zeta = n$. (13.5)

($\#\zeta$ gives the number of elements in the sequence.)

4. Let ζ' be $\langle \nu_{n+1}, \nu_{n+2}, \ldots, \nu_m \rangle$. Then

$\zeta \S \zeta' = \langle \nu_1, \nu_2, \ldots, \nu_n, \nu_{n+1}, \ldots, \nu_m \rangle$. (13.6)

(§ is used for concatenating two sequences.)

Exercise

1. Define a function ⊛ which, given a retract N for a domain such as N, produces ⊛N, a retract for N^*, the domain of finite sequences of elements of N (this ⊛ will then go into our repertoire alongside ⊗, ⊕ and ↠). Define a second version which also includes infinite sequences in the domain.

Stack Semantics In this, the first non-standard semantics for our little language, expressions are evaluated with a stack; the effect is to append the "value" of the expression onto the stack. We define this as follows.

Semantic Domains

$\nu \in N$ (Non-negative integers)
$\zeta \in N^*$ (Stacks: finite sequences of integers)

Semantic Functions

$\mathcal{N}$: Nml → N (as before)

$\mathcal{E}_1$: Exp → $N^* \to N^*$

$$\mathcal{E}_1[\![N]\!]\zeta = \langle \mathcal{N}[\![N]\!]\rangle \S \zeta \tag{13.7}$$

$$\mathcal{E}_1[\![E_1+E_2]\!]\zeta = add(\mathcal{E}_1[\![E_2]\!](\mathcal{E}_1[\![E_1]\!]\zeta)) \tag{13.8}$$

where

$$add(\zeta) = \langle \zeta\downarrow 1 + \zeta\downarrow 2\rangle \S (\zeta\dagger 2) \tag{13.9}$$

Here, *add* replaces the top two elements of a stack by their sum. 13.7 states that evaluating a numeral causes its value to be appended to the front of the given stack. Notice that in 13.8 we have specified an order of evaluation: E_1 is first evaluated on the given stack; then E_2 is evaluated on the stack resulting from that; and the resulting stack is supplied to *add*.

Though an order of evaluation is specified (or at least implied) by this semantics, notice that it is *not* an operational semantics. It is as denotational as the standard semantics, though it is defined in terms of somewhat more complicated values.

Congruence Condition We may easily state the condition that must be satisfied if we are to claim that these two semantics define the same language: the value appended to the stack according to the stack semantics must be that specified by the standard semantics. That is to say:

$$\mathcal{E}_1[\![E]\!]\zeta = \langle \mathcal{E}_0[\![E]\!]\rangle \S \zeta \quad \text{for all E and } \zeta \tag{13.10}$$

Exercise

2. Prove that Condition 13.10 is satisfied.

An Alternative Stack Semantics The previous section does not, of course, give the only stack semantics there is: for example, a trivial amendment would specify right to left evaluation instead of left to right. But any implementation based on these definitions would use a single stack, on which subexpressions would be evaluated one at a time. We next give an alternative stack semantics, which would be more suitable if we wished to evaluate subexpressions in parallel, perhaps on a multiprocessing computer.

The only change from the previous stack semantics is that we replace the semantic function for expressions, $\mathcal{E}_1$, with a new one, $\mathcal{E}_2$, defined as follows.

$$\mathcal{E}_2 : \text{Exp} \to N^* \to N^*$$

$$\mathcal{E}_2[\![N]\!]\zeta = \langle \mathcal{N}[\![N]\!]\rangle \S \zeta \quad (13.11)$$

$$\mathcal{E}_2[\![E_1 + E_2]\!]\zeta = \langle (\mathcal{E}_2[\![E_1]\!]\langle\rangle){\downarrow}1 + (\mathcal{E}_2[\![E_2]\!]\langle\rangle){\downarrow}1\rangle \S \zeta \quad (13.12)$$

Equation 13.12 is the only one that has changed: $\mathcal{E}_2$ is thought of as evaluating subexpressions on "new" empty stacks, so lending itself to an implementation embodying parallelism.

In fact, of course, $\mathcal{E}_2$ does nothing of the kind. The definitions of $\mathcal{E}_1$ and $\mathcal{E}_2$ are merely alternative formulations of the *same* function. But to prove directly that $\mathcal{E}_1 = \mathcal{E}_2$ is difficult; it is far easier to show that $\mathcal{E}_2$ satisfies the same congruence condition as $\mathcal{E}_1$: that is, that they are identically related to $\mathcal{E}_0$.

Exercise

3. Prove that 13.10 remains true when $\mathcal{E}_1$ is replaced by $\mathcal{E}_2$. Hence deduce that $\mathcal{E}_1 = \mathcal{E}_2$.

This provides a good illustration of the *normative* nature of standard semantics. It is easier to relate each implementation semantics separately to the standard than to relate them to each other, simply because the difficulties of reconciling two different implementations are thereby avoided. The moral is that the canonical definition of a language ought, as in our approach, to avoid implementation decisions as much as possible.

A Machine Code and Compiler We now proceed with the implementation of our simple example language, and the next stage is to provide a compiler and machine code for it.

We shall be using the approach suggested by the definition of $\mathcal{E}_1$, and so the obvious choice for a machine code will be one based on Reverse Polish. We therefore define its syntax as follows.

Syntactic Domains

N ∈ Nml (Numerals)

I ∈ Ins (Instructions)

Π ∈ Prg = Ins^* (Programs: finite sequences of instructions)

Syntax

I ::= load N | add

When we define the semantics of this machine code we shall arrange, as might be expected, that ⌜load N⌝ will place the value of N on the stack, and ⌜add⌝ will form the sum of the top two elements on the stack.

First, however, we define the compiling function, which produces the appropriate machine code from expressions in the example language. Notice that this function, $\mathscr{C}$, specifies a translation: it maps expressions to *syntactic* values, which is why quotation marks appear on the right hand side of the defining equations.

Compiling Function

$$\mathscr{C} : \text{Exp} \to \text{Prg}$$

$$\mathscr{C}[\![\text{N}]\!] = \langle\ulcorner \text{load N}\urcorner\rangle \qquad (13.13)$$

$$\mathscr{C}[\![\text{E}_1+\text{E}_2]\!] = (\mathscr{C}[\![\text{E}_1]\!])\S(\mathscr{C}[\![\text{E}_2]\!])\S\langle\ulcorner \text{add}\urcorner\rangle \qquad (13.14)$$

Before we can say whether this compiler is correct, we must give some semantics for the machine code programs it produces. There is no reason why a machine code should not have a *denotational* semantics. For the present example this would have been easier if we had chosen to define programs by the syntax

$$\Pi ::= \text{load N} \mid \Pi_1;\Pi_2;\text{add}$$

rather than simply as a sequence of instructions: then the denotational semantics would be very like the various versions for our original example language. But it is perhaps more natural to give an *operational* semantics for a machine code; and, in order to do so, we now define our machine.

A Machine We may think of the operation of any single sequential computer (that is, any computer which does not employ parallel processing) as being described informally by the following little program.

$$\text{until } \mathit{term}(\sigma) \text{ do } \sigma := \mathit{step}(\sigma) \qquad (13.15)$$

At each stage of the machine's operation the state, σ, is modified to a new state as specified by the single step state transformation function *step*; this is repeated until a terminal state, recognised by the predicate *term*, is reached. The structure of the domain of states, S, and the definitions of the functions *step* : S→S and *term* : S→T depend, of course, on the particular machine. More formally, we can define the general function *machine* as follows.

$$\mathit{machine}(\mathit{step},\mathit{term}) = \mathit{fix}(\lambda\phi\lambda\sigma.\mathit{term}(\sigma)\rightarrow\sigma,\ \phi(\mathit{step}(\sigma))) \qquad (13.16)$$

Then to define any particular machine we have merely to give definitions of *step* and *term*.

For the machine code of our example language it is convenient to consider the relevant states as being triples, comprised of a program, a program counter and a stack. So we define

$$S = \mathrm{Prg}\times\mathrm{N}\times\mathrm{N}^*$$

and let $\sigma = \langle \Pi,\nu,\zeta\rangle$ be a typical member of S. To define the single step function it is convenient first to specify the effect of any single instruction on the stack, which we do by defining a function $\mathscr{I}$.

$$\mathscr{I} : \mathrm{Ins} \rightarrow \mathrm{N}^* \rightarrow \mathrm{N}^*$$

$$\mathscr{I}[\![\mathrm{load}\ \mathrm{N}]\!]\zeta = \langle \mathscr{N}[\![\mathrm{N}]\!]\rangle \S \zeta \qquad (13.17)$$

$$\mathscr{I}[\![\mathrm{add}]\!]\zeta = \mathit{add}(\zeta). \qquad (13.18)$$

Then we may simply define

$$\mathit{step}_1(\langle \Pi,\nu,\zeta\rangle) = \langle \Pi,\ \nu+1,\ \mathscr{I}(\Pi\downarrow\nu)\zeta\rangle . \qquad (13.19)$$

A terminal state is reached when the program counter points beyond the end of the program. So:

$$term_1(\langle \Pi, \nu, \zeta \rangle) = (\nu > \#\Pi). \tag{13.20}$$

Thus when the machine executes a program Π with a starting stack ζ, a final stack is obtained as specified by the semantic function $\mathscr{M}$, defined as follows.

$$\mathscr{M} : \text{Prg} \to N^* \to N^*$$

$$\mathscr{M}[\![\Pi]\!]\zeta = (machine(step_1, term_1)\langle \Pi, 1, \zeta \rangle)\downarrow 3 \tag{13.21}$$

Notice that this definition is no longer denotational semantics: the value denoted by Π is no longer defined in terms of the values denoted by the syntactic subcomponents of Π. Instead, the whole program is fed to the machine, which is then left to behave according to its own rules.

The congruence condition for this semantics is simply that the effect of running a compiled expression should be that given by the stack semantics for the expression itself. More specifically:

$$\mathscr{M}(\mathscr{C}[\![E]\!])\zeta = \mathscr{E}_1[\![E]\!]\zeta \quad \text{for all } E, \zeta. \tag{13.22}$$

Exercises

4. Prove that Condition 13.22 is satisfied.
[Lemmas: (i) If $\#\Pi \geqslant \nu \geqslant 1$ then $\mu\langle \Pi, \nu, \zeta \rangle = \mu\langle \Pi\dagger 1, \nu-1, \zeta \rangle$, where $\mu\sigma = (machine(step_1, term_1)\sigma)\downarrow 3$.
(ii) $\mathscr{M}(\Pi_1 \S \Pi_2) = \mathscr{M}(\Pi_2) \circ \mathscr{M}(\Pi_1)$.]

5. The machine we have defined is still somewhat more abstract than it need be. Specify and prove correct an implementation in which the values kept on the stack are (binary) numerals rather than numbers

(that is, a stack is in Nml^* rather than N^*).

An Interpreter A compiler is not a necessary part of an operational semantics. To illustrate this, we give an alternative machine, which interprets expressions directly.

The state of this machine is comprised of two stacks. One is the usual stack of operands; the other is a stack of expressions waiting to be evaluated, interspersed with a special value, $\ulcorner plus \urcorner$, signifying that an addition is to be done. The way it works is as follows.

State

$\sigma = \langle \eta, \zeta \rangle \quad \in \quad S = [Exp + \{\ulcorner plus \urcorner\}]^* \times N^*$

Auxiliary Semantic Function

$$\mathscr{I} : [Exp + \{\ulcorner plus \urcorner\}] \to S \to S$$

$$\mathscr{I}[\![N]\!]\langle \eta, \zeta \rangle = \langle \eta, \langle \mathscr{N}[\![N]\!] \rangle \S \zeta \rangle \tag{13.23}$$

$$\mathscr{I}[\![E_1 + E_2]\!]\langle \eta, \zeta \rangle = \langle \langle E_1, E_2, \ulcorner plus \urcorner \rangle \S \eta, \zeta \rangle \tag{13.24}$$

$$\mathscr{I}[\![plus]\!]\langle \eta, \zeta \rangle = \langle \eta, add(\zeta) \rangle \tag{13.25}$$

Machine Definition

$$step_2(\langle \eta, \zeta \rangle) = \mathscr{I}(\eta \downarrow 1)\langle \eta \dagger 1, \zeta \rangle \tag{13.26}$$

$$term_2(\langle \eta, \zeta \rangle) = (\#\eta = 0) \tag{13.27}$$

Machine Semantic Function

$$\mathscr{T} : Exp \to N^* \to N^*$$

$$\mathscr{T}[\![E]\!]\zeta = (machine(step_2, term_2)\langle \langle E \rangle, \zeta \rangle) \downarrow 2 \tag{13.28}$$

Exercises

6. State and prove the appropriate congruence condition for this implementation.

7. Define and prove correct a "quick and dirty"

implementation of our simple example language; namely one for which the machine code is merely a list of the numerals in the expression, and the machine scans it, forming the sum in a single accumulator. Comment on the style of this implementation.

Application to Bigger languages

A realistic programming language is, of course, far removed in complexity from the very simple language we have been using for our examples. Nevertheless the same overall strategy may be used to justify a claim that a proposed implementation of such a language is correct. For example, in [34] Milne and Strachey discuss two implementations (involving direct interpretation and compilation, respectively) for a language called Sal which is about as complex as Algol 68. For the compiling implementation they distinguish the following stages in the sequence of semantic definitions.

1. Standard Semantics This is a denotational definition with continuations, very much as described in earlier chapters of this book. (For some simple languages, though not for Sal, it would be possible to define the semantics without using continuations. That would then be the standard semantics; but because continuations are required at a later stage it would be necessary to introduce as an extra stage a definition with continuations, and to prove it congruent with the standard semantics. A simple example of this is the substance of Exercise 9 below (page 356)).

2. Store Semantics The process of making state manipulations more explicit is now begun. Objects such as procedure values now correspond quite closely with the closures of our Chapter 4: they have one component which may be thought of as pure code (involving only information known at compile time) and a second component (an environment or, equivalently, a free variable list) giving details of all the denoted entities which the procedure can use. Labels are somewhat more complicated: since labelled commands can occur within expressions (in valof blocks, for example), a label value must include as a third component a "stack" for the anonymous subexpression values of partially evaluated expressions. Thus a piece of pure code can be thought of as running on a "state" comprised of a current environment, a current stack and a current store.

3. Stack Semantics The next stage is to use the stack for keeping denoted values, as well as anonymous ones; environments now associate names with pointers into the stack, using (in the particular example we are describing) the display mechanism of Dijkstra [8]. The continuation associated with a procedure call is also now kept on the stack, so that we now have a form of the usual return link mechanism. Since identifiers now denote stack positions rather than the values in those positions, it is possible to know where a value will be and to construct references to it before the value itself is worked out: this allows a recursive use of a procedure name, for example, to be treated just like any other free variable of the procedure body. Thus recursive procedures, and label blocks, no longer involve *fix* explicitly in their semantics (though *fix* might still be used explicitly at this stage for loops).

4. Syntactic Constraints As denoted values are now kept on the stack they can no longer have indefinite extents. Store semantics, however, had no such constraints; so store semantics and stack semantics are congruent only for programs which do not try to exploit the wider extents. The next step is therefore to define constraints on the *syntax* of programs, which are intended to guarantee that programs cannot use any of the facilities which rely on indefinite extents. Store semantics and stack semantics are then proved congruent for all programs satisfying these constraints.

5. Compiler and Relocating Loader A translation function is now defined, into a machine language called Sam. A relocating loader function is also provided, to allow separately compiled segments to be concatenated: the loader makes appropriate changes to those instructions whose operand fields contain code addresses.

6. Consecution Semantics The next step is to give a semantic definition for Sam. In fact the first one to be given is denotational, in which the meaning of an instruction depends only on its own subcomponents, or fields. Some of these fields are code addresses specifying, for example, the targets of jumps; for a denotational semantics these must be regarded as denoting some kind of continuation. The semantic function for instructions must therefore be supplied with an extra parameter giving a mapping between possible numerical field values and continuations. This mapping is called a *consecution*: it is defined by means of an iterative composition of the effect of each successive instruction in the program code.

7. Pointer Semantics Finally an operational semantics for Sam is given. Now code address fields are indeed regarded as pointers to more code, to which the interpreter is to be redirected. The semantics no longer involve abstract infinitary entities such as continuations; they may be expressed solely in terms of realistic atomic operations on a realistic machine.

Further details of these stages of definition and the proofs of their congruence will be found in [34]. We shall now turn to a simpler example, by considering another tiny language (devised by Robert Milne). This will allow us to discuss some of the techniques used in these congruence proofs, and the particular problem of relating a denotational semantics to an operational one, without involving us in the overwhelming mass of fine detail which the implementation of a large language inevitably brings.

A Second Simple Language

Unlike our first example language, the semantics of this language involve reflexive domains; the language is intended to be as simple as possible while still exhibiting this feature. The syntax and standard semantics are as follows.

Syntactic Domains

$B \in \mathsf{Bas}$ (Basic constants)

$I \in \mathsf{Ide}$ (Identifiers)

$E \in \mathsf{Exp}$ (Expressions)

Syntax

$E ::= B \mid I \mid (\lambda I.E_0)E_1$

Standard Semantics

Semantic Domains

$\beta \in \mathsf{B}$ (Basic values)

$\rho \in \mathsf{U} = [\mathsf{Ide} \to \mathsf{D}]$ (Environments)

$\delta \in \mathsf{D} = [\mathsf{U} \to \mathsf{B}]$ (Denoted values)

Semantic Functions

$\mathscr{B} : \mathsf{Bas} \to \mathsf{B}$ (not further defined)

$\mathscr{E} : \mathsf{Exp} \to \mathsf{U} \to \mathsf{B}$ (or $\mathscr{E} : \mathsf{Exp} \to \mathsf{D}$)

$$\mathscr{E}[\![B]\!]\rho = \mathscr{B}[\![B]\!] \quad (13.29)$$

$$\mathscr{E}[\![I]\!]\rho = (\rho[\![I]\!])\rho \quad (13.30)$$

$$\mathscr{E}[\![(\lambda I.E_0)E_1]\!]\rho = \mathscr{E}[\![E_0]\!](\rho[\mathscr{E}[\![E_1]\!]/I]) \quad (13.31)$$

Notice that this is an example of a language with dynamic (Lisp-like) scope rules. Actual parameters are evaluated in the environment governing the occurrences of the formal parameter name within the abstraction body. That is why the values denoted by names are of functionality $[U \rightarrow B]$ rather than simply B. The definition may easily be revised so as to conform to the Algol-like scope rules; but this would make the language far less interesting for our purposes.

Operational Semantics As is obvious and well-known, in the implementation of languages with dynamic scope rules unevaluated subexpressions may be represented simply by their text. In our particular case this actually makes life more complicated rather than less, as the alternative scope rules would not require named subexpressions to remain unevaluated, so that names would denote only basic values. But it does simplify the implementations of languages involving values such as functions, which would otherwise have to be represented by closures or something equivalent. That is why Lisp, and many other languages usually implemented by interpreters, acquired such scope rules. There is something of a culture clash as to whether this is a good thing. (For compiled languages the tendency to have dynamic scope rules is absent, as the text is not usually available at run time.)

In the interpreter for our language, then, names will denote unevaluated text, so the values corresponding to environments will be of the form $\rho \in U = [\text{Ide} \rightarrow \text{Exp}]$. The state of the interpreter will consist of an expression and such an environment; so it is of the form $\langle E,\rho\rangle \in [\mathrm{Exp}\times \mathrm{U}]$. We use the same general scheme for the definitions of machines as previously (13.15 and 13.16 above), so we must define the two functions *step* and *term*.

$$term(\langle E,\rho\rangle) = (E \in \mathrm{Bas}) \qquad (13.32)$$

$$step(\langle E,\rho\rangle) = \mathscr{G}[\![E]\!]\rho \qquad (13.33)$$

where $\mathscr{G}$ is defined as follows:

$$\mathscr{G} : \mathrm{Exp} \to \mathrm{U} \to [\mathrm{Exp} \times \mathrm{U}]$$

$$\mathscr{G}[\![B]\!]\rho = \langle B,\rho\rangle \qquad (13.34)$$

$$\mathscr{G}[\![I]\!]\rho = \langle \rho[\![I]\!],\ \rho\rangle \qquad (13.35)$$

$$\mathscr{G}[\![(\lambda I.E_0)E_1]\!]\rho = \langle E_0,\ \rho[E_1/I]\rangle \qquad (13.36)$$

Then, as before, we may define a function giving the overall effect of the whole machine.

$$\mathscr{E} : \mathrm{Exp} \to \mathrm{U} \to \mathrm{B}$$

$$\mathscr{E}[\![E]\!]\rho = \mathscr{B}((machine(step,term)\langle E,\rho\rangle)\downarrow 1) \qquad (13.37)$$

In fact a little manipulation leads to the following equations for $\mathscr{E}$.

$$\mathscr{E}[\![B]\!]\rho = \mathscr{B}[\![B]\!] \qquad (13.38)$$

$$\mathscr{E}[\![I]\!]\rho = \mathscr{E}(\rho[\![I]\!])\rho \qquad (13.39)$$

$$\mathscr{E}[\![(\lambda I.E_0)E_1]\!]\rho = \mathscr{E}[\![E_0]\!](\rho[E_1/I]) \qquad (13.40)$$

At first sight this looks like a conventional set of denotational semantic equations for $\mathscr{E}$. Notice, however, that this initial appearance is really illusory. The reason is that 13.39 breaks the rule about the value associated with a construct being defined in terms of the values associated with its subcomponents: $\rho[\![I]\!]$ is not a subcomponent of I. A structural induction proof cannot therefore be used to show that $\mathcal{E}$ is well-defined; instead we must rely on the existence of solutions to 13.16, which leads to a quite different argument.

We must now try to show the congruence of these two semantic definitions.

The Diacritical Convention When making proofs about two semantic definitions we are frequently required to consider and to compare pairs of values, one from each definition scheme, which are both called by the same name. They are usually elements of domains which may or may not be of the same structure but which also share one name. In our example, for instance, each form of definition involves a form of environment; both kinds of environment are elements of domains called U, and ρ is used for a typical element of either domain. We often need some convenient and systematic way of telling them apart.

Our solution is to decorate the names with accents. All names which belong solely to one of the definitions are given acute accents, and the names belonging to the other get grave accents: by convention we shall use acute accents for whichever definition is closer to the standard semantics. Thus $\acute{\rho}$ is an element of $\acute{U}$ = Ide → $\acute{D}$ and plays a part in the standard semantics, while $\grave{\rho} \in \grave{U}$ = Ide → Exp is used in the operational semantics.

We shall often wish, too, to mention pairs of values, one from each definition, in order to discuss whether they correspond. It is convenient to use circumflex accents for these pairs: thus $\hat{\rho}$ denotes $\langle \acute{\rho}, \grave{\rho} \rangle$, and $\acute{\rho}$ and $\grave{\rho}$ are $\hat{\rho}{\downarrow}1$ and $\hat{\rho}{\downarrow}2$ respectively.

The Congruence of the Two Definitions Our first task is to formulate the condition which must be satisfied if we are to regard the definitions as congruent. Since both versions of $\mathcal{E}$ produce final values from the same domain B, we can demand that in appropriate circumstances they give equal results when applied to any one expression. Here, "appropriate circumstances" implies that the evaluations should be carried out in corresponding environments. To express this it is convenient to define a function, which we shall call *Acute*, for converting any $\grave{\rho}$ to the corresponding $\acute{\rho}$. This function, an element of $\grave{U} \to \acute{U}$, may be defined as follows.

$$Acute(\grave{\rho}) = \lambda I.\acute{\mathcal{E}}(\grave{\rho}[\![I]\!]). \tag{13.41}$$

Our required condition is then given by the following theorem.

13.42. Theorem. For all E and $\grave{\rho}$,

$$\acute{\mathcal{E}}[\![E]\!](Acute\ \grave{\rho}) \equiv \grave{\mathcal{E}}[\![E]\!]\grave{\rho}.$$

Notice that for our environments we are ranging over all $\grave{\rho}$. We are agreeing, as is reasonable, not to worry about any peculiar environments in $\acute{U}$ which do not correspond to any $\grave{\rho}$ in $\grave{U}$.

First Attempt at Proof of 13.42 We first recall that the interpretive semantic function $\grave{\mathcal{E}}$ is based on a recursive definition; so we might be able to prove what we want by fixpoint induction. In fact

$$\grave{\mathcal{E}} = \mathit{fix}(H)$$

where

$$\begin{aligned} H = \lambda\mathcal{E}\lambda E\lambda\grave{\rho}.\ & E{=}\ulcorner B\urcorner & \rightarrow\ & \mathcal{B}[\![B]\!], \\ & E{=}\ulcorner I\urcorner & \rightarrow\ & \mathcal{E}(\grave{\rho}[\![I]\!])\grave{\rho}, \\ & E{=}\ulcorner(\lambda I.E_0)E_1\urcorner & \rightarrow\ & \mathcal{E}[\![E_0]\!](\grave{\rho}[E_1/I]), \\ & ?_B. \end{aligned} \tag{13.43}$$

(Notice that for this definition we have somewhat extended our notational conventions: a test in the conditional expression not only performs a kind of pattern-matching test on the syntactic structure of E, but also introduces new local names for the components, whose scopes include the branch invoked by a successful match.)

Let us define the assertion q as follows:

$$q(X) \;\Leftrightarrow\; X[\![E]\!]\grave{\rho} \equiv \acute{\mathcal{E}}[\![E]\!](\mathit{Acute}\ \grave{\rho}) \quad \text{for all E and } \grave{\rho} \tag{13.44}$$

and let us try to prove $q(\mathit{fix}\ H)$ by fixpoint induction.

Inductive step: Assume $q(\mathcal{E})$ and prove $q(H\mathcal{E})$ for all $\grave{\rho}$ by cases of E. For example, if E is $\ulcorner I\urcorner$, we have

$$\begin{aligned} (H\mathcal{E})[\![E]\!]\grave{\rho} &= \mathcal{E}(\grave{\rho}[\![I]\!])\grave{\rho} && \text{(by 13.43)} \\ &= \acute{\mathcal{E}}(\grave{\rho}[\![I]\!])(\mathit{Acute}\ \grave{\rho}). && \text{(induction hypothesis)} \end{aligned}$$

On the other hand,

$$\begin{aligned} \acute{\mathcal{E}}[\![E]\!](\mathit{Acute}\ \grave{\rho}) &= ((\mathit{Acute}\ \grave{\rho})[\![I]\!])(\mathit{Acute}\ \grave{\rho}) && \text{(by 13.30)} \\ &= \acute{\mathcal{E}}(\grave{\rho}[\![I]\!])(\mathit{Acute}\ \grave{\rho}). && \text{(by 13.41)} \end{aligned}$$

So $q(H\mathcal{E})$ holds in this case as required.

Basis step: We have to show $q(\bot)$. Unfortunately this is simply not true, since $\acute{\mathcal{E}}[\![E]\!](\mathit{Acute}\ \grave{\rho})$ is not $\bot$ for all E and $\grave{\rho}$ (not, at any rate, for any reasonable definition of $\mathcal{B}$).

This first attempt is therefore a failure. We can, however, salvage something from it: if we weaken q to

$$q(X) \Leftrightarrow X[\![E]\!]\grave{\rho} \sqsubseteq \acute{\mathcal{E}}[\![E]\!](\mathit{Acute}\ \grave{\rho}) \quad \text{for all E and } \grave{\rho} \qquad (13.45)$$

the basis step is now trivially satisfied, and the rest of the proof is still valid. So at least we have the following lemma.

13.46. Lemma. For all E and $\grave{\rho}$,

$\acute{\mathcal{E}}[\![E]\!](\mathit{Acute}\ \grave{\rho}) \sqsupseteq \grave{\mathcal{E}}[\![E]\!]\grave{\rho}$.

Exercise

8′. Complete the proof of 13.46. [You will need to prove the subsidiary result that

$\mathit{Acute}(\grave{\rho}[E/I]) = (\mathit{Acute}\ \grave{\rho})[\acute{\mathcal{E}}[\![E]\!]/I]$.]

We should not be surprised that this strategy gives us only an inequality result. The analysis of an algorithm by fixpoint induction is effectively an induction on the length of a computation. In this example, the inductive step is a matter of showing that if the computation is OK after n steps of execution it will still be OK after $n+1$ steps. Obviously in this context we cannot expect "OK" to mean "has produced the right answer", since for any particular n there will be some programs that go on for longer than n steps. "OK" can mean no more than "on the right lines" - and this is the meaning more precisely captured by 13.46.

Second Attempt at Proof of 13.42 We now turn our attention to $\acute{\&}$, which also has a recursive definition. We could try to proceed by expressing $\acute{\&}$ as $\acute{\&} = fix(H_1)$, where H_1 is defined along the lines suggested by 13.29 to 13.31, just as H was previously defined (in 13.43) along the lines suggested by 13.38 to 13.40. Then we could define the assertion

$$q_1(X) \Leftrightarrow X[\![\mathrm{E}]\!](Acute\ \grave{\rho}) \equiv \grave{\&}[\![\mathrm{E}]\!]\grave{\rho} \quad \text{for all E and } \grave{\rho} \tag{13.47}$$

and attempt to prove $q_1(fix\ H_1)$ by fixpoint induction. As before, we would have to relax q_1 to an inequality to get the basis step to hold; but this time the induction step goes wrong too. For example, assuming $q_1(\&)$ and attempting to prove $q_1(H_1\&)$, for the case where E is $\ulcorner \mathrm{I} \urcorner$ we would have to show

$$((Acute\ \grave{\rho})[\![\mathrm{I}]\!])(Acute\ \grave{\rho}) = \grave{\&}(\grave{\rho}[\![\mathrm{I}]\!])\grave{\rho}.$$

The use of 13.41 transforms this to

$$\acute{\&}(\grave{\rho}[\![\mathrm{I}]\!])(Acute\ \grave{\rho}) = \grave{\&}(\grave{\rho}[\![\mathrm{I}]\!])\grave{\rho}$$

and we can get no further without begging the whole question. Alternatively, if we try to spell out the definition of *Acute* explicitly in the original assertion, so that $q_1(X)$ becomes

$$X[\![\mathrm{E}]\!](\lambda \mathrm{I}.X(\grave{\rho}[\![\mathrm{I}]\!])) \equiv \grave{\&}[\![\mathrm{E}]\!]\grave{\rho} \quad \text{for all E and } \grave{\rho},$$

then for the case where E is $\ulcorner \mathrm{I} \urcorner$, the proof that

$$(H_1\&)[\![\mathrm{E}]\!](\lambda \mathrm{I}.(H_1\&)(\grave{\rho}[\![\mathrm{I}]\!])) = \grave{\&}[\![\mathrm{E}]\!]\grave{\rho}$$

reduces to showing that

$$(H_1\&)(\grave{\rho}[\![\mathrm{I}]\!])(\lambda \mathrm{I}.(H_1\&)(\grave{\rho}[\![\mathrm{I}]\!])) = \grave{\&}(\grave{\rho}[\![\mathrm{I}]\!])\grave{\rho},$$

which leads to an infinite regress.

Third Attempt at Proof of 13.42 To make progress with our analysis of the denotational semantic function $\acute{\&}$ we need some way of relating a pair of environments, $\grave{\rho}$ and a corresponding $\acute{\rho}$, which does not use *Acute* and hence involve the function we are trying to analyse. So we try to define a predicate, u, which asserts that two environments, $\hat{\rho}$, correspond: they do so if they map every identifier to denoted values which correspond. Denoted values are elements of $\acute{\mathrm{U}}\to\mathrm{B}$, for the denotational semantics, or of Exp for the operational semantics: each needs an environment in order to produce a basic value. So we need another predicate, d, for relating denoted values: two values correspond if they yield corresponding basic values when supplied with corresponding environments. The relationship between these two predicates is given by the following equations.

$$d\langle \acute{\delta},\mathrm{E}\rangle \Leftrightarrow \bigwedge\{\acute{\delta}\acute{\rho} \equiv \grave{\&}[\![\mathrm{E}]\!]\grave{\rho} \mid u\hat{\rho}\} \qquad (13.48)$$

$$u\hat{\rho} \Leftrightarrow \bigwedge\{d\langle \acute{\rho}[\![\mathrm{I}]\!], \grave{\rho}[\![\mathrm{I}]\!]\rangle \mid \mathrm{I}\} \qquad (13.49)$$

Here we use the $\bigwedge$P notation, introduced in 9.31, for the conjunction of a (possibly infinite) set of assertions; in 13.49 it asserts that $d\langle \acute{\rho}[\![\mathrm{I}]\!],\grave{\rho}[\![\mathrm{I}]\!]\rangle$ holds for all I. (If we were being really systematic we could perhaps define a third predicate, $b\hat{\beta} \Leftrightarrow (\acute{\beta}\equiv\grave{\beta})$, for relating basic values, and use $b\langle \acute{\delta}\acute{\rho},\grave{\&}[\![\mathrm{E}]\!]\grave{\rho}\rangle$ in 13.48; but for this example such modularity would merely confuse.)

If, then, the predicates d and u are defined as in 13.48 and 13.49, we have only to prove

$$d\langle \acute{\mathcal{E}}[\![E]\!], E\rangle \quad \text{for all } E, \tag{13.50}$$

for then it will immediately follow that

$$u\langle \mathit{Acute}\ \grave{\rho}, \grave{\rho}\rangle \tag{13.51}$$

and these two results combined will give us

$$\acute{\mathcal{E}}[\![E]\!](\mathit{Acute}\ \grave{\rho}) \equiv \grave{\mathcal{E}}[\![E]\!]\grave{\rho}$$

as required.

The proof of 13.50 is a simple structural induction on E. If E is $\ulcorner I \urcorner$, then for any $\hat{\rho}$ such that $u\hat{\rho}$ we have to show $\acute{\mathcal{E}}[\![E]\!]\acute{\rho} \equiv \grave{\mathcal{E}}[\![E]\!]\grave{\rho}$. We have

$$\acute{\mathcal{E}}[\![E]\!]\acute{\rho} = (\acute{\rho}[\![I]\!])\acute{\rho} \qquad \text{(by 13.30)}$$

and

$$\grave{\mathcal{E}}[\![E]\!]\grave{\rho} = \grave{\mathcal{E}}(\grave{\rho}[\![I]\!])\grave{\rho}. \qquad \text{(by 13.39)}$$

But since $u\hat{\rho}$ holds, we know that $d\langle \acute{\rho}[\![I]\!], \grave{\rho}[\![I]\!]\rangle$ is true; so, also since $u\hat{\rho}$ holds, we have $(\acute{\rho}[\![I]\!])\acute{\rho} = \grave{\mathcal{E}}(\grave{\rho}[\![I]\!])\grave{\rho}$. If E is $\ulcorner(\lambda I.E_0)E_1\urcorner$, we note that if $u\hat{\rho}$ then also $u\langle \acute{\rho}[\acute{\mathcal{E}}[\![E_1]\!]/I], \grave{\rho}[E_1/I]\rangle$; so by the inductive hypothesis $\acute{\mathcal{E}}[\![E_0]\!](\acute{\rho}[\acute{\mathcal{E}}[\![E_1]\!]/I]) = \grave{\mathcal{E}}[\![E_0]\!](\grave{\rho}[E_1/I])$ as required. The third case is trivial.

Thus we have constructed what seems, at least at first sight, to be a proof of 13.42. Yet we have labelled it only an attempt at a proof, though the reader may have noticed that such timidity is not our usual style when we believe we have something valid to say. The reader is urged, therefore, before continuing, to review this argument carefully, and to consider where a possible mistake could lie.

The Snag The trouble with the previous section is the pair of equations 13.48 and 13.49 which purports to be a definition of two mutually recursive predicates. We have earlier talked about the danger of assuming that any equation has a solution, though previously whenever this kind of question arose we developed the habit of appealing to the theorem of Tarski [60] that any monotonic function on a complete lattice has a (minimal) fixed point. That is no use here, however, as the predicates (if any) described by 13.48 and 13.49 are not expected to be the fixed points of monotonic functions. For example, suppose *d* in 13.49 is so restrictive that there are *no* pairs of values for which it gives a *true* result. Then there will be no pairs of environments related by *u*; so the set of assertions in 13.48 will be empty, and thus the *d* in 13.48 is trivially satisfied for *all* pairs of values. As the *d* in 13.49 is relaxed, so that it begins to return *true* for some values, the *d* in 13.48 begins to reject some. This behaviour cannot be described by a monotonic function. As in our discussion of fixpoint induction (in Chapter 9), we may prefer to think of these predicates as mapping their arguments into T′, the two-element lattice {*true*,*untrue*}, where *true* $\sqsubseteq$ *untrue*: but this is no help in the present predicament.

This problem is not a feature of *all* predicate definitions that arise in the course of constructing congruence proofs. In 13.49, for example, u is monotonically (and even continuously) related to d. The difficulty typically arises when a circularity occurs through using a predicate to limit the membership of a set of assertions (an example is the $u\hat{\rho}$ in 13.48). This usually happens when specifying a set of congruent argument pairs for which a pair of functions must give congruent results if the functions themselves are to be considered congruent; thus the difficult situation is when a reflexive domain occurs to the left of an arrow in its own defining equation: that is, it is part of the argument space of some function space involved in its own structure (in our present example we have $\mathrm{D} = [\mathrm{Ide} \to \mathrm{D}] \to \mathrm{B}$).

We must therefore now discuss techniques which in most situations are sufficient to demonstrate the existence of the predicates we want. Unfortunately, however, our present example has further difficulties: for reasons which we shall discuss later, the general techniques are not successful in showing the existence of predicates satisfying 13.48 and 13.49. We are forced to weaken our requirements a little, and to accept a predicate d satisfying the equations

$$d\langle \acute{\delta}, \mathrm{E}\rangle \;\Leftrightarrow\; \bigwedge\{\acute{\delta}\acute{\rho} \sqsubseteq \grave{\mathcal{E}}[\![\mathrm{E}]\!]\grave{\rho} \mid u\hat{\rho}\} \qquad (13.52)$$

$$u\hat{\rho} \;\Leftrightarrow\; \bigwedge\{d\langle \acute{\rho}[\![\mathrm{I}]\!], \grave{\rho}[\![\mathrm{I}]\!]\rangle \mid \mathrm{I}\}. \qquad (13.53)$$

The Existence of the Required Predicates The domain $\acute{\mathrm{D}}$, one of the domains on which d is to be defined, is given by the equation

$$\mathrm{D} = [\mathrm{Ide} \to \mathrm{D}] \to \mathrm{B}.$$

As we explained in Chapter 7, this domain is the range of the retract D defined by

$$D = fix(\lambda D.(Ide \circ\!\!\rightarrow D) \circ\!\!\rightarrow B) \qquad (13.54)$$

where *Ide* and B are given retracts. So, since

$$D = \bigsqcup_{n=0}^{\infty} (\lambda D.(Ide \circ\!\!\rightarrow D) \circ\!\!\rightarrow B)^n (\perp)$$

we may express D by

$$D = \bigsqcup_{n=0}^{\infty} D_n \qquad (13.55)$$

where

$$D_0 = \perp \qquad (13.56)$$

$$D_{n+1} = U_n \circ\!\!\rightarrow B \qquad (n \geq 0) \qquad (13.57)$$

$$U_n = Ide \circ\!\!\rightarrow D_n \qquad (n \geq 0). \qquad (13.58)$$

Each D_n and U_n is itself a retract. Our strategy is to define sequences of predicates d_n and u_n on the domains given by D_n and U_n respectively (for $n \geq 0$). This does not involve any circularity. Then, just as D and U are defined in terms of the D_n and U_n, so we define d and u, acting on D and U, in terms of the d_n and u_n, and show that they satisfy 13.52 and 13.53 as required.

First we remind ourselves of a couple of properties of the retract sequences. Not only is each element weaker than its successor, when they are considered as functions, but it is also *included* in its successor when they are considered as domains. This latter idea is contained in the following definition.

13.59. Definition. For retracts X and Y, $X \lessdot Y$ if

$X \circ Y = Y \circ X = X$.

13.60. Lemma. $D_n \sqsubseteq D_{n+1}$ for all $n \geq 0$.

13.61. Lemma. $D_n \leqslant D_{n+1}$ for all $n \geq 0$.

Proofs: Straightforward inductions, using monotonicity and the definition of $\bullet\!\!\rightarrow$ (7.42).

We now define the sequences of predicates.

13.62. Definition. For $n \geq 0$, d_n and u_n are defined as follows.

$$d_0\langle \acute{\delta}, \mathrm{E}\rangle \;\Leftrightarrow\; \mathit{true} \qquad \text{(for all } \acute{\delta}, \mathrm{E})$$

$$d_{n+1}\langle \acute{\delta}, \mathrm{E}\rangle \;\Leftrightarrow\; \bigwedge\{D_{n+1}(\acute{\delta})\acute{\rho} \sqsubseteq \grave{\mathcal{E}}[\![\mathrm{E}]\!]\grave{\rho} \mid u_n\hat{\rho}\}$$
$$\text{(for all } \acute{\delta}, \mathrm{E} \text{ and } n \geq 0)$$

$$u_n\hat{\rho} \;\Leftrightarrow\; \bigwedge\{d_n\langle \acute{\rho}[\![\mathrm{I}]\!], \grave{\rho}[\![\mathrm{I}]\!]\rangle \mid \mathrm{I}\} \qquad \text{(for } n \geq 0).$$

Remember that we are thinking of our predicates as mapping to the lattice T′, in which *true* is the minimal element; thus d_0 is the bottom predicate. Since there is no circularity in their definitions, there is no question but that all these predicates are well defined.

We now use these sequences to define the predicates on the "limit spaces" D and U.

13.63. Definition. $d\langle \acute{\delta}, \mathrm{E}\rangle \Leftrightarrow \bigwedge_{n=0}^{\infty} d_n\langle D_n \acute{\delta}, \mathrm{E}\rangle$.

u is defined in terms of d, as in equation 13.53.

We may immediately prove the following lemma.

13.64. Lemma. $u\hat{\rho} \Leftrightarrow \bigwedge_{n=0}^{\infty} u_n\langle U_n \acute{\rho}, \grave{\rho}\rangle$.

It now remains to show that the d defined by 13.63 satisfies equation 13.52. There is a general strategy for such tasks: it involves proving lemmas like the following.

13.65. Lemma. For all $\acute{\delta}$ and E, and all $n \geq 0$,

1. $d_n\langle \acute{\delta}, E\rangle \Rightarrow d_{n+1}\langle \acute{D}_n \acute{\delta}, E\rangle$;
2. $d_{n+1}\langle \acute{\delta}, E\rangle \Rightarrow d_n\langle \acute{D}_n \acute{\delta}, E\rangle$.

Proof: We prove these two results together, by induction on n.

Inductive step: Assume the results hold for all $n<m$; note that since $U_n = Ide \to D_n$, this assumption immediately implies that for all $n<m$,

$u_n \hat{\rho} \Rightarrow u_{n+1}\langle \acute{U}_n \acute{\rho}, \grave{\rho}\rangle$, and

$u_{n+1} \hat{\rho} \Rightarrow u_n\langle \acute{U}_n \acute{\rho}, \grave{\rho}\rangle$.

Now, suppose $d_m\langle \acute{\delta}, E\rangle$ holds for some $\acute{\delta}$ and E; that is,

$$\bigwedge\{\acute{D}_m \acute{\delta} \acute{\rho} \sqsubseteq \grave{\&}[\![E]\!]\grave{\rho} \mid u_{m-1}\hat{\rho}\}.$$

Thus, in particular, since by hypothesis

$u_m \hat{\rho} \Rightarrow u_{m-1}\langle \acute{U}_{m-1} \acute{\rho}, \grave{\rho}\rangle$,

$$\bigwedge\{\acute{D}_m \acute{\delta}(\acute{U}_{m-1}\acute{\rho}) \sqsubseteq \grave{\&}[\![E]\!]\grave{\rho} \mid u_m\hat{\rho}\}.$$

But, since $\acute{D}_m \acute{\delta} = (\acute{U}_{m-1} \to B)\acute{\delta} = B \circ \acute{\delta} \circ \acute{U}_{m-1}$, this reduces to

$$\bigwedge\{\acute{D}_m \acute{\delta} \acute{\rho} \sqsubseteq \grave{\&}[\![E]\!]\grave{\rho} \mid u_m\hat{\rho}\}.$$

So, by Lemma 13.61,

$$\bigwedge\{\acute{D}_{m+1}(\acute{D}_m \acute{\delta})\acute{\rho} \sqsubseteq \grave{\&}[\![E]\!]\grave{\rho} \mid u_m\hat{\rho}\},$$

and thus $d_{m+1}\langle \acute{D}_m \acute{\delta}, E\rangle$, as required for Part 1. For Part 2, suppose $d_{m+1}\langle \acute{\delta}, E\rangle$ for some $\acute{\delta}$ and E; that is,

$$\bigwedge\{\acute{D}_{m+1} \acute{\delta} \acute{\rho} \sqsubseteq \grave{\&}[\![E]\!]\grave{\rho} \mid u_m\hat{\rho}\}.$$

Thus, in particular, since by hypothesis

$u_{m-1}\hat{\rho} \Rightarrow u_m\langle \acute{U}_{m-1}\acute{\rho},\grave{\rho}\rangle$,

$\bigwedge\{\acute{D}_{m+1}\delta(\acute{U}_{m-1}\acute{\rho}) \sqsubseteq \grave{\mathcal{E}}[\![E]\!]\grave{\rho} \mid u_{m-1}\hat{\rho}\}$.

But, since $\acute{D}_{m+1}\delta(\acute{U}_{m-1}\acute{\rho}) = (B\circ\delta\circ\acute{U}_m)(\acute{U}_{m-1}\acute{\rho})$
$= B(\acute{\delta}((\acute{U}_m\circ\acute{U}_{m-1})\acute{\rho})) = B(\acute{\delta}(\acute{U}_{m-1}\acute{\rho})) = \acute{D}_m\acute{\delta}\acute{\rho}$ by Lemma 13.61, this becomes

$\bigwedge\{\acute{D}_m\acute{\delta}\acute{\rho} \sqsubseteq \grave{\mathcal{E}}[\![E]\!]\grave{\rho} \mid u_{m-1}\hat{\rho}\}$,

and so $d_m\langle \acute{D}_m\acute{\delta},E\rangle$ holds, as required.

Basis step: We must show

1. $d_0\langle \acute{\delta},E\rangle \Rightarrow d_1\langle \acute{D}_0\acute{\delta},E\rangle$
2. $d_1\langle \acute{\delta},E\rangle \Rightarrow d_0\langle \acute{D}_0\acute{\delta},E\rangle$

where $d_0\langle \acute{\delta},E\rangle = true$ for all $\acute{\delta}$ and E, and $\acute{D}_0 = \bot$. Part 2 is therefore trivial, and Part 1 amounts to showing $\bigwedge\{\bot \sqsubseteq \grave{\mathcal{E}}[\![E]\!]\grave{\rho} \mid u_0\hat{\rho}\}$ for all E, which is also trivial. (Note, however, that it is this last step which would break down if we were trying to construct predicates satisfying the original equations, 13.48 and 13.49.)

<u>*13.66. Corollary.*</u> For all $\hat{\rho}$ and all $n\geq 0$,

$u_n\hat{\rho} \Rightarrow u_{n+1}\langle \acute{U}_n\acute{\rho},\grave{\rho}\rangle$, and

$u_{n+1}\hat{\rho} \Rightarrow u_n\langle \acute{U}_n\acute{\rho},\grave{\rho}\rangle$.

<u>*13.67. Lemma.*</u> If for some $\hat{\rho}$ and n, $u_n\hat{\rho}$ holds, then $u\langle \acute{U}_n\acute{\rho},\grave{\rho}\rangle$ holds.

Proof: $u_n\hat{\rho}$ immediately implies $u_n\langle \acute{U}_n\acute{\rho},\grave{\rho}\rangle$. Moreover, by inductions using 13.66, we also have

$u_n\hat{\rho} \Rightarrow u_m\langle \acute{U}_m\acute{\rho},\grave{\rho}\rangle$ (for all $m<n$)
$u_n\hat{\rho} \Rightarrow u_m\langle \acute{U}_n\acute{\rho},\grave{\rho}\rangle$ (for all $m>n$).

So, by 13.61, $u_n\hat{\rho} \Rightarrow u_m\langle \acute{U}_m(\acute{U}_n\acute{\rho}),\grave{\rho}\rangle$ for all m, and thus $u\langle \acute{U}_n\acute{\rho},\grave{\rho}\rangle$ holds as required.

Now that we have established these relationships between the elements of the various sequences, we continue with our general strategy by using them in proving the following theorem.

13.68. Theorem. d (as defined in 13.63) satisfies the equation

$$d\langle \acute{\delta},\mathrm{E}\rangle \Leftrightarrow \bigwedge\{\acute{D}\acute{\delta}\acute{\rho} \sqsubseteq \grave{\mathcal{E}}[\![\mathrm{E}]\!]\grave{\rho} \mid u\hat{\rho}\}.$$

Proof: Suppose $d\langle \acute{\delta},\mathrm{E}\rangle$ holds for some $\acute{\delta}$ and E; that is, for all $n\geq 0$, $d_n\langle \acute{D}_n\acute{\delta},\mathrm{E}\rangle$ holds. Now for any $\hat{\rho}$ such that $u\hat{\rho}$ holds, we know that for all $n>0$ $u_{n-1}\langle \acute{U}_{n-1}\acute{\rho},\grave{\rho}\rangle$ holds. Combining these two facts gives, since

$\acute{D}_n = \acute{U}_{n-1}\to B$,

$\acute{D}_n\acute{\delta}\acute{\rho} \sqsubseteq \grave{\mathcal{E}}[\![\mathrm{E}]\!]\grave{\rho}$.

Hence, since all our functions are continuous and $\{\acute{D}_n \mid n\geq 0\}$ is a chain with l.u.b. D, we have

$$\bigwedge\{\acute{D}\acute{\delta}\acute{\rho} \sqsubseteq \grave{\mathcal{E}}[\![\mathrm{E}]\!]\grave{\rho} \mid u\hat{\rho}\}$$

as required. (If we were being more general, and working with a predicate $b\langle \acute{\delta}\acute{\rho},\grave{\mathcal{E}}[\![\mathrm{E}]\!]\grave{\rho}\rangle$ instead of $\acute{\delta}\acute{\rho} \sqsubseteq \grave{\mathcal{E}}[\![\mathrm{E}]\!]\grave{\rho}$, we should be relying here on b being inclusive.)

Conversely, suppose that for some $\acute{\delta}$ and E,

$$\bigwedge\{\acute{D}\acute{\delta}\acute{\rho} \sqsubseteq \grave{\mathcal{E}}[\![\mathrm{E}]\!]\grave{\rho} \mid u\hat{\rho}\}$$

holds, and let $\hat{\rho}$ be such that $u_n\hat{\rho}$ holds for some n, so that (by 13.67) $u\langle \acute{U}_n\acute{\rho},\grave{\rho}\rangle$ holds. Then

$\acute{D}\acute{\delta}(\acute{U}_n\acute{\rho}) \sqsubseteq \grave{\mathcal{E}}[\![\mathrm{E}]\!]\grave{\rho}$.

Hence, by monotonicity $\acute{D}_{n+1}\acute{\delta}(\acute{U}_n\acute{\hat{\rho}}) \sqsubseteq \grave{\mathcal{E}}[\![E]\!]\grave{\hat{\rho}}$, and so $\acute{D}_{n+1}\acute{\delta}\acute{\hat{\rho}} \sqsubseteq \grave{\mathcal{E}}[\![E]\!]\grave{\hat{\rho}}$ for all $\hat{\rho}$ such that $u_n\hat{\rho}$.

Thus $d_{n+1}\langle \acute{D}_{n+1}\acute{\delta},E\rangle$ holds for any $n \geqslant 0$, and so $d\langle \acute{\delta},E\rangle$ holds as required.

We have thus shown the existence of predicates satisfying equations 13.52 and 13.53 (since values denoted by $\acute{\delta}$ in these equations are all in D, and thus fixed points of D), and we can therefore use them in order, finally, to prove 13.42.

13.69. Lemma. For all E and $\grave{\hat{\rho}}$,
$\acute{\mathcal{E}}[\![E]\!](Acute\ \grave{\hat{\rho}}) \sqsubseteq \grave{\mathcal{E}}[\![E]\!]\grave{\hat{\rho}}$.

Proof: Use the argument of the third attempt to prove 13.42 (page 344), using the new version of the equation for d.

Proof of Theorem 13.42. The theorem is an immediate consequence of 13.46 and 13.69.

At last we have succeeded in proving the congruence of the denotational and the operational semantics of our little language, but only by a rather complicated process of proving that each was an approximation to the standard set by the other. The reason for this complication was the large disparity between the two kinds of semantic definition. On the one hand is an interpreter, naturally analysed by means of an induction on the number of program steps executed; on the other, a denotational definition normally subjected to analysis by a structural induction on parse trees. This denotational definition, moreover, is based on reflexive domains, and analysing the properties of these domains involves us in an induction (as in 13.65) on the level of functional complexity of the values being considered (that is, on the n in the $\hat{D}_n$ sequence). However, an induction on execution length cannot be used to demonstrate complete congruence with the denotational standard, since at any stage there will always be some programs that require longer time (a concept outside the denotational scheme); similarly, an induction on functional complexity cannot be used to set up a predicate expressing complete congruence with an interpreter, since at each stage there will always be some programs which manipulate objects of still higher type (an abstract concept outside the interpretive scheme). This is not to say that the predicates expressing complete congruence do not exist: that is an open question. It is simply that we cannot *demonstrate* that they exist, and therefore we cannot use them in our proofs.

Actually, *both* domains related by our predicate d were reflexive. However, though our construction of d involved a sequence of approximations of $\hat{D}$, we did not consider introducing a similar sequence of approximations for the other domain, Exp. In this example, indeed, doing so would have been unhelpful: one sequence was based on increasing functional complexity, while the other would have been based on increasing syntactic complexity - again there would have been no correlation.

Sometimes, especially when two denotational definitions are being related, the domains involved are not so dissimilar. Then the sequences of approximations do correspond more closely; and since at each level approximation is being compared with approximation, the predicates expressing precise equivalence at each level do satisfy the required relationships with each other (in our example, Lemma 13.65). Thus in such cases congruence can be proved at once: there is no need to analyse each side separately. An example of this situation is provided by the concluding exercise.

The comparison of two operational definitions is less straightforward: often the two implementation techniques will differ so widely that there will be no correlation between the execution times of programs run under the two schemes. In such cases, as we have already suggested, it is usually simpler to relate each separately to a normative denotational semantics.

The "inclusive predicate" strategy which we have been describing was devised by Robert Milne, who used it in his thesis [33] to investigate mode declarations in Algol 68. John Reynolds [43] has also done similar work, in connection with the congruence of alternative semantic definitions for the λ-calculus (see the concluding exercise of this chapter). His formulation is a little different, however: he uses "directed complete" relations in place of our inclusive predicates. Michael Gordon [15] has used different but related techniques in an investigation into the correctness of a LISP interpreter.

As we have seen, the construction of congruence

proofs is complicated. Part of this complexity is inevitable: language definitions and implementations both contain quantities of "small print", all of which has to be either used as a standard or verified against one. We must hope that programs for algebraic manipulation will be developed to provide some automated assistance in this task. But some, at least, of the complexity of our second example can be encapsulated in a general theory. Just as our results about retracts and methods of combining them provided us with all the domains we needed without requiring us to construct them from scratch each time, so we can also develop more general results allowing us to use predicates on pairs of domains, and to combine them, without explicit examination of the sequences of domains and predicates involved in their construction. For example, given suitable predicates a, defined on the pair of domains $\hat{A}$, and b, defined on $\hat{B}$, we can use the predicate $(a{\to}b)$ defined on $[\acute{A}{\to}\acute{B}]\times[\grave{A}{\to}\grave{B}]$: two functions are related by $(a{\to}b)$ if they give results related by b for all pairs of arguments related by a. Of course, the difficulties we have encountered earlier in this chapter indicate that such a general theory is not always applicable - and, as might be imagined, it is itself of some complexity. Readers interested in studying it are once again referred to Milne and Strachey [34].

Exercise

9. Table 13.1 gives two semantic definitions (based on Reynolds [43]) for a version of the λ-calculus

containing forms of abstraction for both call by name and call by value. Suggest suitable predicates for proving the congruence of these two definitions. Show that the predicates exist, and prove that the definitions are congruent.

Table 13.1. Two Definitions of a λ-calculus

Syntactic Domains

$I \in \mathrm{Ide}$ (Identifiers)

$E \in \mathrm{Exp}$ (Expressions)

Syntax

$E ::= I \mid E_1(E_2) \mid \lambda I.E \mid \lambda_{\mathrm{val}} I.E$

First Semantics

Semantic Domains

B (Basic values)

$\varepsilon \in \mathrm{E} = \mathrm{B} + [\mathrm{E} \to \mathrm{E}]$ (Expression values)

$\rho \in \mathrm{U} = [\mathrm{Ide} \to \mathrm{E}]$ (Environments)

Semantic Function

$\mathcal{E} : \mathrm{Exp} \to \mathrm{U} \to \mathrm{E}$

$\mathcal{E}[\![I]\!]\rho = \rho[\![I]\!]$

$\mathcal{E}[\![E_1(E_2)]\!]\rho = (\mathcal{E}[\![E_1]\!]\rho \mid [\mathrm{E}\to\mathrm{E}])(\mathcal{E}[\![E_2]\!]\rho)$

$\mathcal{E}[\![\lambda I.E]\!]\rho = (\lambda\varepsilon.\mathcal{E}[\![E]\!](\rho[\varepsilon/I]))$ in E

$\mathcal{E}[\![\lambda_{\mathrm{val}} I.E]\!]\rho = (\mathit{strict}(\lambda\varepsilon.\mathcal{E}[\![E]\!](\rho[\varepsilon/I])))$ in E

Table 13.1 (continued)

Second Semantics

Semantic Domains

B	(Basic values)
A	(Answers)
$\omega \in W = K \to A$	(Expression closures)
$\kappa \in K = E \to A$	(Expression continuations)
$\varepsilon \in E = B + [W \to W]$	(Expression values)
$\rho \in U = Ide \to W$	(Environments)

Semantic Function

$$\mathcal{E} : Exp \to U \to W$$

$$\mathcal{E}[\![I]\!]\rho\kappa = \rho[\![I]\!]\kappa$$

$$\mathcal{E}[\![E_1(E_2)]\!]\rho\kappa = \mathcal{E}[\![E_1]\!]\rho\{\lambda\varepsilon.\ \varepsilon \equiv [W{\to}W] \to (\varepsilon|[W{\to}W])(\mathcal{E}[\![E_2]\!]\rho)\kappa,\ \mathit{Wrong}\ \}$$

$$\mathcal{E}[\![\lambda I.E]\!]\rho\kappa = \kappa(\lambda\omega.\mathcal{E}[\![E]\!](\rho[\omega/I])\ \text{in}\ E)$$

$$\mathcal{E}[\![\lambda_{val} I.E]\!]\rho\kappa = \kappa((\lambda\omega.\lambda\kappa'.\omega\{\lambda\varepsilon.\mathcal{E}[\![E]\!](\rho[(\lambda\kappa.\kappa\varepsilon)/I])\kappa'\})\ \text{in}\ E)$$

where *Wrong* is an element of A.

Chapter 14

MISCELLANEOUS MATTERS

Relation to the Axiomatic Approach

We remarked back in Chapter 2 that the axiomatic approach has made an important contribution to the art of proving the correctness of programs. In this methodology the effects of the various command constructs in a programming language are described by means of proof rules, which are couched largely in terms of the language itself. We also remarked that the justification of these rules is an important application of denotational semantics. By way of example, we shall shortly obtain the appropriate rule for one particular construct (a jump-free while-loop); but first we make a few remarks about the axiomatic approach itself, and introduce the notation.

At the end of Chapter 8 we drew attention to the fact that the λ-calculus was a referentially transparent language. This allowed us to use the normal machinery of mathematics in our analysis of the various expressions in the language. We could introduce new names for subexpressions, for example, and manipulate them freely, provided only that we observed the discipline of the scope rules, which in any case corresponded to normal practice. But in the language we have since been developing, the behaviour is not so accommodating. To be sure, the relationship between names and the objects they denote is still referentially transparent, but in practice this is frequently confined to the relationship between names and the corresponding locations, or L-values, which is for most purposes of analysis unimportant. Except when we are explicitly considering some concept such as sharing, for which the identity of locations is crucial, we are normally concerned rather with the relationship between names and R-values: and this, because of the assignment command, is not referentially transparent. Our formal semantics has described this relationship in terms of the behaviour of the environment ρ and the state σ; and although the notation we have introduced for this is indeed referentially transparent, it is far too complicated to invoke every time we write a program. Moreover, the state is itself a complicated object, and contains information about *all* the R-values, whereas frequently we would prefer to concentrate our attention upon just a few. So instead of working with the whole state we make assertions relating the values of just some of the variables in it; instead of manipulating states in a referentially transparent calculus of state values, we manipulate and transform the assertions according to rules in a calculus of assertions. In a sense, the non-transparent behaviour of variables has caused us to take one step backwards from the program: we no longer work formally with the variables themselves, because their values are liable to change; instead we work formally with assertions about the variables.

The most common notation for describing this calculus of assertions was introduced by Tony Hoare

[19]. In this notation statements are made of the form

$$P \{ S \} Q$$

where S is a command of the programming language, and P and Q are assertions, perhaps involving the names in S's environment (strictly, in the environments which hold immediately before and after S, respectively). The intended meaning of the above statement is as follows:

"If P is true before the execution of S is begun,
and if S terminates normally,
then Q will be true afterwards."

Notice that if S fails to terminate, or if it terminates abnormally (that is, comes to an error stop or causes control to jump away from S), the statement is vacuously true. For each command construct in the language a rule of inference (called an "axiom") is given. The notation for these (which is quite conventional) is illustrated by the following example.

$$\frac{P \{ S_1 \} Q \qquad Q \{ S_2 \} R}{P \{ S_1 ; S_2 \} R} \tag{14.1}$$

If all the statements above the line can be shown to be true, then the truth of the statement below the line may be inferred. A definition of much of the language PASCAL [70] has been given in this way [20].

For the purposes of the present discussion, we shall assume that P and Q etc. are expressions in our programming language, and that they are without side effects. We are using these assertions to describe a state, and we do not intend them actually to be evaluated by the machine: an expression with a side effect would therefore be *prima facie* meaningless in this context. But, by the same token, the fact that these assertions are never going to be computed implies that they need not necessarily be computable, or even continuous: so our restriction to expressions in the programming language is something of an oversimplification. Indeed, discontinuous predicates are sometimes useful in practice. If they are going to be employed, their semantics must be defined and care must be taken to avoid any arguments based on continuity. These extra complications are by no means insoluble, but we shall nevertheless avoid them for this introduction.

Exercise

1. Devise a situation in which the use of a discontinuous predicate might help in analysing the correctness of a program.

The Rule for the **while**-*loop* In the notation just introduced, the rule of inference for the while-loop is as follows.

$$\frac{(P \wedge B)\ \{\ S\ \}\ P}{P\ \{\ \textbf{while}\ B\ \textbf{do}\ S\ \}\ (P \wedge \sim B)} \qquad (14.2)$$

We now prove the validity of this rule from the semantic definition of our language. For simplicity we shall assume that S is jump-free. Notice also that since B appears as part of an assertion we are assuming that it is without side effects.

Let us make the same simplifying assumption as we did in Chapter 11, namely that *Wrong* is $\lambda\sigma.?_A$. Then, using all these assumptions, we may translate the rule into our own terms as follows. Let

$$\gamma_0 = \mathscr{C}[\![S]\!]\rho$$
$$\gamma_1 = \mathscr{C}[\![\text{while B do S}]\!]\rho$$
$$\omega = \mathscr{R}[\![B]\!]\rho.$$

We are assuming:

1. There exists a completely strict ψ_0 such that, for all θ, $\gamma_0\theta = (\mathit{strict}\ \theta)\circ\psi_0$.
2. There exists a completely strict χ_0 such that $\omega\kappa = (\mathit{strict}\ \kappa)\circledast\chi_0$ for all κ.

Then by Theorem 11.34, we know that the entire loop is jump-free, so that $\gamma_1\theta = (\mathit{strict}\ \theta)\circ\psi_1$ for all θ and some particular completely strict ψ_1.

Now since P is without side effects, there is a completely strict χ_P such that $\mathscr{R}[\![P]\!]\rho\kappa = (\mathit{strict}\ \kappa)\circledast\chi_P$ for all κ; let us put $P'(\sigma) = (\chi_P(\sigma)|T)$ and $\chi'(\sigma) = (\chi_0(\sigma)|T)$, so that the value for state σ of an expression like $\ulcorner B \wedge P\urcorner$, for example, is given by $\chi'(\sigma) \wedge P'(\sigma)$.

The theorem we must prove is then as follows.

<u>*14.3. Theorem.*</u> Suppose that

if $P'(\sigma) \equiv \mathit{true}$ and $\chi'(\sigma) \equiv \mathit{true}$
then either $P'(\psi_0\sigma) \equiv \mathit{true}$
or $\psi_0\sigma$ is improper
or $\gamma_0\theta\sigma \equiv \mathit{Wrong}(\sigma')$ for all θ and some σ';

then

$P'(\sigma_0) \equiv true$ implies
that either $P'(\psi_1\sigma_0) \equiv true$ and $\chi'(\psi_1\sigma_0) \equiv false$,
or $\psi_1\sigma_0$ is improper,
or $\gamma_1\theta\sigma_0 \equiv Wrong(\sigma')$ for all θ and some σ'.

Proof: We may assume that σ_0 is proper, for otherwise, since P' is completely strict, the result holds trivially. Writing σ_n for $\psi_0{}^n\sigma_0$, for any particular σ_0 one of the following three cases must be true (because of the limited range, T, of χ'):

1. $\exists m \geq 0$: $\chi'\sigma_m \equiv false$,
2. $\exists m \geq 0$: $\chi'\sigma_m$ is improper,
   and, in either case, $\forall n$: $0 \leq n < m$: $\chi'\sigma_n \equiv true$;
3. $\forall n$: $0 \leq n$: $\chi'\sigma_n \equiv true$.

Now from the proof of 11.34 we see that

$$\psi_1 = fix(H) \quad \text{where} \quad H(\psi) = Cond((strict\ \psi)\circ\psi_0,\ I)\circledast\chi_0$$

and that ψ_1 is completely strict. So

$$\psi_1 = Cond(\psi_1\circ\psi_0,\ I)\circledast\chi_0.$$

Thus, for any σ, if $\chi_0\sigma \not\equiv$ T then $\gamma_1\theta\sigma = Wrong(\sigma)$ for any θ, and otherwise

$$\psi_1\sigma = \begin{cases} \psi_1(\psi_0\sigma) & \text{if } \chi'\sigma = true \\ \sigma & \text{if } \chi'\sigma = false \\ \text{improper} & \text{if } \chi'\sigma \text{ is improper.} \end{cases}$$

So for our three cases above, we have

$$\psi_1\sigma_n = \psi_1\sigma_{n+1} \begin{cases} 0 \leq n < m & \text{for cases 1 and 2;} \\ n \geq 0 & \text{for case 3.} \end{cases}$$

Hence, assuming that the alternatives involving *Wrong* are never invoked (for if one is, then the theorem is immediately satisfied), we have

$\psi_1\sigma_0 = \psi_1\sigma_m$ (cases 1 and 2)
$\psi_1\sigma_0 = \psi_1\sigma_n$ $(n\geq 0)$ (case 3)

and

$\psi_1\sigma_m = \sigma_m$ (case 1)
$\psi_1\sigma_m$ is improper (case 2).

So the theorem is satisfied for case 2.

We next complete case 1. From the premise of the theorem we know that if $P'(\sigma_n) \equiv true$ and $\chi'(\sigma_n) \equiv true$ then either $P'(\sigma_{n+1}) \equiv true$, or σ_{n+1} is improper, or *Wrong* is applied. Now we are assuming that $\chi'(\sigma_n)$, and hence σ_n, have proper values for all n such that $0\leq n\leq m$, and that *Wrong* is not invoked. Hence if $P'(\sigma_0) \equiv true$ then $P'(\sigma_m) \equiv true$, and for case 1 we also know that $\chi'(\sigma_m) \equiv false$. So $P'(\sigma_0) \equiv true$ implies $P'(\psi_1\sigma_0) \equiv true$ and $\chi'(\psi_1\sigma_0) \equiv false$, and the theorem is satisfied for case 1.

We are left with case 3. For this case we aim to prove that $\psi_1\sigma_0 \equiv \bot$, which would satisfy the theorem. (That is to say, if the test of the **while**-loop is always true, we prove that the loop never terminates.)

Let $S' = \{\sigma_n \mid n\geq 0\}$, so that $\chi'\sigma \equiv true$ for all $\sigma \in S'$. Remembering that

$$\psi_1 = fix(\lambda\psi.Cond((strict\ \psi)\circ\psi_0,\ I)\circledast\chi_0)$$

we prove by fixpoint induction that $\psi_1\sigma \equiv \bot$ for all $\sigma \in S'$.

Basis: $\bot\sigma \equiv \bot$ for all σ.

Induction: For all $\sigma \in S'$, assume $\psi\sigma \equiv \bot$. Then

$(\lambda\psi.\mathit{Cond}((\mathit{strict}\ \psi)\circ\psi_0,\ I)\circledast\chi_0)\psi\sigma$

$= (\mathit{Cond}((\mathit{strict}\ \psi)\circ\psi_0,\ I)\circledast\chi_0)\sigma$

$= (\mathit{strict}\ \psi)\sigma'$ where $\sigma' = \psi_0\sigma$

(since $\chi'\sigma \equiv \mathit{true}$ for all $\sigma \in S'$)

$= \bot$ (by hypothesis, since $\sigma' \in S'$, and is also therefore proper).

So by fixpoint induction $\psi_1\sigma \equiv \bot$ for all $\sigma \in S'$, and in particular when $\sigma = \sigma_0$, as required. So the theorem is satisfied in all cases.

Further Comments We have thus proved the validity of the rule for while-loops, under several simplifying assumptions. The assumption that the body was jump-free was admittedly introduced for the sake of simplicity. If jumps are allowed, the particular loop can no longer be considered as an isolated piece of text, but must be analysed in the larger context within which jumps may occur; nevertheless, provided suitable assertions can be attached to (and verified for) the jumps and labels in the program, it is still possible to use the while-loop proof rule.

On the other hand, the assumption that there are no side-effects in the test expression is an essential qualifier to the validity of the result. If side-effects are allowed in the test expression the proof rule is not in general valid (even assuming that we give some meaning to the appearance of such an expression in an assertion, such as agreeing simply to ignore the state change). Most of the rules of a language require qualifications of this sort. Sometimes the design of a language guarantees that a particular qualification is always satisfied and can be taken for granted. For example, one insidious difficulty is sharing: proof rules concerned with assignment generally do not take account of the possibility that another name, not appearing at all in the assignment command, might also denote the updated location. (The most common cause of this is a location supplied as a parameter by reference to a procedure and also accessible as a free variable.) Dealing properly with this would involve making explicit the two-fold mapping between names and R-values (ρ and σ), and would make the rules much more complicated. Some simple languages guarantee that this sort of situation can never occur. Otherwise, if such an assurance is not available, each qualification must be checked whenever the rule is applied. George Ligler [26] lists no less than six such qualifications to the proof rule for assignment in Algol 60 (he includes an assumption about successful termination, which we took into account by allowing the rules to be satisfied if the final state were improper; other qualifications involve matters ranging from side-effects in subexpresions within the assignment command to unexpected real to integer conversions).

It is the job of a good language designer to provide languages in which the proof rules have as few qualifications as possible. In our particular case, for instance, Ligler suggests a syntactically distinguishable subclass of expressions which can be guaranteed to be free from side-effects, and to which the tests of while-loops (among other things) would be confined. (In our example language this subclass would exclude the valof expression, and all but a restricted subclass of functions.)

We reiterate what we said in Chapter 2, that it is important for the language designer to provide simple rules of this sort: the qualifications should be few, and those which are necessary should wherever possible be capable of simple, preferably purely syntactic, verification. The use of these simple rules is the technique which practising programmers are most likely to employ for showing the correctness of their programs; moreover it will usually be employed more or less informally, when extra complications are likely to be ignored. We believe that the denotational approach helps by allowing us to show that a language can be constructed which has the rules we want, and putting precise bounds on their applicability.

Termination The notation we have been using was defined in such a way that proof rules were satisfied by programs which failed to terminate. In order to show that a program actually produces a satisfactory answer, a separate proof of termination is necessary. For these an operational approach is usually adopted: for each cycle in the program one seeks some kind of value which strictly decreases each time round the cycle and which cannot go on decreasing indefinitely (for example, an integer constrained to be positive which is decremented in the body of a loop). In this way one proves that none of the cycles can fail to terminate. Recursive procedures are analysed similarly. It is claimed that it is frequently easier to split the proof of a program into two separate parts, correctness and termination, each with its own battery of techniques.

Alternatively the whole problem may be faced at once. In this approach, pioneered by Dijkstra [10], we speak of the "weakest precondition" for a command Γ and assertion P, and write it

$wp(\Gamma, P)$.

For any Γ, *wp* specifies a "predicate transformer" which maps assertions to assertions. Γ will terminate successfully and P will be true afterwards if and only if $wp(\Gamma, P)$ holds beforehand. Thus $wp(\Gamma, P)$ is stronger than the P′ of P′{Γ}P: P′ is sufficient for *partial* correctness ("*if* it terminates the result will be right"), whereas $wp(\Gamma, P)$ is sufficient (and necessary) for *total* correctness ("it *will* terminate with the right result"). Of course the two formalisms are related, in that

$wp(\Gamma, P)\ \{\ \Gamma\ \}\ P$.

It remains to be seen which strategy is easier to apply in practice.

Further Extensions: Arrays and Structures

We are now reaching the end of this introduction to the techniques of denotational semantics. There are, of course, many topics we have left undiscussed: some of these we now very briefly consider.

In the first place, there are several language features we have not described, some of which could be incorporated with little trouble. Arrays, for instance, may be treated as elements of the domain $[\mathbb{N}^* \to L]$ (that is, as mappings from tuples of subscripts to locations), or of $[N^* \to E]$ for constant arrays. Structures, similarly, may be regarded as elements of $[\mathrm{Sel} \to [L \times T]]$ (for structures with updateable fields) or $[\mathrm{Sel} \to [E \times T]]$ (for those with unvarying fields), where Sel is a domain of selectors (possibly strings, or perhaps identifiers), and the T component is introduced to allow the semantics to record the fact that a given structure has a particular component.

Definitions

Another extension we might make to our formalism allows us to accommodate more elaborate forms of declaration. Instead of our commands such as

let I=E in Γ

with other versions for all the other ways of declaring new names, we introduce a new syntactic category of definitions

Δ ∈ Def

and change our syntax to:

Δ ::= I=E | I:=E
Γ ::= let Δ in Γ
E ::= let Δ in E .

The result of evaluating a definition is to

associate one or more names with the denoted value or values. This little set of name-value pairs corresponds, of course, to an element of U, the domain of environments; and the intended semantics for ⌜let Δ in Γ⌝, for example, is that this little environment is to be combined with the environment in which the whole construct is evaluated in order to provide the environment for Γ. So the continuation argument for $\mathscr{D}$, the semantic function for definitions, will be one which accepts the little environment produced; it is therefore of the form

$\chi \in X = U \to C$ (definition continuations)

(compare this with the domain $K = E \to C$ for expression continuations). Thus $\mathscr{D}$ is of functionality $Def \to U \to X \to C$, and the equations for the two forms of definition given in the syntax so far are as follows.

$$\mathscr{D}[\![I=E]\!]\rho\chi = \mathscr{E}[\![E]\!]\rho\{\lambda\varepsilon.\chi(arid[\varepsilon/I])\} \qquad (14.4)$$

$$\mathscr{D}[\![I:=E]\!]\rho\chi = \mathscr{R}[\![E]\!]\rho\{\lambda\beta.Newstore\{\lambda\alpha.Assign\alpha\beta\{\chi(arid[\alpha \text{ in } D/I])\}\}\} \qquad (14.5)$$

In these equations *arid* is the empty environment, which may be defined as follows, if $U = Ide \to D$:

$$arid = \lambda I.?. \qquad (14.6)$$

(Alternatively, if we are using the extended form of the environment domain $[Ide \to D] \times K \times C \times C$, then

$$arid = \langle \lambda I.?, \lambda\varepsilon.Wrong, Wrong, Wrong\rangle . \qquad (14.7))$$

We must also give equations for the new forms of command and ex ression embodying definitions. They are very similar to each other; the equation for the command is as follows.

$$\mathscr{C}[\![\texttt{let } \Delta \texttt{ in } \Gamma]\!]\rho\theta = \mathscr{D}[\![\Delta]\!]\rho\{\lambda\rho'.\mathscr{C}[\![\Gamma]\!](\mathit{Join}\rho\rho')\theta\} \tag{14.8}$$

where *Join*, the function for combining two environments (and therefore an element of U→U→U), is defined by

$$\mathit{Join}\rho\rho' = \lambda I.\ \rho'[\![I]\!]=? \rightarrow \rho[\![I]\!],\ \rho'[\![I]\!] \tag{14.9}$$

when U = Ide→D; the reader is invited to choose a suitable definition for the more complicated form of environment.

Recursion We may now revise our earlier forms for recursive abstractions so as to accommodate them in our new scheme. We may add two new forms of definition:

$$\Delta ::= \texttt{rec } I_0 = \texttt{fn } I_1.E \mid \texttt{rec } I = \texttt{rt } \Gamma$$

with the semantic equations

$$\mathscr{D}[\![\texttt{rec } I_0 = \texttt{fn } I_1.E]\!]\rho\chi = \chi(\mathit{arid}[\mathit{fix}(\lambda\phi\lambda\delta.\mathscr{E}[\![E]\!](\rho[\phi \texttt{ in } D/I_0][\delta/I_1])) \texttt{ in } D/I_0]) \tag{14.10}$$

$$\mathscr{D}[\![\texttt{rec } I = \texttt{rt } \Gamma]\!]\rho\chi = \chi(\mathit{arid}[\mathit{fix}(\lambda\gamma.\mathscr{C}[\![\Gamma]\!](\rho[\gamma \texttt{ in } D/I])) \texttt{ in } D/I]) \tag{14.11}$$

Since we introduced recursion in Chapter 11, however, we have dealt with assignment and with initialised declarations. We now therefore have the opportunity to give a new form of recursion, for recursive initialised definitions.

Δ ::= rec I:=E

$\mathscr{D}[\![\text{rec I:=E}]\!]\rho\chi =$
$\quad Newstore\{\lambda\alpha.\mathscr{R}[\![E]\!](\rho[\alpha \text{ in } D/I])\{\lambda\beta.Assign\alpha\beta$
$\qquad \{\chi(arid[\alpha \text{ in } D/I])\}\}\}$ (14.12)

This is defined without restriction on the form of the expression E but, as E is evaluated before the location denoted by I is initialised, it will give a sensible result only if the value of E does not depend on the *R-value* of I. This is quite sufficient for the usual case; that is, when E is an abstraction. If E is a function we have, for example:

$\mathscr{D}[\![\text{rec } I_0 := \text{fn } I_1.E]\!]\rho\chi = Newstore\{\lambda\alpha.Assign\alpha$
$\quad (\lambda\delta.\mathscr{E}[\![E]\!](\rho[\alpha \text{ in } D/I_0][\delta/I_1]) \text{ in } E)$
$\qquad \{\chi(arid[\alpha \text{ in } D/I_0])\}\}.$ (14.13)

Using the previous form for recursion, on the other hand, we would obtain

$\mathscr{D}[\![I_0 := \text{rec } I_0 \text{ fn } I_1.E]\!]\rho\chi = Newstore\{\lambda\alpha.Assign\alpha$
$\quad (fix(\lambda\phi\lambda\delta.\mathscr{E}[\![E]\!](\rho[\phi \text{ in } D/I_0][\delta/I_1]) \text{ in } E))$
$\qquad \{\chi(arid[\alpha \text{ in } D/I_0])\}\}.$ (14.14)

It cannot be claimed that these two forms are equivalent, as they use the store in different ways. For example, in an environment in which f had been declared in one or other of the ways given above, a program such as

$\ulcorner g := f;\;\; f := sqrt\urcorner$

would behave differently: in the first case g would be affected by the assignment to f, while in the second case it would not. 14.14 makes an entry in the *environment* to provide a means for the function to refer to itself, while 14.13 uses an entry in the *store* for the same purpose. (Of course, behind the scenes the implementation of 14.14 will almost certainly be using the method implied by 14.13.) Nevertheless, in programs in which the initialised location is *not* subsequently updated, the results of applying the functions defined by the two methods should be the same. To formulate and to prove this, however, it is necessary to work with the store semantics rather than standard semantics since, as described on page 333, it is only then that the identifiers referred to in an abstraction are explicitly available in the abstraction value.

In fact we could, if we wished, now avoid incorporating recursion explicitly in our language; for we can achieve the same kind of effect as in 14.12 using the apparatus already available. Consider the following definition.

```
⌜fix = fn F.
    let f := IRRELEVANT in valof
      (  f := F(f);
         resultis f
      )⌝
```

Remember that according to our semantic definition *F* will take its parameter by denotation, which is in this case by L-value. For any function *G* which does not refer to the R-value of its parameter, a definition such as ⌜*g*:=*fix*(*G*)⌝ has a very similar effect to ⌜rec *g*:=*G*(*g*)⌝ (though in the former case the location used by *fix* is not the location *g*, and the circular pointer is thus protected from subsequent updating).

Exercise

2. Investigate the behaviour of a program incorporating *fix* as defined above, and a definition such as the following:

⌜*FactKernel* = fn *f*.
  fn *n*. if *n*=0 then 1 else *n*×*f*(*n*-1)
within
Factorial = *fix*(*FactKernel*)⌝.

Combining definitions The extra flexibility of our new method of treating definitions allows us to discuss ways in which two definitions may be combined into one. We briefly mention three such ways, which may be expressed by the following syntax:

$$\Delta \ ::= \ \Delta_1 \text{ around } \Delta_2 \mid \Delta_1 \text{ and } \Delta_2 \mid \Delta_1 \text{ within } \Delta_2 \ .$$

In fact the first of these forms is not strictly necessary, as it is intended for a succession of definitions, whose effects accumulate as they are evaluated from left to right; thus, for example,

$$\ulcorner \text{let } I_1{=}E_1 \text{ around } I_2{=}E_2 \text{ in } \Gamma \urcorner \ \equiv \ \ulcorner \text{let } I_1{=}E_1 \text{ in let } I_2{=}E_2 \text{ in } \Gamma \urcorner.$$

The second form indicates that Δ_1 and Δ_2 are to be evaluated together, both of them in the original environment, and their effects combined. The third form indicates that the effect of Δ_1 is to change the environment in which Δ_2 is evaluated, but the names declared in Δ_1 are not part of the result of the definition as a whole. The equations for these three forms are therefore as follows.

$$\mathscr{D}[\![\Delta_1 \text{ around } \Delta_2]\!]\rho\chi = \mathscr{D}[\![\Delta_1]\!]\rho\{\lambda\rho'.\mathscr{D}[\![\Delta_2]\!](Join\rho\rho')\{\lambda\rho''.\chi(Join\rho'\rho'')\}\} \quad (14.15)$$

$$\mathscr{D}[\![\Delta_1 \text{ and } \Delta_2]\!]\rho\chi = \mathscr{D}[\![\Delta_1]\!]\rho\{\lambda\rho'.\mathscr{D}[\![\Delta_2]\!]\rho\{\lambda\rho''.\chi(Join\rho'\rho'')\}\} \quad (14.16)$$

$$\mathscr{D}[\![\Delta_1 \text{ within } \Delta_2]\!]\rho\chi = \mathscr{D}[\![\Delta_1]\!]\rho\{\lambda\rho'.\mathscr{D}[\![\Delta_2]\!](Join\rho\rho')\chi\} \quad (14.17)$$

The second of these could be replaced by a version involving a variant of the list evaluation function *le*, so so as to leave the order of evaluation unspecified.

Notice that in examples such as

```
⌜let i:=0 within
   Count = fn(n).valof ( i:=i+n; resultis i )
 in Γ⌝
```

the within form provides facilities akin to the own variables of Algol 60 (but without the difficulties of initialising the latter). Here the scope of *i* is merely the definition of *Count*; but its extent would survive from activation to activation of *Count*, enabling a running total to be kept.

Input/Output

A more fundamental change would be the introduction of input/output facilities. Let us look briefly at the case of a language with just one input and one output stream (the method can be extended to cover more elaborate schemes with little difficulty). We adjoin two more components to the state σ, namely the sequence of values not yet input, and the sequence so far output; so now

$S = [[L \to V] \times [L \to T] \times B^* \times B^*]$

where B can be any domain containing those values which can be expressed in the I/O medium. Then the write command, ⌜write E⌝, applied to state σ, would lead to a state in which the value of E was appended as a new final element in the sequence constituting the output component of the state; similarly, the ⌜read⌝ expression would give as its value the first element in the input sequence, and as a side effect would remove that element from the sequence (note that this is one of the most important examples of a side effect).

Exercise

3. Write the semantic equations for these two new constructs.

We have included the input and output in the state of the machine, which is the most natural place, but our doing so raises an interesting question. What of a program that outputs some preliminary results before going into a nonterminating loop? According to our theory (the final section of the proof of 14.3, for example) the final state is ⊥. But we know that certain preliminary results have been output and cannot be revoked: so we have some information about at least one component of the state, which cannot therefore be ⊥. This argument, however, confuses the final state with some actual state arising some arbitrary, but finite, time along the way. For the sequence of actual states we can certainly show that once values are output they are never revoked, and that moreover the values output do not thereby affect the subsequent course of the computation: this assures us that we can implement such semantics on a line-printer or some other device that having writ moves on - or alternatively, depending on one's point of view, that our equations satisfactorily model a line-printer's behaviour. But none of these actual states is the "final" state, and our result says nothing at all about that, just as a proof by induction demonstrates that some particular property holds, say, for each finite integer n, but says nothing about what happens when n tends to infinity. In our discussion of fixpoint induction (in Chapter 9), we relied on inclusivity to allow results which had been proved about some sequence of states to be inferred for the limit of the sequence too. But the final state of a computation is *not* the limit of the intermediate states arising during the course of the execution.

State Sequences This last point leads us to think that the final state, or an "answer" related to it, is not always what interests us: perhaps we are sometimes more concerned with the sequence of intermediate states, or answers. This is especially true for programs, such as operating systems, which are *intended* not to terminate. It is fairly easy to adapt the semantic equations to produce such a sequence. To obtain a sequence of states, for example, we change the functionality of continuations, so that command continuations are now* in $[S \to S^{\circledast}]$ instead of $[S \to A]$, and expression continuations are now in $[E \to [S \to S^{\circledast}]]$. The initial continuation, which is supplied to the entire program, is $\lambda\sigma.\langle\sigma\rangle$, and the equations are changed so that at each stage the current state is concatenated to the front of the sequence produced by the remainder of the program. For example, 12.32 becomes

$$\mathscr{C}[\![\Gamma_1;\Gamma_2]\!]\rho\theta = \mathscr{C}[\![\Gamma_1]\!]\rho\{\lambda\sigma.\langle\sigma\rangle\ \S\,(\mathscr{C}[\![\Gamma_2]\!]\rho\theta\sigma)\}. \tag{14.18}$$

The sequence so produced contains, of course, far more detail than is usually required: but the features which we wish to analyse may be extracted from it.

This is obviously just another example of a non-standard semantics, devised to suit a particular problem in hand. As usual, if using such a non-standard definition, we should state and prove its congruence with the standard.

Parallel Processing

We turn now to another new topic, also discussed by Milne [33]. Up to now, continuations have been supplied to commands (and expressions) in order that they may either be applied to the resulting state or ignored completely. Sometimes, in addition, the con-

---

* The notation $V^{\circledast}$ differs from V^* in that it defines a domain which also includes infinitely long sequences of values. (See Exercise 1 of the previous chapter.)

tinuation is placed in the command's environment for use by certain commands (such as ⌜return⌝) occurring within. We now extend this third possibility - that is, of reserving a continuation for possible use later. In particular, we form a collection from which, from time to time and under various constraints, one of them may be selected and applied. This technique enables us to describe such features as coroutines, and also parallel processing.

Thus for the latter feature Milne suggests a flat lattice I of "processes" (rather like the domain of locations); and a function, τ (rather like the contents mapping of the store), which for each element ι of I gives the "status" of that process. One component of this status is a continuation, which must be applied to σ to enable the process to continue; other components may include store area functions (elements of $[L \to T]$) to specify what store is reserved for that process, semaphores, flags controlling interlocks, and any other values required for protection and control. Inserted into the semantic equations at convenient points is a function which decides whether the current process should continue (in which case the continuation is applied to σ as usual) or whether another should be selected; in this case τ is updated so that the status of the current process is preserved, and the continuation of a suitable new process obtained and applied to σ. The function which selects the new process need not be defined completely; as with *New*, which selects new locations in the store, we need only specify a set of constraints which it must satisfy, and can leave the rest of the details to the implementation. This technique is a sort of formalised time-slicing, but notice that it does not imply that the implementation must necessarily be on a single processor. Provided processes do not interfere with each other (for example, provided they confine their activities to separate parts of the state) their execution can indeed proceed in parallel: the process "current" in the semantics is merely the one on which our mathematical attention happens to be fixed at the moment. Our list evaluation function *le* can also of course be modified so that it uses separate processes for the evaluation of each component. In general the semantic functions will require two extra parameters: the function τ and also some information about the scheduling of processes (such as a list of them).

Another interesting approach to the semantics of parallel programs is that of Robin Milner [35]. The main difference from the approach we have just described is that whereas in Milne's work there is just one process associated with each thread of control through a program, Milner uses processes to model each of many different kinds of object. So, for example, he has a separate process for each sequence of instructions in a program, and a separate process associated with each location in the store, replaced by a different process whenever the location is updated. Carl Hewitt's "actors" [17] somewhat resemble these processes of Milner's, though Milner's semantics is functional (and immediately based on lattice-theoretic foundations) whereas Hewitt's is interpretive.

Type-Checking and Coercion

Another topic which also leads to yet more parameters for some of the semantic functions is manifest types, type-checking and coercion. So far our language has had "dynamic" types: any location could have as its contents any value in V, though an error would occur if an attempt was made to use a value wrongly - for example, to multiply a number by a truth-value. But in languages such as Algol, locations are declared to be of a particular type and can contain only appropriate values. To describe this situation we introduce a lattice of "types" (more precisely, of typenames); an element of this domain is supplied as parameter to the function *New* which finds new locations, and also to the semantic functions for expressions to specify the required type of the result. If it is desired to specify "compile-time" type-checking, a further set of semantic functions may be defined which, instead of evaluating the syntactic constructs supplied as arguments, merely check them for type errors. (Such functions would, for example, have analogues of ρ drawn from the domain [Ide→Type] rather than [Ide→D].) For examples and further discussion of this technique for Algol 60 and the much more complicated case of Algol 68 see, respectively, Mosses [36] and Milne [33].

Networks of Processes

We resist the temptation to set a final exercise asking for a complete definition of a language embodying all the features discussed above. Instead we briefly mention some work of Gilles Kahn [22] in which the lattice-theoretic apparatus is used in a slightly different way in order to describe the behaviour of some interconnected system of processes such as the tasks of an operating system.

In this model a number of computers are connected together in a network. Each computer is a single sequential process; at any time it is either computing or is waiting for input along some particular input line. There is no limit to the rate at which output can occur down a computer's output lines: no output gets lost, and sooner or later it all arrives (in order) at the computer at the far end, though the time it takes is unpredictable.

The traffic from one of these computers to another may be thought of as a sequence of values from some domain D. These values are assumed to be discrete and perfectly known: our idea of approximations to a particular value does not occur. Instead, the sequences themselves are ordered: one sequence is weaker than another in the ordering if the one is an initial segment of the other. So the weakest sequence of all is the empty sequence $\langle\rangle$, which corresponds to $\perp$. Two sequences with unequal nth components (for any n) are incomparable: their upper bound is the "contradictory" sequence $\top$. Just below $\top$ in the ordering come the sequences of countably infinite length, and below them the finite sequences. (Such a sequence domain is actually a special case of a somewhat more general concept studied and axiomatised by Kahn and Gordon Plotkin - their "concrete" domains - which characterises precisely those domains whose values are capable in principle of being output from a computer on a peripheral, or a communication line, etc.)

Axioms of monotonicity and continuity apply to this system. The monotonicity axiom says that sending more input to a computer can do nothing other than perhaps provoke more output: the computer cannot change anything it would have output before reading the new input. The continuity axiom says that if a computer is going to output at all it must begin to do so after only a finite amount of input. So, just as before, the axioms derive from the basic fact that computing is a finitary activity.

Then cyclic networks, for example, lead to fixed point equations and, just as before, the theory guarantees the existence of a minimal solution (that is, a minimal sequence of values along a particular line). One of the examples Kahn gives is as shown in Fig.14.1, where f's program is the function

$y = cons('a', x)$.

That is, f outputs 'a' first, and then everything that arrives on the input line. The minimal solution for this system is that the traffic on the line is the infinite sequence

$\langle 'a', 'a', 'a', \ldots \rangle$.

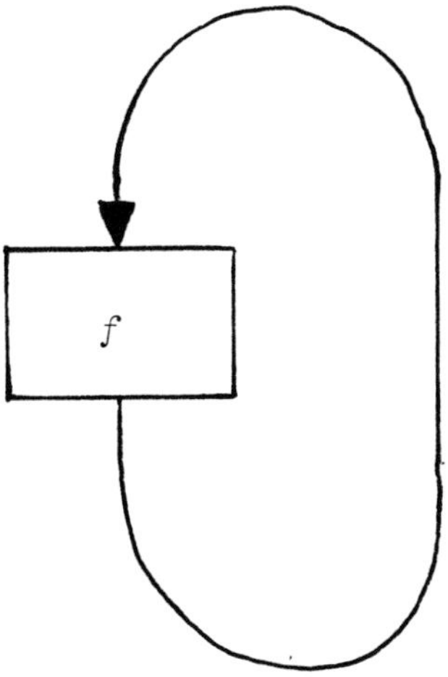

Fig.14.1. A simple cyclic network.

Notice that this is quite different from Milne's approach to parallel processing, which we discussed earlier. We mention it principally to show how an analysis begun from a rather different viewpoint from ours nevertheless uses the same basic insights into the nature of computing, and arrives at a very similar mathematical theory.

The Semantic Bridge

We have now completed this introduction to the ideas of denotational semantics, and it is appropriate to survey what we have achieved.

The core of the subject has been the standard semantics of high-level programming languages, by which a precise meaning is given to any construct a programmer might use. This descriptive technique is supported on the one hand by a mathematical apparatus based on lattice theory and logic, which provides it

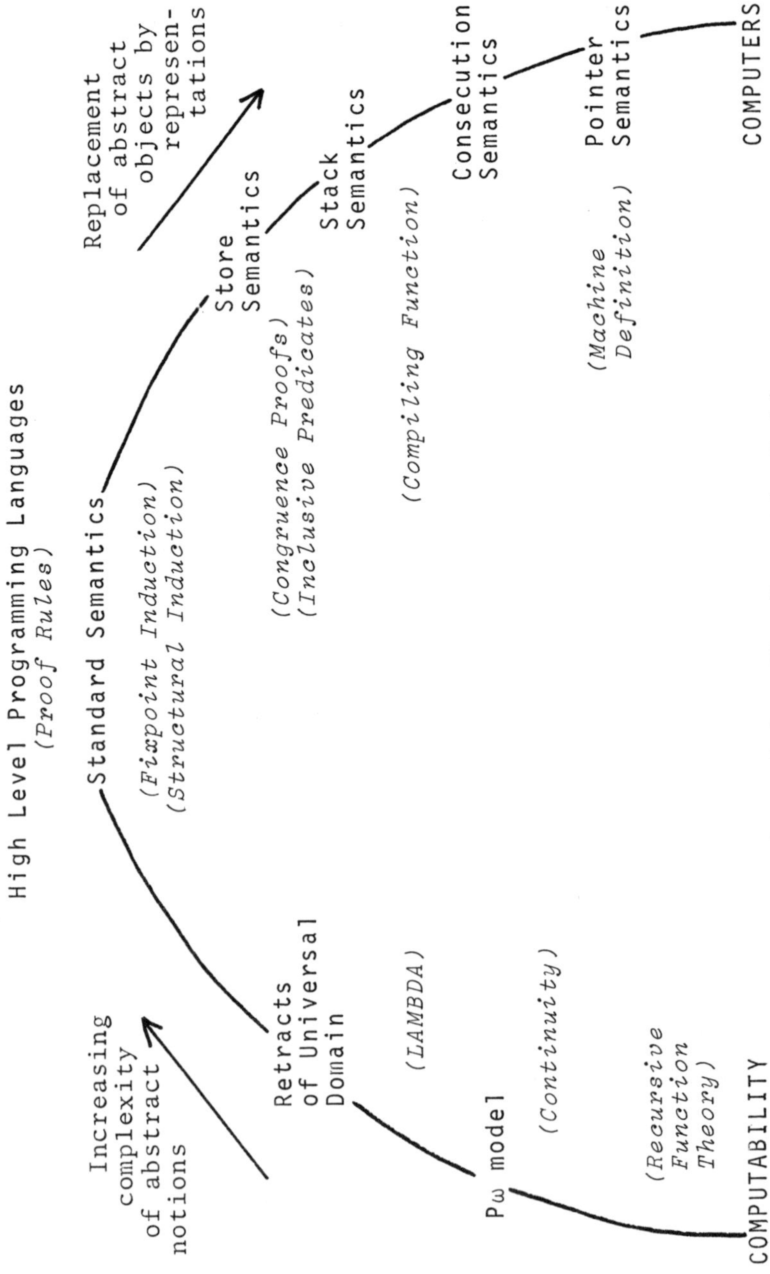

Fig. 14.2. The Semantic Bridge.

with firm theoretical foundations, and on the other by the techniques of non-standard semantics, which provide the possibility of correct implementations. Thus the theory forms a kind of bridge (Fig.14.2) between fundamental computability theory and realistic engineering practice: between Turing machines and commercially available computers. Standard semantics, at the apex of the bridge, by providing justification for various tools, such as the proof rules of the axiomatic approach, is of direct help to users of programming languages, and also provides insight to the designers of the next generation.

Much work remains to be done. In places this scheme of things is still very messy, sometimes because of the unwieldiness of existing languages, and sometimes because we have not yet found the ideal way of expressing some of our concepts. But perhaps this system of denotational semantics may provide the basis of a coherent and unified theory of "how to compute the computable", and thus help in the task of increasing the usefulness of computers and their programmers.

FIRST CLASS FUNCTIONS (continued)

In this appendix we give a further example of the use of functions as "first class citizens". The example concerns one possible way of doing input/output.

Suppose an input stream *S* is an anadic* function with side effects. The basic function *Next*, which given a stream *S* produces the next object in the stream, is defined as follows:

```
let Next(S) = S()                                    (A1)
```

The side effects are arranged so that successive calls of *Next*(*S*) (that is, successive calls of *S*()) produce different values, the whole sequence of which makes up the stream of data.

New streams are constructed by *stream functions*, which usually take a stream as a parameter and produce another stream as result. Let us consider a few examples of such stream functions.

1. OmitSpaces Suppose we have a stream of characters, and that we wish to produce a stream which is identical except that all space characters are left out. A suitable stream function is as follows:

```
function OmitSpaces(S);                              (A2)
begin function T();
      begin let x = Next(S)
          while x = SPACE do x := Next(S)
```

* that is, a function of no parameters: cf. anadic, monadic, dyadic, triadic, ..., polyadic, ...

```
        resultis x                      || result of T
     end;
resultis T                        || result of OmitSpaces
end
```

An alternative, shorter, recursive definition is:

```
let OmitSpaces(S) = T                                (A3)
    where T() =
        ((if x = SPACE then T() else x)
            where x = S())
```

Notice once more, as in Chapter 4, the need for semi-infinite extents.

2. Repeat Given a stream of characters, *Repeat* is to produce a stream in which each character appears twice.

```
function Repeat(S);                                  (A4)
begin let x = NIL                || NIL is not a character.
    function R();
    begin test x = NIL
            ifso  begin x := Next(S);
                        resultis x       ||result of R
                  end
            ifnot begin let y = x
                        x := NIL
                        resultis y       || result of R
                  end
    end
resultis R                          || result of Repeat
end
```

It would be most satisfactory if we could prove the equivalence, in some sense, of the following two expressions:

Repeat(OmitSpaces(S))
OmitSpaces(Repeat(S))

but we shall not deal with that problem here.

3. PutBack The call *PutBack(x,S)*, where *x* is an object and *S* is a stream, is to create a new stream such that the first time *Next* is applied to it *x* will result, and afterwards *Next* will produce the objects in *S*. We give two formulations: the first uses a boolean *Flag* to recognise the first time, while the second uses the fact that functions can be assigned.

1.

```
function PutBack(x,S);                                  (A5)
begin let Flag = true
   function T();
   begin test Flag
            ifso begin Flag := false;
                       resultis x        || result of T
                 end
            ifnot resultis Next(S)       || result of T
   end;
resultis T                         || result of PutBack
end
```

2.

```
function PutBack(x,S);                                  (A6)
begin function T();
      begin T := S;
```

```
            resultis x                      || result of T
      end;
      function U();
          resultis T();                     || result of U
resultis U                            || result of PutBack
end
```

Why, in this second formulation of *PutBack*, is *U* needed at all? Why should not the result be simply *T*? The answer is that it is the function which is the *contents* of the location called *T* which would be passed out as the result. After that had happened, the variable *T* would be no longer relevant, so the assignment to it would have no effect. The extra function ensures that *T* continues to be referenced. In pictures, the two situations are as follows.

Suppose we have obeyed

A := *PutBack*(*x*,*S*)

In the first case, without *U*, the final situation is as shown in Fig.A1. *T* does occur in the FVL of *A*, but it is used only as the object of an assignment, and its contents are never used. Assignment to *T* makes no difference; in particular, it does not alter *A*.

In the second case, using the extra function *U*, the situation is also shown in Fig.A1. Now it is the contents of *U* that are passed out as the result and are irrelevant thereafter, and so the assignment to *T* now has the desired effect.

Without *U*

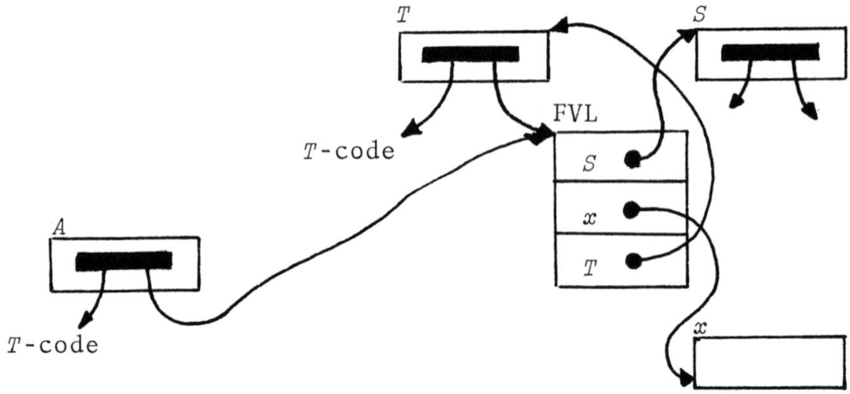

With *U*

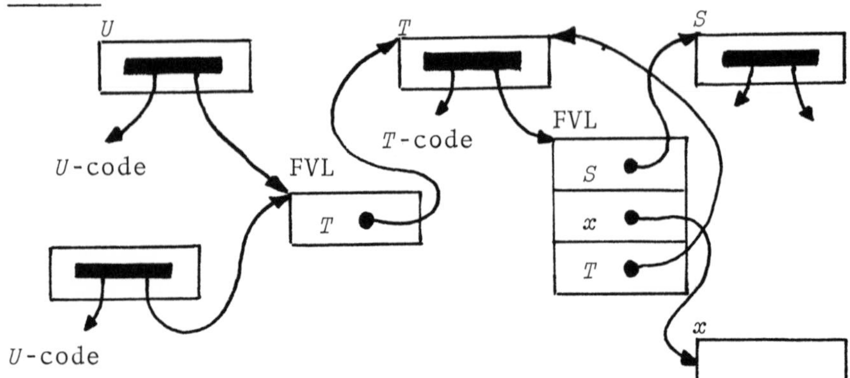

Fig.A1. Implementations of *PutBack*.

We conclude with a few exercises on streams.

Exercises Write programs for the following functions.

1. *Peep(S)*. This, like *Next(S)*, is to return the next object in the stream *S*. However, the object is not to be removed from *S*, but will be returned by the following call of *Next*, too, and also by any intervening calls of *Peep*. [Hints: use *PutBack*; *S* must be called by reference, as *Peep* will require to assign to it.]

2. *Addto(S,x)*. This is to produce a new stream in which the object *x* occurs after the last object in *S*. Note that for any stream *S*, *Next(S)* is assumed to produce the value *NIL* after all the objects in *S* have been exhausted. You may assume the existence of a stream *NullStream*; *Next(NullStream)* is always equal to *NIL*.

3. *Split(S)*. This produces a pair ⟨*S1*,*S2*⟩, each component of which is a stream. *S1* and *S2* are independent copies of *S*: that is, a sequence of calls of *Next(S1)* and a similar sequence of *Next(S2)* each produces the same sequence of objects as would a sequence of *Next(S)*. Calls of *Next(S1)* and *Next(S2)* may be interleaved in any order. [Hint: use *Addto* and *NullStream*.]

BIBLIOGRAPHY

1. Backus, J.W.: *Programming Language Semantics and Closed Applicative Languages*; pp. 71-86 of Proceedings of the ACM Symposium on Principles of Programming Languages (1973).

2. de Bakker, J.W., and Scott, D.S.: *A Theory of Programs* (manuscript); Seminar on Programming Theory, Vienna (1969).

3. Birkhoff, G.: *Lattice Theory*; American Mathematical Society Colloquium Publications, vol.25, Third (new) edition (1967).

4. Böhm, C.: *Alcune proprieta della forme β- η-normali del λ-K-calcolo*; Pubblicazioni del' istituto per le applicazioni del calcolo (Consiglio nazionali delle ricerche, Roma) no. 696 (1968). The proof is now reprinted at pp.156-162 of Curry, H.B., Hindley, J.R., and Seldin, J.P.: *Combinatory Logic*, Vol. II; North-Holland, Amsterdam (1972).

5. Böhm, C.: *The CUCH as a Formal and Description Language*; pp.179-197 of *Formal Language Description Languages for Computer Programming* (ed. Steel, T.B., Jr.), North-Holland, Amsterdam (1966).

6. Church, A.: *The Calculi of Lambda-Conversion*; Annals of Mathematical Studies 6, Princeton University Press, Princeton (1951).

7. Curry, H.B., and Feys, R.: *Combinatory Logic*, Vol. I; North-Holland, Amsterdam (1968).

8. Dijkstra, E.W.: *An Algol 60 Translator for the X1*; pp.329-345 of Annual Review in Automatic Programming 3 (ed. Goodman, R.), Pergamon Press, Oxford (1963).

9. Dijkstra, E.W.: *Talks on Programming Methodology*; Advanced Course on Systems Architecture, Grenoble (1972) (memo. EWD 356).

10. Dijkstra, E.W.: *Guarded Commands, Nondeterminacy and Formal Derivation of Programs*; pp.453-457 of Communications of the ACM, 18 (1975).

11. Escher, M.C.: *Pedalternorotandomovens centroculatus articulosus*; "*Wentelteefje*" (Curl-up) Lithograph (1951).

12. Fischer, M.J.: *Lambda Calculus Schemata*; pp.105-109 of Proceedings of the ACM Conference on Proving Assertions about Programs, Las Cruces (1972).

13. Floyd, R.W.: *Assigning Meanings to Programs*; pp.19-32 of Proceedings of Symposia in Applied Mathematics 19 (1967).

14. Gericke, H.: *Lattice Theory*; Harrap (1966).

15. Gordon, M.J.C.: *Models of Pure LISP (a worked example in semantics)*; Experimental Programming Reports 31, Department of Machine Intelligence, University of Edinburgh (1973).

16. Henderson, D.A., Jr.: *The Binding Model: A Semantic Base for Modular Programming*; Ph.D. Thesis, MIT (1975) (Project MAC Technical Report MAC TR-145).

17. Hewitt, C., *et al.*: *Actor Induction and Meta-evaluation*; pp.153-168 of Proceedings of ACM Symposium on Principles of Programming Languages, Boston (1973).

18. Hindley, J.R., Lercher, B., and Seldin, J.P.: *Introduction to Combinatory Logic*; London Mathematical Society Lecture Note Series 7, Cambridge University Press (1972).

19. Hoare, C.A.R.: *An Axiomatic Basis for Computer Programming*; pp. 576-580,583 of Communications of the ACM, 12 (1969).

20. Hoare, C.A.R., and Wirth, N.: *An Axiomatic Definition of the Programming Language Pascal*; pp.335-355 of Acta Informatica, 2 (1973).

21. Jones, C.M.: D.Phil. thesis on the detection of potential parallelism in sequential programs; University of Oxford (1977).

22. Kahn, G.: *A Preliminary Theory for Parallel*

Programs; internal memo., IRIA (Laboria) (1973).

23. Knuth, D.E.: *Semantics of Context-Free Languages*; pp.127-145 of Mathematical Systems Theory, 2 (1968).

24. Landin, P.J.: *A Correspondence Between Algol 60 and Church's Lambda-Notation*; pp.89-101,158-165 of Communications of the ACM, 8 (1965).

25. Landin, P.J.: *The Mechanical Evaluation of Expressions*; pp.308-320 of Computer Journal, 6 (1964). See also: *A Lambda-Calculus Approach*; pp.97-141 of *Advances in Programming and Non-Numerical Computation* (ed. Fox, L.), Pergamon Press, Oxford (1966).

26. Ligler, G.T.: *A Mathematical Approach to Language Design*; Proceedings of 2nd ACM Symposium on Principles of Programming Languages, Palo Alto (1975).

27. Lucas, P., and Walk, K.: *On the Formal Description of PL/I*; pp.105-182 of Annual Review in Automatic Programming 6 (ed. Halpern, M.I., and Shaw, C.J.), Pergamon Press, Oxford (1971).

28. Manna, Z., Ness, S., and Vuillemin, J.E.: *Inductive Methods for Proving Properties of Programs*; Proceedings of ACM Conference, New York (1972).

29. Mazurkiewicz, A.: *Proving Algorithms by Tail Functions*; pp.220-226 of Information and Control 18 (1970).

30. McCarthy, J.: *Towards a Mathematical Science of Computation*; pp.21-28 of *Information Processing (1962)*, North-Holland, Amsterdam (1963).

31. McCarthy, J. *et al.*: *LISP1.5 Programmer's Manual*; MIT Press (1962). See also: *Problems in the Theory of Computation*; pp.219-222 of Proceedings of the IFIP Congress (1965).

32. McCarthy, J.: *A Basis for a Mathematical Theory of Computation*; pp.33-70 of *Computer Programming and*

Formal Systems (ed. Braffort, P., and Hirschberg, D.), North-Holland, Amsterdam (1963).

33. Milne, R.E.: *The Formal Semantics of Computer Languages and Their Implementations*; Ph.D. Thesis, University of Cambridge (1974), and Technical Microfiche TCF-2, Programming Research Group, University of Oxford (1974).

34. Milne, R.E., and Strachey, C.: *A Theory of Programming Language Semantics*; Chapman and Hall, London, and John Wiley, New York (1976).

35. Milner, A.J.R.G.: *An Approach to the Semantics of Parallel Programs*; Proc. Convegno di Information Teorica, Istituto di Elaborazione della Informazione, Pisa (1973). See also: *Processes: A Mathematical Model of Computing Agents*; pp.157-174 of Logic Colloquium '73 (ed. Rose, H.E., and Shepherdson, J.C.), North-Holland, Amsterdam (1975).

36. Mosses, P.D.: *The Mathematical Semantics of Algol 60*; Technical Monograph PRG-12, Programming Research Group, University of Oxford (1974).

37. Mosses, P.D.: *Mathematical Semantics and Compiler Generation*; D.Phil. thesis, University of Oxford (1975).

38. Naur, P., *et al.*: *Revised Report on the Algorithmic Language Algol 60*; pp.349-367 of the Computer Journal, 5 (1963).

39. Plotkin, G.D.: *A Power Domain Construction*; pp.452-487 of the SIAM Journal on Computing, 5 (1976).

40. Quine, W.V.O.: *Word and Object*; MIT Press, Cambridge (1960).

41. Randell, B.: *System Structure for Software Fault Tolerance*; pp.220-232 of IEEE Transactions on Software Engineering, SE-1 (1975).

42. Reynolds, J.C.: *Definitional Interpreters for Higher-order Programming Languages*; pp.717-740 of

Proceedings of the 25th ACM National Conference, Boston, ACM, New York (1972)..

43. Reynolds, J.C.: *On the Relation Between Direct and Continuation Semantics*; pp.141-156 of Proceedings of the Second Colloquium on Automata, Languages and Programming, Saarbrücken (ed. Loeckx, J.), Springer-verlag, Berlin (1974).

44. Richards, M.: *BCPL: A Tool for Compiler Writing and System Programming*; pp.557-566 of Proceedings of the 1969 Spring Joint Computer Conference, Boston, AFIPS, Montvale (1969).

45. Rogers, H., Jr.: *Theory of Recursive Functions and Effective Computability*; McGraw-Hill, New York (1967).

46. Sanderson, J.G.: *The Lambda Calculus, Lattice Theory and Reflexive Domains*; Mathematical Institute Lecture Notes, University of Oxford (1973).

47. Schönfinkel, M.: *Uber die Bausteine der mathematischen Logik*; pp.305-316 of Mathematische Annalen, 92 (1924).

48. Scott, D.S.: *Outline of a Mathematical Theory of Computation*; pp.169-176 of Proceedings of the Fourth Annual Princeton Conference on Information Sciences and Systems, Princeton University (1970); and Technical Monograph PRG-2, Programming Research Group, University of Oxford (1970).

49. Scott, D.S.: *The Lattice of Flow Diagrams*; pp. 311-366 of Symposium on the Semantics of Algorithmic Languages (ed. Engeler, E.), Springer-Verlag, Berlin (1971); and Technical Monograph PRG-3, Programming Research Group, University of Oxford (1970).

50. Scott, D.S.: *Continuous Lattices*; pp.97-136 of *Toposes, Algebraic Geometry and Logic* (ed. Lawvere, F.W.), Springer-Verlag, Berlin (1972); and Technical Monograph PRG-7, Programming Research Group, University of Oxford (1971).

51. Scott, D.S.: *Lattice Theory, Data Types and*

Semantics; pp.64-106 of NYU Symposium on Formal Semantics (ed. R. Rustin), Prentice-Hall, New York (1972).

52. Scott, D.S.: *Models for Various Type-free Calculi*; pp.157-187 of *Logic, Methodology and Philosophy of Science IV* (ed. Suppes, P., Henkin, L., Joja, A., and Moisil, G.C.), North-Holland, Amsterdam (1973).

53. Scott, D.S.: *Data Types as Lattices*; pp.522-587 of the SIAM Journal on Computing, 5 (1976).

54. Scott, D.S., and Strachey, C.: *Toward a Mathematical Semantics for Computer Languages*; pp.19-46 of Proceedings of the Symposium on Computers and Automata (ed. Fox, J.), Polytechnic Institute of Brooklyn Press, New York (1971); and Technical Monograph PRG-6, Programming Research Group, University of Oxford (1971).

55. Smyth, M.B.: *Powerdomains*; Theory of Computation Report 12, Department of Computer Science, University of Warwick (1976).

56. Strachey, C.: *Towards a Formal Semantics*; pp.198-220 of *Formal Language Description Languages for Computer Programming* (ed. Steel, T.B.), North-Holland, Amsterdam (1966).

57. Strachey, C.: *Fundamental Concepts in Programming Languages*; International Summer School in Computer Programming, Copenhagen (unpublished) (1967).

58. Strachey, C.: *The Varieties of Programming Language*; pp.222-233 of Proceedings of the International Computing Symposium, Cini Foundation, Venice (1972); and Technical Monograph PRG-10, Programming Research Group, University of Oxford (1973).

59. Strachey, C., and Wadsworth, C.P.: *Continuations - a Mathematical Semantics for Handling Full Jumps*; Technical Monograph PRG-11, Programming Research Group, University of Oxford (1974).

60. Tarski, A.: *A Lattice-theoretical Fixpoint Theorem and its Applications*; pp.285-309 of Pacific Journal of Mathematics, 5 (1955).

61. Tennent, R.D.: *The Denotational Semantics of Programming Languages*; pp.437-453 of Communications of the ACM, 19 (1976).

62. van Wijngaarden, A., *et al.*: *Revised Report on the Algorithmic Language Algol 68*; pp.1-236 of Acta Informatica, 5 (1975).

63. van Wijngaarden, A.: *Recursive Definition of Syntax and Semantics*; pp.13-24 of *Formal Language Description Languages for Computer Programming* (ed. Steel, T.B., Jr.), North-Holland, Amsterdam (1966).

64. Wadsworth, C.P.: *Semantics and Pragmatics of the Lambda-Calculus*; D.Phil. Thesis, University of Oxford (1971).

65. Wadsworth, C.P.: *The Relation between Computational and Denotational Properties for Scott's* D_∞ *models of the Lambda-Calculus*; pp.488-521 of the SIAM Journal on Computing, 5 (1976).

66. Wadsworth, C.P.: *Approximate Reduction and Lambda-Calculus Models*; the SIAM Journal on Computing (to appear).

67. Ward, S.A.: *Functional Domains of Applicative Languages*; Ph.D. Thesis, Massachusetts Institute of Technology (1974).

68. Whitehead, A.N.: *An Introduction to Mathematics*; Williams and Norgate (1911).

69. Whitehead, A.N., and Russell, B.: *Principia Mathematica*; Cambridge (1910-1913) (2nd ed. 1925-1927).

70. Wirth, N.: *The Programming Language Pascal*; pp.35-63 of Acta Informatica, 1 (1971).